# AMERICANA
# science
# annual
### A Modern Science Anthology for the Family

AMERICANA

science
annual

A Modern Science Anthology for the Family

'79

ISBN 0-7172-1509-1
Library of Congress Catalog Card Number: 64-7603

# contents

# staff

# contributors

**ROBIN M. AKERT,** Department of Social Psychology, Princeton University
co-author BODY LANGUAGE

**LAWRENCE K. ALTMAN, M.D.,** Medical reporter, *The New York Times*
REVIEW OF THE YEAR— HEALTH AND DISEASE

**DANE ARCHER,** Associate Professor of Sociology, University of California at Santa Cruz
co-author BODY LANGUAGE

**JOAN AREHART-TREICHEL,** Biomedical Sciences Editor, *Science News*
LAETRILE

**ROBERT D. BALLARD,** Associate Scientist in the Department of Geology and Geophysics at Woods Hole Oceanographic Institution
THE GALAPAGOS RIFT

**ROMAINE BAMFORD,** Free-lance science writer
DESERTIFICATION

**ROBERT O. BECKER,** Chief of Orthopedic Surgery at Veterans Administration Hospital and Research Professor at Upstate Medical Center in Syracuse, New York
co-author
ELECTROMAGNETIC POLLUTION

**RICHARD B. BORGENS,** Research Fellow, Purdue University
BIOELECTRICITY

**PETER BRITTON,** Free-lance writer
AN ADVANCED SOLAR HOUSE

**MALCOLM BROWNE,** Staff reporter, *The New York Times*
CATASTROPHE THEORY

**FRED BRUEMMER,** Free-lance nature writer
GREENLAND'S HUNGRY ESKIMOS

**GILBERT CANT,** Free-lance medical writer
ULCERS

**PETER CAPEN,** Free-lance writer and underwater photographer
THROUGH A KELP FOREST

**LOUIS S. CLAPPER,** Director of Conservation, National Wildlife Federation
REVIEW OF THE YEAR— ENVIRONMENTAL SCIENCES

**GEORGE F. DALES,** Archaeologist
RELICS OF THE INDUS CULTURE

**PAUL CHARLES WILLIAM DAVIES,** Lecturer in Applied Mathematics, Kings College, London; author of *Space and Time in the Modern Universe*
GRAVITY'S RAINBOW

**LEE DEMBART,** Staff reporter, *The New York Times*
IF COMPUTERS COULD REASON

**RICHARD DEMPWOLFF,** Free-lance science writer
ENERGY FROM OUTER SPACE

**JOHN DERR,** Staff member, U.S. Geological Survey
EARTHQUAKE LIGHTS

**GEORGE ENGEL,** Professor of Psychiatry and Medicine at the University of Rochester School of Medicine and Dentistry
SUDDEN DEATH

**DAVID M. EVANS,** Energy consultant; former

Director, Potential Gas Agency, Mineral Resources Institute, Colorado School of Mines Foundation, Inc.
REVIEW OF THE YEAR— ENERGY

**NEIL GLUCKIN,** Free-lance writer
ELECTRIC VEHICLES

**JOHN GRIBBIN,** Author of *White Holes: Cosmic Gushers in the Universe*
WHITE HOLES

**PETER GWYNNE,** Free-lance science writer; Science Editor, *Newsweek* magazine
DOOMED JUNGLES

**ALLEN L. HAMMOND,** Editor, Research News, *Science*
ALCOHOL: BRAZIL'S ANSWER TO THE ENERGY CRISIS

**KATHERINE HARAMUNDANIS,** Research Associate, Smithsonian Astrophysical Observatory; co-author, *Introduction to Astronomy*
REVIEW OF THE YEAR— ASTRONOMY

**GUY HARTMAN, M.D.,** Pediatrician, Kaiser Permante Medical Center in Fontana, California
POISONOUS GARDEN PLANTS

**WILLIAM K. HARTMANN,** Senior Scientist at the Planetary Science Institute in Tucson, Arizona; author of *Astronomy: The Cosmic Journey*
STARS WITH COMPANIONS

**WILLIAM J. HAWKINS,** Electronics Editor, *Popular Science*
THE HOME COMPUTER

**DAVID HENDIN,** Vice-President and Executive Editor, Newspaper Enterprise Association; author of *The Genetic Connection*
THE 1977 NOBEL PRIZE IN PHYSIOLOGY OR MEDICINE

**WALTER B. HENDRICKSON, JR.,** Free-lance writer
VOICES IN THE DEEP

**HUGH F. HENRY,** Head, Department of Physics, Depauw University
co-author REVIEW OF THE YEAR— PHYSICAL SCIENCES

**JOHN IRWIN,** Associate Professor, Department of Earth Sciences, Newark State College, New Jersey
SUNSETS

**PETER A. JORDAN,** Associate Professor, Department of Entomology, Fisheries, and Wildlife, University of Minnesota
co-author
THE WOLF THAT LOST ITS GENES

**STEPHEN KALLIS, JR.,** Engineer and Free-lance writer
ROBOT PROBES

**EUGENIA KELLER,** Managing Editor, *Chemistry*
co-author REVIEW OF THE YEAR— PHYSICAL SCIENCES

**FRASER KENT,** Author of *Nothing to Fear: Coping with Phobias*
AGORAPHOBIA

**GINA BARI KOLATA,** Research News Editor, *Science*
CRYPTOGRAPHY
HUMAN EVOLUTION

**ANNE LaBASTILLE,** Consultant on environmental concerns; Adirondacks guide
MAKING IT THROUGH THE WINTER

**DAVID N. LEFF,** Free-lance medical writer
ENDOSCOPY

**RICHARD D. LYONS,** Staff reporter, *The New York Times*
METHANOGENS

**MARTIN M. McLAUGHLIN,** Senior fellow, Overseas Development Council
REVIEW OF THE YEAR— PEOPLES OF THE WORLD

**PABLO MACERA,** Professor of History, University of San Marcos, Lima, Peru; Director of Centre of Andean Rural History
LIVING LEGACY OF THE ANDES

**ANDREW A. MARINO,** Research Physicist at the Veterans Administration Hospital and Assistant Professor at Upstate Medical Center of Syracuse, New York
co-author
ELECTROMAGNETIC POLLUTION

**RICHARD MARTIN,** Staff reporter, *The Wall Street Journal*
GLAUCOMA

**WILLIAM H. MATTHEWS, III,** Regent's Professor of Geology, Lamar University; Director of Education, American Geological

Institute
REVIEW OF THE YEAR—
EARTH SCIENCES

**JULIE ANN MILLER,** Life Sciences Editor, *Science News*
REVIEW OF THE YEAR—
BIOLOGY

**J. MURRAY MITCHELL, JR.,** Project Scientist, National Oceanic and Atmospheric Administration
FUTURE CLIMATE

**FRED NISBET,** Co-author of *The Golden Guide to Flowers* and author of numerous articles on landscaping and gardening
SHELTERBELTS

**PETER NULTY,** Free-lance writer
WHEN WE'LL START RUNNING OUT OF OIL

**JOHN OSTROM,** Professor of Geology and Curator of Vertebrate Paleontology, Yale University
WERE DINOSAURS WARM-BLOODED?

**BETTY PRATT-JOHNSON,** author of *141 Dives in the protected waters of Washington and British Columbia*
EVERYBODY LOVES AN OCTOPUS

**MICHAEL REEVE,** Staff member, Rosenthal School of Marine and Atmospheric Science, University of Miami
co-author PROJECT CEPEX

**EDWARD RICCIUTI,** author of *Killer Animals: The Menace of Animals in the World of Man* and many articles on wildlife and conservation
MOUNTAINS BESIEGED

**MAXINE ROCK,** Science writer specializing in conservation and ecology
ORANGUTAN—ENDANGERED "MAN OF THE FOREST"

**DAVID F. SALISBURY,** Staff correspondent, Science, *The Christian Science Monitor*
IS THE DREAM OF NUCLEAR POWER FADING?

**ROBERT M. SALTER,** Physicist at Rand Corporation, California
PLANETRAN

**RICHARD SALTONSTALL,** Free-lance writer; President of Wilderness Public Rights; guide for non-commercial canoe trips
WILDERNESS PERMITS

**JANE SAMZ,** Assistant Editor, *Science World*
REVIEW OF THE YEAR—
COMPUTERS AND MATHEMATICS

**RICHARD SEVERO,** Staff reporter, *The New York Times*
THE STIGMA OF CANCER

**JAMES A. SHAW,** Assistant Professor of Biology, Oklahoma State University
co-author
THE WOLF THAT LOST ITS GENES

**ROBERT STROHM,** Managing Editor, *International Wildlife*
REVIEW OF THE YEAR—
WILDLIFE

**KENNETH V. THIEMANN,** Professor of Biological Sciences, University of California at Santa Cruz
WHY DO LEAVES TURN COLOR IN THE FALL?

**DIETRICK E. THOMSEN,** Senior Editor and Physical Sciences editor, *Science News*
REVIEW OF THE YEAR—
TECHNOLOGY
MEASURING MINUTE MAGNETICS

**JAMES S. TREFIL,** Professor of Physics, University of Virginia; author of forthcoming book *Physics Appreciation*
TRAVELING FASTER THAN LIGHT

**ROBERT J. TROTTER,** Editor, *Science News*
LEBOYER'S BABIES

**PETER VOGT,** Geophysicist, U.S. Naval Oceanographic Office
HOT SPOTS

**MARY ANN WALTER,** Research Associate, Rosenthal School of Marine and Atmospheric Science, University of Miami
co-author PROJECT CEPEX

**VITA WEST-MUIR,** Free-lance writer
MIGRAINE

**JOHN NOBLE WILFORD,** Director of Science News, *The New York Times*
REVIEW OF THE YEAR—
SPACE SCIENCE

**ROBERT C. YAEGER,** Free-lance medical writer
THE SELF-CARE SURGE

**JOSEPH ZMUDA,** Free-lance science writer
A NEW TELEPHONE SYSTEM

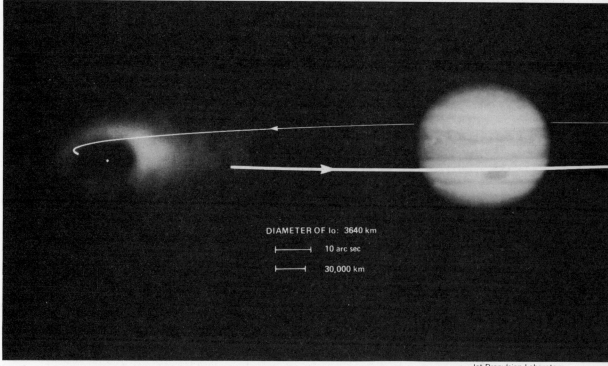

Jet Propulsion Laboratory

Jupiter's moon Io has been found to have a sodium cloud surrounding it. The photo above shows the image of Io's extended sodium cloud along with a picture of Jupiter (right) and drawings of the orbital path and Io's disk. Io's sodium cloud is thought to play a role in inducing radio noise from the region around Jupiter.

# ASTRONOMY AND SPACE SCIENCE

## contents

# ASTRONOMY AND SPACE SCIENCE

## review of the year

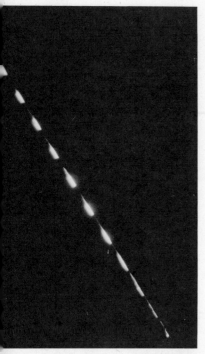

**Asteroids and meteorites.** A new planetoid, or minor planet, was discovered by Charles Kowal of the Hale Observatories and confirmed by colleagues at the University of Arizona and the California Institute of Technology. When first observed, the object was identified as a planet, but further observation showed that it was really a planetoid. It has a diameter estimated at 480 kilometers (300 miles). Its orbit, which is inclined about 7° to the ecliptic, lies inside that of Saturn and Uranus. It takes the minor planet from 47 to 51 years to complete one revolution. ■ Two new Apollo asteroids—those asteroids that have orbits that come inside the orbit of earth or Venus at their closest approach to the sun— were discovered in 1977. Named 1977 HA and 1977 HB, they were discovered by Eleanor Helin and Charles Kowal respectively and bring to 24 the number of known Apollo asteroids. ■ The largest known asteroid—Ceres—was studied extensively during the year by Larry Lebovsky of the University of Arizona. He found the first evidence of water in the surface material of an asteroid.

A two-kilogram (one-pound) chondrite meteorite was found in a rural area in Innisfree, Alberta, Canada, during the year. The meteorite was one of the few recovered soon after it reached the surface of the earth, because its passage through the sky had been recorded by special cameras designed to track meteors. ■ A group of Soviet scientists at Tomsk University have analyzed soil samples taken from the site where the famous Tunguska fireball fell to earth on June 30, 1908. They have concluded that the fireball was a comet made of the same material as carbonaceous chondrite meteorites.

**The planets and their moons.** A more detailed picture of the planet Venus is now being unveiled. Soviet scientists have analyzed the two photographs taken by the Venera 9 and 10 probes that landed on the planet in October 1975 and report that they show the planet surface strewn with heaps of slablike stones possibly made of crystalline basalts. At Venusian temperatures of around 460° Celsius (850° Fahrenheit) and wind less than one meter per second (two miles per hour) there is apparently no wind erosion to affect the stones. ■ The object called "Beta" in the northern hemisphere of Venus has been identified as a gigantic volcano by Richard M. Goldstein of the Jet Propulsion Laboratory using the Goldstone radio antennas. The volcano is thought to be over 700 kilometers (more than 425 miles) in diameter.

The year 1977 marked the first time a major ground tremor was ever recorded on another world. The Viking lander 2 recorded the occurrence of a "Marsquake" that had a shock with a magnitude of 6 on the Richter scale. This scale is used as an indication of quake activity on earth. The spacecraft that recorded the quake has landed in the Plains of Utopia. ■

both, Herzberg Institute of Astrophysics, National Research Council of Canada

Top: the Innisfree meteorite photographed as it passed through the sky about 50 kilometers (30 miles) from where it fell to earth. Bottom: main piece of the meteorite recovered at Innisfree, Canada.

Frost was seen in photographs of the Martian surface taken on September 13, 1977. At the time the temperature on Mars was about 175° Kelvin (−98° Celsius, or −144° Fahrenheit), a temperature too warm for carbon dioxide to freeze. Scientists suggest that the frost is possibly composed of clathrate, a combination of ice (water) and dry ice (carbon dioxide). ■ The two moons of Mars—Phobos and Deimos—have also been extensively studied by the Viking craft. Analyses of Viking 1 orbiter observations by Joseph Veverka of Cornell University suggest that the two moons are captured asteroids. The estimated density of the moons—two grams per cubic centimeter—and their dark appearance as revealed by Viking 2 closeup photographs are characteristics similar to those of some known meteorites. Deimos seems relatively smooth, but Phobos is heavily pock-marked with craters and is lined with parallel grooves; the largest crater on Phobos has been named Stickney. Studies by Thomas C. Duxbury indicate that Phobos is so close to Mars that after a certain time it will be broken apart by the gravitational forces of the planet.

Io, a satellite of Jupiter, has been found to be surrounded by a remarkably bright sodium cloud that is brightest close to the planet and fades in the other direction. The cloud appears to induce Jovian radio noise. ■ A possible 11th moon of Saturn has been described by Stephen Larson and John Fountain of the University of Arizona. Its image appears within 15,000 kilometers (9,500 miles) of the outer edge of Saturn's rings.

In March 1977 James Elliot of Cornell University's Center for Radiophysics and Space Research and Robert Millis of Lowell Observatory made a surprising discovery—that the planet Uranus is encircled by a system of rings of satellites, with perhaps up to 18 moons. It appears that there are five separate rings in a band about 7,000 kilometers (about 4,500 miles) wide. For a discussion of the discovery of the rings of Uranus, see "Another Ringed Planet" in the 1977-78 *Science Supplement.* ■ Scientists also learned more about the planet Uranus itself during the year. Using new equipment and techniques, they found that the planet is larger than previously thought with a diameter of about 55,800 kilometers (almost 35,000 miles) and that it takes much longer to rotate on its axis than previously believed; the Uranian "day" is about 23 hours long, not 10.8 as previously thought. ■ Even distant Neptune came under scrutiny during the year. Its brightness, once thought to be constant, has been observed to change.

**Our galaxy.** Our galaxy—the Milky Way—is traveling through space nearly on edge at a speed of about 450 kilometers (280 miles) per second, or more than 1,600,000 kilometers (1,000,000 miles) per hour, according to the reports of several astronomers who used measurements taken from balloons, from high-altitude planes, and other observations. ■ For the first time, a stellar object undergoing possible formation into a planetary system, has been found. Roger I. Thompson of the University of Arizona and colleagues at Steward Observatory and NASA's Ames Laboratory observed a possible pre-planetary disk forming around a star in the constellation Cygnus, about 8,000 light years away from us. ■ Many new molecules were discovered in the space of our galaxy during the year. They include cyanotriacetylene ($HC_7N$) seen in the constellation Taurus and isocyanide (DNC) observed in several locations including Orion. Isocyanide contains deuterium (D), or heavy hydrogen, a substance that is not believed to be formed in stars and thus must have either been in the universe since its beginning or have been formed by some non-stellar process.

NASA

Photograph of Mars' smaller and outermost satellite, Deimos, taken by Viking Orbiter 1 from a range of about 3,300 kilometers (2,000 miles).

Ames Research Center, NASA

Artist's conception of pre-planetary disk formation around a star. In 1977 a star undergoing possible formation into a planetary system was discovered for the first time.

**The Universe.** Halton C. Arp of the Hale Observatories, a long-time observer of galaxies, has suggested that quasars may be material ejected from galaxies. This theory is not new but is now receiving increased attention. It would explain the origin of quasars, their brightness, and their apparent rapid speed without resorting to arguments that they are many millions upon millions of light years away.

Katherine Haramundanis

**Space science.** The year 1977 was the twentieth anniversary of the dawn of the space age, which began with the launching of Sputnik by the Soviet Union on October 4, 1957. As perhaps was appropriate, the Soviet Union dominated events in space during the anniversary year and in early 1978. For the United States it was a year of beginnings and preparations for future major events.

**Soviet manned launchings.** The primary thrust of the Soviet program during 1977 and early 1978 was the development and testing of vehicles for long-duration manned flight in earth orbit, with the assembling of more or less permanent orbital stations as the eventual goal.

In February 1977 two cosmonauts, Colonel Viktor Gorbatko and Yuri Glazbo, flew Soyuz 24 to the orbiting Salyut 5 space station. They spent 18 days in orbit. ■ On September 29, 1977, the 19-metric-ton Salyut 6 was launched into orbit, replacing Salyut 5 and setting the stage for a succession of manned missions. On October 9, 1977, Lt. Col. Vladimir Kovalenok and Valery Ryumin rode Soyuz 25 to a rendezvous with the Salyut, but they failed in their attempt to link up with the station and returned to earth two days later.

Success did come, however, with the Soyuz 26 mission, launched December 10, 1977. Lt. Col. Yuri Romanenko and Georgi M. Grechko docked with the Salyut on December 11, and took a "space walk," to check the exterior of the Salyut space station for any evidence of damage from the Soyuz 25 unsuccessful docking attempt. Finding the space station in good condition, they then settled down to set a new record for human space endurance.

The Soyuz 26 crew was visited by another crew of cosmonauts, Lt. Col. Vladimir Dzhanibekov and Oleg Makarov, who were launched in Soyuz 27 on January 10, 1978. The Soyuz 27 craft nosed into the Salyut's second docking port to effect the first double docking in space, creating a cluster of three vehicles. After five days, the Soyuz 27 crew returned to earth in the Soyuz 26 capsule, leaving their own capsule filled with extra supplies for Romanenko and Grechko. Later, an unmanned supply ship, a modified Soyuz named Progress 1, linked with the Salyut to deliver rocket fuel, scientific apparatus, and "materials for life support of the crew." The maneuver of refueling in orbit was another "space first."

On March 2, 1978, Soyuz 28 was launched, bringing two more visitors, Col. Aleksei A. Gubarev and Capt. Vladimir Remek, to the Salyut space station. Remek, a Czeckoslovakian, was the first person in space from a country other than the United States or the Soviet Union. Soyuz 28 returned to earth with its crew on March 10.

While being visited by the Soyuz 28 crew the Soyuz 26 crew—Romanenko and Grechko—surpassed the U.S. spaceflight endurance record of 84 days. They eventually stayed in orbit 96 days, returning to earth in

Tass from Sovfoto

The Soviet Union dominated space events in 1977 with several successful manned launches and some space "firsts." Here a photo of a Soviet rocket about to be launched with a Soyuz craft.

Tass from Sovfoto

Cosmonauts Romanenko and Grechko at the central control desk of the Soyuz 26—Salyut 6—Soyuz 27 cluster.

the Soyuz 27 craft on March 16. While in space, the Soviet cosmonauts spent much of their time photographing earth, operating a prototype radiotelescope, conducting numerous experiments, and, most of all, serving as test subjects on the physiological effects of long-term space flight and weightlessness. Soviet physicians, after examining the two men, concluded that even longer space flights were possible.

**Soviet unmanned launchings.** The Soviet Union also launched more than 90 unmanned vehicles during 1977. Most of these were military reconnaissance flights, but there were also weather, navigation, and communications satellites and a biological satellite. They continued launchings in early 1978, reaching 1,000 in their Cosmos series, which has included nearly all Soviet unmanned satellites.

NASA

NASA's Space Shuttle Enterprise Orbiter is shown atop a 747 carrier jet during a test flight.

Cosmos 954, a Soviet naval reconnaissance satellite with a nuclear reactor to power its radar systems, caused great interest and concern in January 1978 when, crippled and beyond ground control, it plunged back into the earth and disintegrated over northern Canada. Fragments of the satellite, some of which were radioactive, were found scattered along a 800-kilometer (500-mile) region from Yellowknife to Baker Lake in the Northwest Territories. No one was hurt, but scientists will observe the area for many months to see if there are any lingering hazards.

**U.S. space flights.** The United States launched 25 vehicles in 1977. Two unmanned Voyager spacecraft were launched in mid-1977 on 10-year journeys to the outer reaches of the solar system. (See "Voyager" on page 33.)

The first High Energy Astronomy Observatory (HEAO-1) was launched in August 1977, inaugurating a three-mission program to study some of the most intriguing mysteries of the universe—pulsars, quasars, exploding galaxies, and black holes.

The U.S. Landsat program with its orbiting observatories with multi-scanning sensors for studying and mapping the earth's resources continued during 1977 and early 1978. Landsat 1 was switched off after more than five years of service, but Landsat 2 continued to return a steady stream of data, and Landsat 3 was launched in March 1978.

NASA

A High Energy Astronomy Observatory undergoing tests before launch. HEAO's will study X rays, cosmic rays, and gamma rays emitted by stellar and stellarlike sources.

Looking toward the future, the National Aeronautics and Space Administration (NASA) began the landing tests of the space shuttle, the hybrid aircraft-spacecraft under development as the next-generation vehicle for space travel. In three tests, between August and October, the shuttle prototype, called Enterprise, was dropped from a Boeing 747 and astronauts steered it to a glide landing at Edwards Air Force Base in California. A reusable craft, the shuttle is supposed to return from orbit using aerodynamic forces to brake and control its descent.

As currently planned, the first manned orbital test of the shuttle should come in mid-1979, though difficulties in the development of its rocket engines could cause some delay. Four two-person crews have been selected to begin training for the first orbital test flights. They are: John W. Young and Robert L. Crippen; Joe H. Engle and Richard H. Truly; Fred W. Haise and Jack R. Lousma; and Vance D. Brand and Charles G. Fullerton. ■ NASA has also named 35 new astronaut candidates in the space shuttle program. They include the U.S. space program's first black astronauts and first women astronauts.

John Noble Wilford

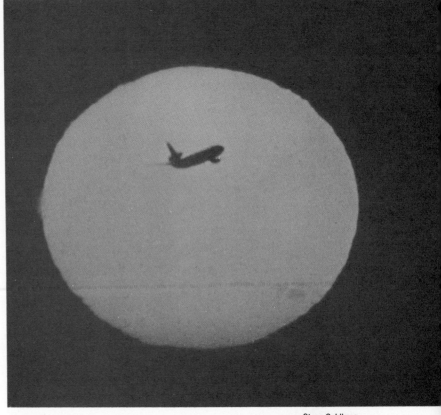

A jet aircraft silhouetted against the setting sun. The plane's exhaust blurs the left edge of the flattened solar disk.

# SUNSETS

## by John D. Irwin

A setting sun can be a colorful, even majestic affair, especially for someone on a mountaintop with a clear and unobstructed view of the distant horizon. If conditions are just right, the last diminishing bit of the yellow-orange sun suddenly changes to a brilliant emerald green. This green flash puts an exciting exclamation point to the end of a day, but is seldom seen even by astronomers living at mountain observatories near the ocean, where conditions are the most favorable for viewing the flash.

In this article, we will concern ourselves with some more common events that occur a few minutes earlier, when the solar disk is just about to touch the horizon. The setting sun presents a typical astronomical problem—an observational problem rather than an experimental one since we can do little or nothing to change what is happening. But we can frame a theory to explain the observa-tions and then verify or disprove the theory with other observations or laboratory experiments, perhaps uncovering new questions. Thus, the study of sunsets can be used to illustrate scientific method.

### WHAT WE SEE

When the setting sun is seen just above the western horizon, many effects can be observed. We list only six, some of them so obvious as to be almost overlooked. The sun is:

1. Dimmer than when it is higher in the sky.

2. Yellower or redder than when it is higher up.

3. Oblate in shape, not circular.

4. In a direction above the western horizon.

5. Moving downward.

6. Larger, considerably larger, than when higher up.

All these observations are correct in the sense that they are made repeatedly and can be verified by independent observers. But the events all are basically illusory. The sun is not, in itself, actually fainter or redder or more oblate than at other times. It is about a diameter from being in the direction seen, and it has not changed in size.

EFFECT OF LIGHT SCATTERING

The first two observations are the easiest to account for. A naive but effective method of checking this would be for a person observing the setting sun to telephone a friend in another part of the world where it is the middle of the day and be assured that the sun, there much higher in the sky, has its normal brightness, color, and shape. The effects seen by the first observer must be due to something else, perhaps to the changed conditions at sunset.

The first thing that comes to mind is that the sun's rays are reaching the observer's eye very obliquely through the earth's atmosphere, through an increased thickness of air. A rough check on this hypothesis is easily made in a smoggy city. On very clear days the setting sun is relatively bright and only slightly yellowed, but on days when the air is loaded with smoke and dust the setting sun can become very dim and almost blood red.

As a more critical test, the astronomer can measure with a high-precision photoelectric device the brightnesses and colors of rising and setting stars. The astronomer can then determine that the greater the zenith distance the greater the dimming is and the redder the observed color.

In a perfectly clean atmosphere, the absorption of light is really a scattering by the air molecules. The beautiful blue of the daytime sky is scattered sunlight. The yellow-red rays of the setting sun, although somewhat scattered, come through much more effectively than rays of shorter wavelength. Similarly, the rising sun is also dimmed and reddened, but normally not as much as the setting sun because in the morning the air is not as dusty or smoggy as it becomes later in the day.

EFFECT OF REFRACTION

Observations that the setting sun is oblate and above the western horizon are closely related. Both are explained by atmospheric refraction, an effect known to the Danish astronomer Tycho Brahe in the late 16th century from his careful measurements of star positions. Light entering the earth's atmosphere obliquely is bent downward, causing all celestial objects to appear higher in the sky than they actually are. This shift is

The earth's atmosphere absorbs and scatters the sun's rays, producing varied and beautiful color effects. In the photo below, we see the somewhat hazy yellow red of the setting sun and the shadow that the 3,000-meter Mt. Haleakala volcano casts across the Pacific Ocean.

Leif J. Robinson

both, Dennis di Cicco

As the sun sets, atmospheric refraction causes it to appear oblate, not round. In the top photo, the sun's horizontal diameter is greater than its vertical diameter and the lower part of the disk appears flattened. Under favorable atmospheric conditions the last blue and violet rays of the setting sun are seen as a bright green flash, as in the lower photo.

zero at the zenith, and increases to about 35 minutes of arc at the horizon, which is slightly more than the angular diameter of the sun.

But why does this atmospheric refraction occur? Theory, checked in depth by experiment, tells us the cause: light is slowed down slightly when it travels through air. It slows down only 87 kilometers (52 miles) per second, a very small amount compared to the 300,000-kilometer (186,000 mile) per-second speed of light in empty space.

Another way of saying this is that air, at normal temperature and pressure, has an index of refraction of 1.00029. Glass, on the other hand, has an index of refraction of 1.5 or more, so light is slowed down in glass from 300,000 kilometers (186,000 miles) per second to 200,000 kilometers (124,000 miles) or less. Therefore, a small prism of glass can deviate light by tens of degrees, while kilometers of atmosphere can only bend it by about half a degree for horizon objects.

Blue light is slowed down more than red light in the earth's atmosphere, so the blue image of the sun is refracted vertically a bit more than the red one. The red image sets first, then the yellow, green, blue, and violet

ones in rapid-fire order. The blue and violet are usually weakened to invisibility by the great thickness of air, so that the last rays seen under favorable circumstances are green. The green flash can be seen much better in binoculars, and can be expected if the upper rim of the setting sun has a greenish tinge.

Likewise, the sun's lower edge should have a reddish fringe, and this too can be observed. If one observes stars with a telescope at large zenith distances, and if the air is steady enough to permit fairly high magnification, the stellar images are both enlarged and drawn out vertically. They look like small French flags turned sideways, with blue at the top, red at the bottom, and a white mixture of colors in the middle.

Atmospheric refraction causes the lower limb of the sun's disk to be raised from 35 minutes of arc below the horizon just to the horizon, at the same moment when the upper limb is refracted from three minutes of arc below the horizon to 26½ minutes above. This results in an oblate solar disk whose height is only 83 per cent of its width. This distortion from circularity is easily recog-

The rising sun presents as beautiful a view as the setting sun. The top photo shows the first view: two brilliant points of light. The lower photo shows the crescent of a partially eclipsed sun.

both, Scott Wallace

At a latitude of 42° north, the setting sun appears to move northward along the horizon as quickly as it appears to move downward, as we can see by the silhouetted trees. These effects are caused by the earth's rotation on its axis.

nized by the eye, which sees the sun as oblate, not circular. Furthermore, although the sunset observer sees the entire sun with its lower edge just touching the horizon, the true sun is actually entirely below the horizon, with its upper edge three minutes of arc beneath it.

## EFFECTS OF EARTH MOVEMENT

A sunset observer sees the sun moving downward. This illusion is caused by the fact that the western horizon is moving upward at about the distance of one solar diameter in two minutes of time.

In antiquity there were three main arguments that the sun and celestial sphere were doing the spinning and not the earth. These were:

1. Everyday experience associates motion with bumpiness; since no bumpiness is felt, the earth is not moving.

2. The earth is extremely large and massive; the sky is "obviously" much more tenuous, and therefore it should be much easier for the sky than for the earth to do the rotating.

3. Twenty centuries ago, some Greek scientists knew that the earth was a sphere, and had a reasonably correct idea of its size. But they argued that, if the earth were rotating, a point on the equator would be moving at over 1,600 kilometers (1,000 miles) an hour, and "obviously" the air and everything else on earth would spin off.

These three plausible arguments all break down on close examination. Today we know that forces ("bumpiness") are proportional to changes in velocity and not to velocity itself. Second, the sun is so far away that its velocity around the earth would be unreasonably large; the ancient argument is now turned completely around. Third, as Isaac Newton, the great 17th century British mathematician, first showed, the acceleration of gravity is about 300 times larger than the spin-off acceleration.

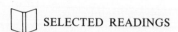
Roger Sinnott

A tranquil evening made majestic by the brilliant sky and the view of the setting sun.

The fact and amount of the earth's rotation can be checked indirectly in a variety of ways, such as the precisely measurable weakening of gravity at the earth's equator and its variation with distance north or south of the equator. Other checks are the earth's equatorial bulge, the deviation of falling objects toward the east, and the curved paths of north- or south-moving projectiles and air masses. In 1851 the French physicist Leon Foucault demonstrated with his famous pendulum how at temperate latitudes the earth literally turns beneath our feet. He made the rotation visible for all to see.

But to a climber sitting on a mountaintop and watching the sun slowly merge into the horizon, the illusion is very strong that the sun is doing the moving.

## PSYCHOLOGICAL EFFECT

As for the observation that the sun is larger near the horizon than when higher up, this is a psychological effect. It is a vivid optical illusion, in which the sun looks some 2½ to 3½ times larger than when it is high in the sky. The effect is more pronounced in a cloudy sky and with a flat rather than a mountainous horizon. The illusion of the corresponding enlargement of the moon (a safer object to look at than the sun) is instantly dispelled by viewing it through a tube that isolates it from all neighboring reference objects. The effect is striking. While many explanations have been offered, there is no generally accepted theory of the moon illusion.

Of the six setting-sun observations we have been considering, the "obvious" explanation has been wrong in every case. Only in the last case have direct measurements shown the observed effect to be completely illusory. Some of the correct explanations were difficult to arrive at, and stemmed from observations seemingly having nothing whatever to do with the setting sun. The scientist is usually not interested, at least in the beginning, in whether or not the things he or she observes are practical or relevant. They may or may not be practical in the long run. The effects encountered here are not only of vital importance to the science of astronomy, but also to physics, meteorology, and psychology□

 SELECTED READINGS

"Cloud Shadow at Sunset." *Sky and Telescope,* June 1977.

The formation of a binary system, as shown here, leaves behind a swarm of smaller asteroids.

ASTRONOMY Magazine painting by Adolf Schaller

# STARS WITH COMPANIONS

## by William K. Hartmann

MANY of us are under the impression that nearly all stars are solitary wanderers through space. When we look into the sky, we see them scattered apparently one by one, and a casual survey with a telescope seems to reveal that there is only a small fraction of stars with companions. Traditional astronomy books and even some astrophysicists therefore discuss stars that have companions as if they were peculiar rarities.

Recent work is changing these preconceptions; in fact, most stars are not single. Stars that have planets as companions and stars that have other stars as companions may even be different end results of the same basic formation process.

We obtain our best statistics from the stars closest to the solar system, because these are the most easily visible. If we investigate all the known nearby systems, we quickly find that most of them are not single. There's a good reason to claim that this "local group" is a representative sample of all the stars in our galaxy's disk, because the disk's stars have been well mixed during the 50 or so trips they've made around the nucleus since the galaxy formed. What statistics on stellar companions can we record from such an investigation? We can determine the masses of stars as compared to that of the

sun. We can also record the orbits of stellar companions in terms of how far they are separated from one another. We measure this distance in astronomical units (A.U.). One astronomical unit is equal to the distance between the earth and the sun, or approximately 150,000,000 kilometers (93,000,000 miles).

### START WITH THE SUN

We begin our survey with the nearest star, our sun. The sun has a mass which is written as $1M_\odot$. Is the sun single? Certainly not. Its most obvious companion, from the viewpoint of a stellar astronaut, is an object with mass $0.001\ M_\odot$—Jupiter. Jupiter isn't a true star because it doesn't have enough mass to generate central pressures or temperatures to create nuclear reactions characteristic of a true star. It would need about 80 times more mass than it has to do that. It does, however, emit more energy than it receives from the sun, and it might be called an "almost-star" that never quite made it.

### THE CLOSEST STARS

After we leave the solar system, the next nearest star system is also multiple—that of Alpha Centauri. Alpha Centauri is about 4.4 light-years away. A light-year is another unit of distance used in astronomy. One light year is the distance that light travels in a vacuum in one year, or approximately 9,600,000,000,000 kilometers (6,000,000,000,000 miles).

The brightest star in that system is Alpha Centauri A, a sunlike star with a mass of 1.1 $M_\odot$. Orbiting about 24 A.U. from it is another sunlike star—Alpha Centauri B—with a mass of 0.9 $M_\odot$. Orbiting around that double system at a distance of some 10,000 A.U. is a small star called Proxima Centauri, with a mass of only 0.1 $M_\odot$. If any of these stars has a Jupiter sized companion, it would be very difficult to detect because of its faintness and small mass. We thus meet our first limitation in the companions we can detect even among the nearest stars.

The next nearest star is a recently discovered object cataloged as CoD31°622. It is believed to be a dwarf type star about 4.4 light-years away, and no companions are known. Therefore, among the three nearest systems, we statistically have about two-thirds with companions.

## TO BARNARD'S STAR AND BEYOND

The next stop on our reconnaissance would be Barnard's star, whose mass is unmeasured but is probably about 0.2 $M_\odot$—about twice the mass of Jupiter. Some models include several secondary planetlike objects around Barnard's star, while another analysis may find no evidence at all of a companion. We will assume there is at least one companion, and list 75 per cent of the star systems out to six light-years as having companions.

At a distance of 7.6 light-years from us is the small star Wolf 359, with mass only about 0.1 $M_\odot$ and no known companion. At 8.1 light-years is a binary system consisting of two small stars of mass 0.35 $M_\odot$ and 0.02 $M_\odot$. These two are reported circling each other at a separation of only 0.07 A.U.

Next, at 8.6 light-years, is the brilliant star Sirius, with 2.3 $M_\odot$. Its famous companion is the first discovered white dwarf, with a mass of 1 $M_\odot$ and a separation distance from Sirius of about 20 A.U. At 8.9 light-years comes still another binary pair—L 726-8. This consists of two small stars of about 0.044 $M_\odot$ and 0.035 $M_\odot$ separated by about

11 A.U. At 9.4 light-years is Ross 154, a star of roughly 0.4 $M_\odot$ and no known companion.

Thus, within a distance of 10 light-years, the statistics of our reconnaissance show at least 14 full-fledged stars organized into nine systems, of which about two-thirds are binary or multiple.

If we continue our search out to a distance of 13 light-years, we pick up a total of some 36 stars arranged in 25 systems, but the fraction known to be either binary or multiple drops to about half. To put it another way, the farther away we point our telescopes, the fewer companions we can see.

## NEARLY ALL HAVE COMPANIONS

Nonetheless, in order to understand the origin of binary stars and any possible connection with the origin of planetary systems, we must at least know the statistics of systems with one member, two members, and so on. We can compare the figures with ours above. Astronomer A. H. Batten, in his 1973 book on binary stars, summarized a number of studies on the percentage of systems with different numbers of members. We can now compare his figures with the statistics we have just generated by surveying nearby systems. Both results show that less than half of all stars are single, with the most probable fraction ranging from about one-third to one-half.

All these statistics have a direct relationship to the problem of whether we will ever find planets and alien civilizations in other parts of the universe. Theories of planet formation, for example, indicate that it is unlikely that planets will form in a system containing two or more big stars. The complicated forces acting on planetary particles from multiple stars are likely to cause the small particles to disperse before they can form planets.

We can approach these statistics in a different way by studying the distribution of masses in multiple systems. This might allow us to guess whether low mass objects like planets are common or rare in the universe. A few decades ago, the American planetary astronomer Gerard Kuiper studied the statistics of binary stars and concluded that the

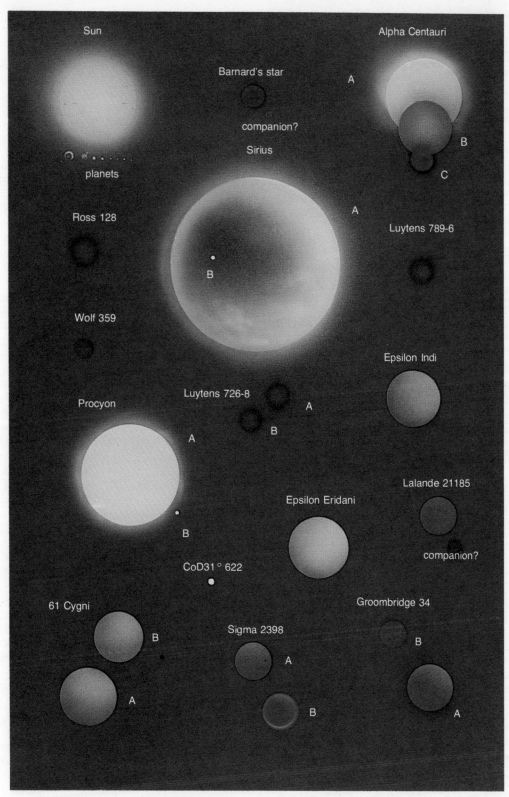

Sun

Barnard's star

companion?

Sirius

Alpha Centauri

A

B

C

Ross 128

A

Luytens 789-6

Wolf 359

B

Epsilon Indi

Procyon

Luytens 726-8

A

B

A

B

Lalande 21185

A

Epsilon Eridani

companion?

B

CoD31° 622

61 Cygni

Groombridge 34

B

Sigma 2398

B

A

A

B

A

planets

ASTRONOMY Magazine painting by Mark Paternostro

The stars in the neighborhood of our own sun vary in size and spectral class. It is estimated that half of all stars have planetary or stellar companions. The farther away a star is, the harder it is to identify its companions. In some cases we can only suspect that the companion exists.

ASTRONOMY Magazine painting by Adolf Schaller

This planet is part of a triple system.

mass ratios, or the mass of the secondary object as compared with that of the primary, were distributed approximately at random, so that a small but definite percentage of all stars should have companions with planet sized masses.

In 1976, Kitt Peak astronomers Helmut Abt and Saul Levy published a survey specifically designed to look at this question. They studied not only the number of stars with companions, but also the masses of the companions. They concluded that about two thirds of all the stars in the universe have detectable companions. But from the statistics of companions' masses, they estimated that of the other third of the stars, nearly all have companions too small to be detected by conventional means. Some of these companions might be stars smaller than one solar mass, but even smaller ones might be planets. According to this new study, nearly all stars may have at least one companion of some size.

## TWO CLASSES OF BINARIES

Still more recently, several astronomical theorists have attempted to study another question: what determines whether all the mass in a system will go into one object, two similar sized objects, or one primary and an array of small secondaries? The angular momentum, or rotational properties of the system, may be a factor. Current studies by Carl Sagan and his colleagues at Cornell University suggest that a rather special, narrow range of conditions may be required to divide the mass into a star-sized primary and planet-sized secondaries. Yet all these results hold out the possibility that at least a few per cent of all stars may have companions in the size range of planetary bodies.

The problem, though, is still not as simple as it may sound. Another characteristic to be studied in comparing binary stars, multiple stars, and planetary systems is the nature of the orbit. The orbits in our solar system are remarkably circular, with all planets lying within 18 degrees of the same plane. Is this true of binary star orbits or orbits in multiple systems? The answer appears to be no.

Batten reported studies of mutual inclinations between groups of orbits among 10 triple and quadruple star systems. Of the 10, none is less than 19 degrees in inclination, and half are more than 40 degrees in inclination. These would appear to be unlike the solar system and may have a fundamentally different mechanism of origin. On the other hand, a system named BD +66°34 may have three low mass stars in co-planar orbits—a clue that some binary systems may originate in a process similar to that involved in planetary systems, while other multiple star systems may originate in completely different ways.

Another clue in this direction comes from the survey by Abt and Levy, who found that widely separated binaries appear to be fundamentally different from close binaries. They found, for example, that companion stars widely separated from their primaries had the same statistical distribution of masses as ordinary field stars, whereas companion stars close to their primaries have a different mass distribution.

They concluded that close binaries might be related to planetary systems formed by some nebula contraction process, whereas widely separated binaries may have formed by a different process.

The orbital statistics of binaries and multiples have always been a problem. As our survey showed, there is a wide range in separation distances, from much less to much more than the size of the solar system. Any naive study of binary star catalogs would reveal two classes of binaries: one with very close orbits, and another in which the orbits are very widely separated.

For many years, however, controversy has raged over whether these two classes are real. A little thought shows that the two classes may result from our observational techniques. If we try to detect binaries photographically or visually, we will see only the ones that are farthest apart, yielding the widely separated class. On the other hand, the search for binaries with spectroscopic techniques usually relies on detecting changes favored by fast orbital motion.

The orbital motion is fastest if the two stars are very close together. Therefore spectroscopic binaries tend to be the closely paired class. So there has always been a question: is there a smooth distribution of orbital types or a separation into close and widely spaced pairs, with no middle ground?

Still another problem exists. Even if we could be positive of the present day orbits of all binaries, we would lack data on the original orbits. Tidal forces and the exchange of mass tend to change orbits' shapes. Just as tidal forces in the earth-moon system cause the moon to recede from earth, tidal forces in binaries could cause the two stars to move farther apart—or closer together.

Also, as either star evolves to the red giant stage, it could blow off mass which may fall onto the other star or escape from the system, altering the mass distribution of the system and the orbital properties. It's therefore hard to be sure that a division into close spaced and wide spaced pairs is really defining two different modes of binary origin.

More than any previous work, the survey of Abt and Levy tried to take these problems into consideration. As described, the result was that there are two groups, and the systems as small as the solar system may have formed by one process, while larger, more loosely bound systems may have formed by another.

## FORMED BY DIFFERENT PROCESSES

It is not hard to think of two processes that might account for these two groups. Those that are solar-system size may have formed by processes similar to those by which the solar system itself formed. Most astronomers and geochemists now believe that this process began during the contraction of just one cloud out of many that were contracting to form stars in an open star cluster, perhaps resembling the Pleiades or the group of stars near the Orion nebula.

In the cloud that formed the solar system, angular momentum and turbulence were such that one major mass formed in the cloud center, leaving the rest of the cloud as a cooling disk of gas. Various minerals condensed into microscopic grains and aggregated into solid meteoritelike objects as the gas cooled further. These eventually accu-

Dumb-bell nebula in *Vulpecula*.

Hale Observatory at Cal Tech

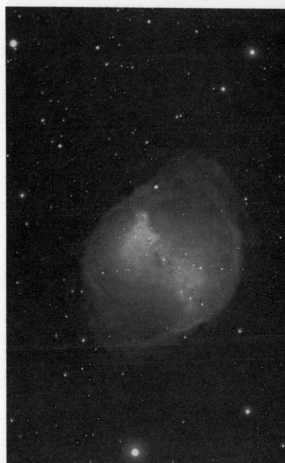

Hale Observatory at Cal Tech

The Pleiades were photographed on spectroscopic film from Mt. Pinos, California.

mulated into planets. Or, to put it another way, the planets were formed by the accretion, or adding together, of small particles.

With slightly altered conditions of angular momentum, turbulence, or mass distribution, two contraction centers might arise, so that the second largest body—instead of being the size of Jupiter (0.001 $M_\odot$.)—might be a much larger planet (0.01 $M_\odot$.) or a small star (0.1 $M_\odot$.), or even a second sun-sized star (1 $M_\odot$.).

Wide-spaced pairs or groups could have formed in the same environment if two stars or protostars (stars-to-be) approached each other at low enough velocity so that one could be captured into an orbit around the other. This capture theory of binary origin was once dismissed by astronomers who calculated that stars in interstellar space could not approach closely or often enough to allow capture. Today, however, we realize that stars begin life in the crowded conditions inside open clusters, because stars form from giant clouds which subdivide into the individual protostars of a cluster.

Close encounters may be quite common in these clusters. In 1973, Massachusetts astronomers Thomas Arny and Paul Weissman analyzed the motions of stars in clusters, and found that fully half undergo collisions or near encounters with each other before the cluster stars disperse into interstellar space. In these crowded conditions—especially with intervening gas clouds—close approaching stars might often be slowed enough to go into wide orbits around each other, creating binary pairs and perhaps occasional triples, or pairs of pairs. This would explain why the orbits of such systems often have seemingly random inclinations, since the capture orbits would occur at random.

## "SINGLE STARS"—MOST INTERESTING?

In summary, the seemingly smooth spectrum ranging from single to multiple stars may really contain two distinct phenomena: formation of systems like our solar system by co-accretion, and formation of systems by capture. The first process may sometimes produce binary stars, but at other times may form a primary object with secondaries too small to be stars—in other words, planets.

If planets form in a system with a single star, then the orbital dynamics may be simple enough for the planets to maintain circular orbits, with consequent stable climates that could permit in some cases liquid water to persist and life to form. Thus, while binary and multiple stars carry interesting clues about star formation and interactions, the one third of all stars that look single may be the ones that most likely have planetary systems.

Perhaps the next generation of astronomers and graduate students, by amassing more statistics, carrying out more theoretical calculations, and using powerful new space telescopes, may reveal what fraction of seemingly single stars actually have unseen companions, including low mass stars and intriguing unknown planets□

 SELECTED READINGS

*Binaries and Multiple Systems of Stars* by A. H. Batten. Pergamon 1973.

"Companions of sunlike stars" by H. A. Abt. *Scientific American,* April 1977.

"Survey of binaries in Magellanic cloud" *Science News,* Oct. 30, 1976.

# WHITE HOLES

George Bakacs

## by John Gribbin

FOR some time now, scientists have been following rabbits down black holes, those pinholes in space and time left by collapsing superstars whose pull of gravity is so strong that nothing, not even light, can escape. But, like Alice on her arrival in Wonderland, they have yet to find a way through the tiny door at the bottom to the garden beyond. They see no way to emerge from the adventure through that astronomical chimera, a white hole.

Black holes, these days, are positively respectable. Theories about their nature have been fine-tuned, and astronomers believe they have detected at least one: an X-ray source in the northern sky known as Cygnus X-1. But white holes—hypothetical points in space that nothing ever went into but from which energy and matter spew out—are still in the realm of speculation. So are the "wormholes," or cosmic subways, that connect the two.

Are white holes, space warps, and instantaneous travel through galaxies about to move from the realm of science fiction to the realm of scientific theory?

Many a theorist, including Albert Einstein, has toyed with the idea of matter and energy disappearing from one part of our universe through a black hole, only to reappear elsewhere through a white hole. Today the idea is in some disrepute because seemingly unsolvable objections have been raised.

The concept of white holes has not been entirely abandoned, however. Astrophysicists and mathematicians on several continents have been caught up in the question of what lies beyond the black hole. They argue that our understanding of white holes today is comparable to what we knew of black holes 10 or 20 years ago, and that the subject needs a lot more work. The last chapter has yet to be written.

### SCIENTIFIC FUN

The idea of white holes is so fascinating, with its implications of instantaneous travel through space and time, that it deserves re-

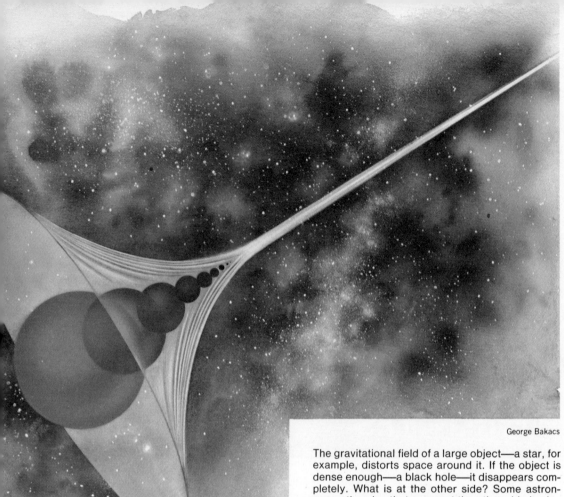

The gravitational field of a large object—a star, for example, distorts space around it. If the object is dense enough—a black hole—it disappears completely. What is at the other side? Some astronomers theorize that space at the other side is also distorted so that matter that disappears in a black hole reappears in a white hole.

porting as one of the more remarkable leaps of the mind, even if we never find the real ones. As a vision of the unseeable and the unknowable, it is a phenomenon in its own right. Even if the naysayers turn out to be right, thinking about white holes is good scientific fun—and gives us an insight into the dreams of scientists, the same kinds of dreams that produce great music and art.

White holes and space tunnels have been part of our culture for half a century or more. Science-fiction writers have long invoked such devices, using names like space warps and hyperspace, for their heroes to bounce around the galaxy at will. Cosmic subways subvert the equations that prove nothing can go faster than light, and thus that a trip across the galaxy must take 100,000 years. Whole flotillas of spaceships have left our universe by diving into hyperspace only to reappear instantly at their destination vast

distances away. For generations of readers, the scene is almost as familiar as the grim-jawed marshal facing the stubble-bearded desperado.

## CAN A WHITE HOLE SURVIVE?

White holes do appear outside the pages of fantasy magazines, but in an equally ethereal way: they show up in the same equations that tell us what we know about the apparently real black holes. Theorists ignore them because, as far as they can see, white holes could not survive in the universe we happen to inhabit.

The problem with white holes, if in fact they do exist, is that they are "inordinately shy." It seems that a white hole would be rather quickly hidden from view by a black hole of its own creation. A spaceship emerging from the white hole would immediately find itself in a black hole and once again would disappear from the universe. Alice could never wake up.

These, at least, are the calculations of Douglas M. Eardley of Yale University and Ya. B. Zel'dovich and Igor D. Novikov of the Institute of Cosmic Research in Moscow. Charles W. Misner of the University of Maryland is equally pessimistic:

"Black holes can be formed and then stay forever; white holes—by definition—have been forever and then dissolve away. Thus even a supergalactic civilization that is able to grow stars to order could not construct a white hole. If there are any white holes, they must be free gifts of the Creator, part of the initial condition of the universe, which is barely visible to modern man and certainly not yet under his intellectual control."

But if white holes are the stuff of fantasy, then black holes ought to be, too. What we call a black hole is a sphere several kilometers across. Anything that goes into it never comes out. But the sphere is really the sphere of influence, the horizon, of a single, dimensionless point in space called a singularity. And it is into this point that matter and energy disappear. The large black holes postulated at the center of galaxies, including perhaps ours, manage to swallow and compress whole stars into a point smaller than the period at the end of this sentence. Curiouser and curiouser, indeed.

## BUT WHAT IS BEYOND A BLACK HOLE?

But what really goes on inside? Do black holes simply sit in space, gulping down whatever comes by like so many cosmic frogs, growing ever more massive? That's the conventional view today, but some cosmologists have raised the question of what might lie beyond the black hole. Is it possible that "what goes in must come out," and that black holes are really the entrances to the cosmic subways our fictional starship captains have traversed for so long?

As long ago as 1935 Albert Einstein and a colleague, Nathan Rosen, now at the Technion in Haifa, Israel, published a paper in which they discussed "bridges," interconnections of our universe by timeless passage. As recently as 1975, the Indian astrophysicist

George Bakacs

If we could hold the earth—compressed to black hole density—between our fingers, then a star collapsed to a black hole would be only a few kilometers across.

J. V. Narlikar, said that studies of what might lie beyond the black hole—the white hole—were in a state "somewhat similar" to those of black holes ten years earlier. Writing with a colleague, K. M. V. Apparao, now at the Massachusetts Institute of Technology, he said: "We feel that the evidence of exploding objects in the universe (including perhaps the universe itself if it started with a Big Bang) indicates the necessity of studying white holes . . . in spite of any possible stability problem seen at present."

The universe is a pretty violent place, which presents a bit of a paradox. All our experience of gravity is as an attractive force, pulling things down and holding them together, culminating in that ultimate attractor, the black hole. But the most interesting objects we see in the universe are all expanding, even exploding, in outbursts of matter, radiation, and energy. Whole galaxies are visibly exploding and radio sources, including the enigmatic quasars, are best explained in terms of expansion, not collapse. Indeed, the universe itself is thought to be expanding with clusters of galaxies getting farther from one another. It looks very much as if the whole universe must have originated in some great cosmic explosion, the so-called Big Bang, in a fashion that sounds remarkably like the description of a white hole.

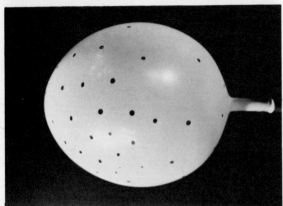

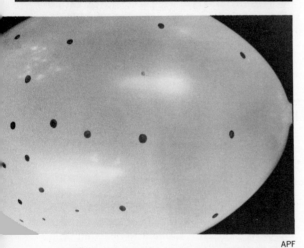

APF

The photographs above show a classic way of explaining the expansion of the universe. As the balloon is inflated, each dot, which represents a galaxy, or island of stars, gets farther from every other dot. No dot is really the center with the others moving; all the dots are moving.

In some cases, true, gravity is triggering the violence, as in the collapse of a star until it explodes as a supernova, or when X rays are emitted by matter spiraling into that black hole in Cygnus. But it is the preponderance of objects expanding blissfully away as if gravity did not exist that invites serious study of what lies beyond the black hole. Up to a point, we can explain what happens to matter inside a black hole. If enough matter is squeezed together in one place (just how much is "enough" isn't quite clear, but it is a quantity expressed in multiples of the mass of our sun), nothing can stop the matter from collapsing indefinitely. The irresistible force of gravity must literally crush out of existence the molecules, atoms, electrons, protons, and other particles of which matter is composed, squeezing everything down into a mathematical point, or singularity, where space, time, and the laws of physics cease to exist.

Ever since astronomers realized that this was what the theory predicts, there has been a widespread feeling of frustration that, by definition, such a singularity could probably never be seen, since it could only occur inside a black hole, and no light could ever escape to be monitored in our telescopes.

Recently we have seen efforts to get around this in two ways. First, the theories have been refined to take into account the effects of rotation, and it turns out that in certain circumstances rotating singularities do not become entirely invisible, but keep a window open on the outside universe. This might make them visible, but it also raises other curious possibilities, of which more later.

Secondly, however, some theorists have made a major step forward by asking: what does it really mean to say that matter is squeezed out of existence at a singularity? In exploding galaxies and the like, matter appears to be in a very dense state and conceivably could be being squeezed into the visible universe. In the last decade several astronomers have had the same idea. These exploding sources, they said, might mark the sites of singularities where matter really is pouring out from a point source, perhaps even a point singularity connected, in some mysterious way, with a black hole which is busily swallowing up matter somewhere else.

## THE ONLY WAY TO GO: THROUGH HYPERSPACE

This is where the cosmic subway or "space-time gateway" comes in—a concept even more speculative than white holes. For matter to get into a black hole and then out of a white hole without crossing the visible space in between would be no mean trick, and would have to mean that in some way it had "tunneled" through the intervening space. In effect, the matter would take a shortcut, a subway, if you will, through some higher dimension or dimensions: a hyperspace. Science-fiction readers will recognize here an old, familiar term. Those writers who have taken the trouble over the years to think about such things have always sought to explain space travel at velocities faster than the speed of light by invoking just this kind of cosmic shortcut. Isaac Asimov's classic *Foundation Series,* or *Trilogy,* which had its origin in the course of a subway ride taken by the author in 1941, is no exception:

"He had steeled himself just a little for the Jump through hyper-space, a phenomenon one did not experience in simple interplanetary trips. The Jump remained, and would probably remain forever, the only practical method of traveling between the stars. Travel through ordinary space could proceed at no more than [the speed] of ordinary light . . . and that would have meant years of travel between even the nearest of inhabited systems. Through hyper-space, that unimaginable region that was neither space nor time, matter nor energy, something nor nothing, one could traverse the length of the Galaxy in the interval between two neighboring instants of time."

In essence, Asimov's spaceship digs itself a black hole, crawls in, and pops out somewhere else. The major snag, though, is that the only way we know of to make a black hole today is by putting the mass of three suns together, and this would make for a rather impracticable, hefty spaceship.

Adrian Berry, a British science writer, has proposed instead that the inhabitants of the solar system build a permanent entrance to the cosmic subway by constructing a black hole outside the orbit of Pluto, the farthest known planet in our solar system. Better, perhaps, to find a natural hole in space and dive right in. It might be difficult to decide "where" and "when" (let alone "how" or even "whether") to emerge again, because hyperspace really could be both timeless and spaceless, a region where "before" and "after" could be as meaningless as "above" and "below," "forward" or "backward." The best solution of all, in theory, would be to find a natural black hole already connected, through the cosmic subway, to a white hole somewhere else, and to use it in much the same way as we would a normal subway. But even this has its problems.

The problem, referred to earlier, is stability. John A. Wheeler, Professor of Physics at the University of Texas, says that even if there were such a "cosmic subway" connection, it has been recognized that any bridge between two universes—*i.e.,* the Einstein-Rosen bridge—or a wormhole connecting two different points in the same universe, would "pinch, melt, squeeze, slough off—or disconnect—in a fantastically short time." Others have calculated the lifetime of a wormhole at 1/10,000 of a second.

Alan P. Lightman of Harvard University and the Smithsonian Astrophysical Observatory compares the stability of this system or structure to sharpened pencils. Well-sharpened pencils are never found standing on their points, he says, because even though in theory they could precisely balance the forces acting on them, in actuality they come tumbling down under the slightest external disturbance.

Even before worrying about whether the tunnel will collapse, a space traveler would have to survive the sheer feat of entering the subway through a black hole. It may be that a collapsing object shaped like a football would be crushed into a long, thin, thread-like singularity, not a mathematical point. And this kind of rotating "hole" could be, as far as we know, free to interact with the outside universe, unlike a simple black hole. It's as though the thread would provide a route for communication between the "inside" of a black hole and the outside universe.

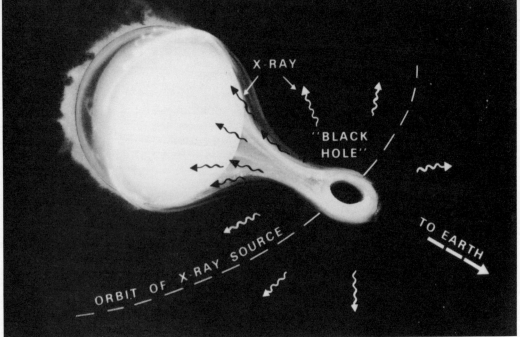

X-RAY

"BLACK HOLE"

ORBIT OF X-RAY SOURCE

TO EARTH

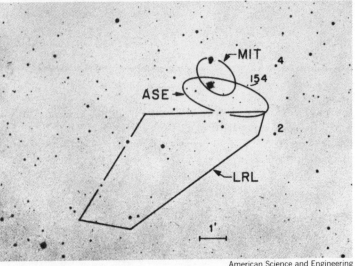

MIT

.4

154

ASE

2

LRL

1'

Astronomers believe that the binary star system HDE 226868 is linked to the X-ray source Cygnus X-1, thought to be a black hole. They have detected evidence of the visible star's gas clouds swirling around and into the X-ray source, or black hole. Cygnus X-1 is in the area of overlap between the MIT and ASE boxes on the illustration at right.

According to John G. Taylor, Professor of Mathematics at the University of London, rotating black holes can form a ring of singularity that could, in principle, be avoided by an expert navigator. Once past the ring, the spaceship would emerge not next door to the singularity in the space it had just left, but in new regions of space—and time. The intrepid traveler would emerge in a different part of the universe, at a different time—and perhaps in a completely different universe, where the laws of physics themselves might be different from those we know and love. Even the journey would be a very strange ex-

perience, with time not necessarily flowing in the everyday sense. As Taylor puts it, "the psychological problems would be as great as the gravitational ones" and "it may not be a world you [would] want to live in."

Other theorists, however, have trouble with the whole idea. They argue that the invocation of rotating black holes requires a special mathematical technique rather than the plausible laws of physics to work. Moreover, Kip S. Thorne of the California Institute of Technology and James M. Bardeen of the University of Washington have calculated that black holes in realistic environments could not spin fast enough to create space-time gateways, anyway.

## A WAY OF UNDERSTANDING EXPANSION

As yet, clearly, black holes and space-time tunnels are of no use for cosmic travel so far as we are concerned. But these bizarre ideas do offer new and perhaps better ways of understanding the violently active phenomena that characterize the universe in which we live. The most fundamental feature of the evolution of our universe is that it is expanding, and the problem of understanding this expansion is the most basic problem in astronomy.

Most cosmologists today have very little doubt that this expansion probably started with the initial Big Bang, blasting outwards from a singularity of just the same kind as has already been discussed here.

The standard way of explaining this universal expansion is to draw the analogy with a rubber balloon that is being inflated. If we imagine spots of paint marked on the surface of the balloon, it is easy to see that all the spots get farther apart from one another as the balloon expands, although no one spot can be picked out as the "center" of the expansion. The balloon's surface is two-dimensional, of course, wrapped around in a third dimension. The universe we live in is three-dimensional, and the analogy would be complete if it were wrapped around in a fourth dimension to make some kind of hyper-balloon. The present state of the observational art cannot tell us how accurate this analogy might be. But with the current speculation about black and white holes, and tunnels through space-time, it is at least possible now to make some educated guesses.

Suppose our balloon also had paint spots, corresponding to the galaxies in our expanding universe, on the inside of its skin. Extending the analogy in this way is open to dispute, but if we do allow it we now find that we have two expanding universes inextricably linked by the expanding fabric of the balloon but never in communication with one another. The balloon fabric would be equivalent to the fabric of space-time that forms the basis of our universe. A black hole singularity would now correspond to a hole in the fabric of the balloon, tunneling through into the "other unverse." From one side, the hole would be a black pit, swallowing matter up; from the other, it would appear as a singularity—a white hole—spewing matter out.

Both universes could be continually gaining and losing matter through these space-time tunnels, so that the laws of mass and energy conservation would apply not just to one universe but to the two taken together. And, although there is no such simple physical analogy, in mathematical terms it is possible, by invoking higher dimensions, to consider more elaborately connected systems of several universes joined by space-time tunnels. This is why our space traveler would have to be intrepid indeed to dive into such a tunnel.

The possibility still remains that both ends of the tunnel could be in our own universe. Perhaps the situation (at least for some tunnels) is more akin to that of a subway with stations all in the same city than to an intercontinental subway with entrances and exits scattered at random across the globe.

## ALL EXITS SEALED

One insuperable difficulty with the cosmic subway concept may be that all the exits are sealed. Many cosmologists have accepted Eardley's argument that any white holes that may have existed in our universe have long since turned into black holes. The idea is that a white hole, just like a black hole, has great mass and would therefore also attract light and all forms of matter by force of gravity. Unlike the situation at a black hole, however, any light, radiation, and cosmic debris that had fallen onto the perimeter of a white hole could not get into the white hole, but would have to float forever at the surface.

An astronaut emerging into our universe through the white hole would have to pass through this layer of "fossil light," Eardley says, and as he did so would see "the entire past history of our universe flash before his eyes." Unfortunately the astronaut would have to wear several tons of lead because the gravity would have compressed the light so radically that he would see not just "a flash

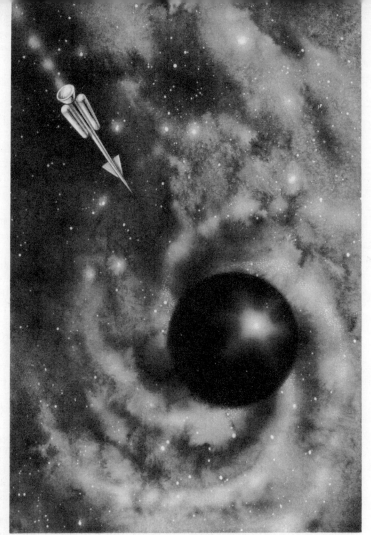

Artist's concept of a starship hurtling toward a black hole, sucked in by the intense gravitational field of the black hole. Will the starship emerge in another universe? Or is there no exit from this cosmic subway?

George Bakacs

of light" but "a blast of extremely energetic X and gamma rays" as well.

The accumulated radiation and matter would eventually produce enough gravity to form a new black hole surrounding the white hole. Now, in turn, that black hole might lead to another white hole . . . and so on. But, Eardley concludes, the astronaut could not emerge into our universe from any such white hole because all white holes would have turned into black holes. And, if a black hole is an entrance to the cosmic subway, "then there is no exit."

In the eyes of many astronomers today, this must be the last word, leaving white holes and cosmic subways firmly in the realm of science fiction. "But yet," we might say, looking at the universe as a whole, "it *does* expand." If white holes must be "part of the initial condition of the universe," then study

of these mysterious concepts must help us to understand the greatest puzzle of all, the origin of the universe itself. The burden of proof is not yet sufficient to decide the issue either way, for or against the existence of white holes, and the enormous implications of the concept certainly justify further investigation. As Carl Sagan, the Cornell astronomer, once put it, "Black holes may be entrances to Wonderlands. But are there Alices or white rabbits?" □

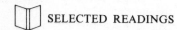 SELECTED READINGS

*Holes in Space* by Larry Niven. Ballantine, 1976.

*The Iron Sun: Crossing the Universe Through Black Holes* by Adrian Berry. Dutton, 1977.

*White Holes: Cosmic Gushers in the Universe* by John Gribbin. Delacorte, 1976.

NASA

Viking lander that was used to photograph the surface of Mars and collect other data—a forerunner of the type of probes scientists hope to develop for the exploration of other planets.

# ROBOT PROBES

## by Stephen A. Kallis, Jr.

THE surface of Venus, the surfaces of the four largest moons of Jupiter, and the atmospheres of the giant gas planets—diverse as they are—all have one characteristic in common: their environments are very hostile to humans. The most optimistic projections for manned space exploration must acknowledge that many areas of extreme astronomical interest and possible abodes of life in the solar system cannot be explored by astronauts for many decades—perhaps centuries. Even with the most favorable projections of current technology, the radiation, pressure, or heat of these various environments places them beyond the capabilities of realistically financeable manned-space programs.

In those areas of the solar system where humans can (and hopefully will) someday explore, preliminary fact gathering will have to be done with unmanned devices—robot explorers. The reason? Time. For unless the extremely near future produces significant new energy sources that would permit faster travel, the basic missions to the near and distant planets must follow orbits that are very time-consuming.

A one-way mission to the outer planets, even with a "grand tour" type of deflection that speeds the mission with a flyby, can take decades. And this is the problem with a

manned mission, which must be less long than a career. Trips that occupy a significant portion of an explorer's lifetime (presuming that the crew is supposed to return after reaching the target) are hardly satisfactory ways to explore space.

### TIME LAG PROBLEM

The alternative is the unmanned or instrumented mission. In the past, automated space probes have proven both useful and highly frustrating. They have returned much useful data, but missions have had to be conducted from orbit, or from a single spot on the surface of the target planet. The sheer size of the solar system, and the resultant time lag in communication, are the causes of most difficulties.

The moon, which is really quite close in terms of astronomical distances, is still sufficiently far away to cause a dangerous time delay of about 1.3 seconds from the time a signal leaves earth to its reception on the moon. Assume that someone "driving" a rover by remote control could react instantly to any problem that might suddenly develop. The driver does not know that the condition—a big rock or hole, for example—is taking place until 1.3 seconds after it has begun. Then the driver's signal to correct or

NASA

The Viking lander was a miniature laboratory, complete with soil sampler, here seen extended. A computer-controlled robot rover would, however, have been able to analyze much more, moving along the surface to explore interesting sites it "sees."

ural than building them into instruments that are sent to the planets?

The main advantage of computerizing unmanned space probes is that a computer can be programmed to make decisions. Given logical choices, the computer is able to act on its own. The addition of a computer can therefore make an unmanned space probe "intelligent"—though the intelligence actually belongs to the people who program it.

Perhaps the most frustrating aspect of the photographs sent back from the Viking mission to Mars was the close Martian horizon. The almost irresistible urge for anyone standing at that location would be to see what was over the horizon (even if it turned out to be more of the same). A rover could theoretically be signaled to see what was over the horizon, but the time lag between earth and Mars is so great—more than four minutes at best, and much longer in the Viking missions—that even the slowest moving rover would be impossible to control from earth. Sooner or later it would fall into a hole or get stuck on a rock. A computer controlled robot rover could, however, protect itself and steer itself safely from place to place.

## WHEELED ROBOTS

For Mars, Mercury, our moon, or the surface of a rocky satellite, a rover could be constructed along the lines of a wheeled vehicle. Use of the rover is almost dictated because there is no other effective way to explore the surface and near surface of these bodies. Unlike remote control rovers, though, the exploring vehicles will have sensors to help them avoid pitfalls.

A typical rover would have some sort of balancing device—perhaps a bubble level or plumb bob. Signals from the device would inform the rover which way is "up" locally, so that it can avoid a slope too steep. Sensors on its wheels would enable it to feel ground that was beginning to give way, so that it could retreat from a dangerous situation. Depending upon the sophistication of the equipment available for the mission, the rover might even be able to see obstructions. If the technology does not permit this, a rover would have to feel its way along. Either way, it would be able to avoid obstacles.

compensate for the problem (to "put on the brakes") would take another 1.3 seconds to reach the moon. That is a total time lapse of 2.6 seconds—even when the driver reacts instantly. One Soviet rover had a solution to this problem, but it was hardly practical for any place but the moon: the rover was geared to move so slowly that it could not get into trouble fast enough so that the time lag would be a factor. Such a slow rover is a solution, but there are better ones.

## "INTELLIGENT" PROBES

Consider, for example, the great strides that have been made in computerization. Today, computers like those that used to fill whole rooms with electronic equipment are available off the shelf in sizes small enough to fit in an attache case. New technologies can provide customized computers much smaller than that. Computers currently are used in conjunction with earthbound astronomical instruments, such as optical and radio telescopes. So what could be more nat-

The boon to astronomy from such a rover would be immense. It could send back a series of photographs from different vantage points. This would permit stereoscopic pictures of the surface revealing a wealth of detail about surface topography. By correlating the surface pictures with those from an orbiting satellite, the details of the planet's characteristics could be extended far beyond what a single panorama from the surface or orbital mapping could produce. The orbiting satellite—like the Viking orbiter—could be used to position the rover's location with great accuracy.

## ROBOT BALLOONS AND GLIDERS

Mars is a relatively friendly environment—compared to Venus or the gas giant planets. Both Venus and the gas giants have thick, high pressure atmospheres, and in addition, Venus is hot. At its closest, Venus is somewhat closer than Mars, but Jupiter is at a vastly greater distance. Each type of planet would require a somewhat different "intelligent" probe.

For a gas giant like Jupiter where there may be no solid surface, neither a rover nor a static lander could be used successfully. The atmosphere of Jupiter, however, could be explored by either of two types of robot probes.

One sort of rover would be based upon the hot air balloon. A balloon can ride through winds of violent force without difficulty. A hot air balloon would be necessary because the atmospheres of most gas giants are composed of very light gases, so that even a balloon filled with hydrogen, the lightest gas known, might be insufficient to create proper lift. But a hot air (or hot Jupiter-atmosphere) balloon could. It would be necessary, therefore, to use some sort of heat source, perhaps generated by thermonuclear means (beyond current technology) to maintain the balloon indefinitely in flight. In theory, since a balloon travels with wind, atmospheric motion should be virtually undetectable; in practice, atmospheric turbulence might make itself felt.

More practical would be the albatross type of rover in which a robot glider could be used. On earth, many birds (notably the albatross and the condor) can soar for hundreds of kilometers without flapping their wings by taking advantage of thermal air currents. Human glider pilots have been able to guide their craft hundreds of kilometers by similar techniques.

A glider-rover would have to be programmed to detect favorable air conditions—thermals and other updrafts found in

Artist's conception of a Mars Rover—a free wheeling laboratory that would be able to cover some five kilometers (three miles) of Martian surface a day, sending back photographs and other data from different vantage points.

NASA

Artist's conception of slightly different type of robot probe equipped to travel along the surface of the planet or satellite it is sent to.

an active atmosphere. But the degree of mobility that a glider rover would have would put it in a class far beyond that of a balloon rover. Unlike the balloon, which is at the mercy of the winds, the glider could take advantage of conditions to travel over more selectable routes. It could, for instance, be directed to explore such atmospherically interesting features as Jupiter's Great Red Spot. Even a pre-programmed system could have enough flexibility to be told the general area to investigate—only the second-to-second reactions would have to be made by the rover. Its basic instructions would come from earth.

On an outer planet like a gas giant, a glider rover would have to be carefully designed. It would need sufficient power to control its maneuvering surfaces. It also would need to be sufficiently rugged to permit maneuvers normal to flight in a gravity that in the case of Jupiter is more than 2½ times that of

earth, while at the same time carrying a payload of cameras and scientific gear.

Robot exploration of Venus could involve several other types of rover. A wheeled rover is theoretically possible, but the extremely high temperatures found at the surface might deactivate it fairly rapidly. The ultradense atmosphere of Venus favors glider rovers and balloons, which could take closer readings than an orbiting satellite, but which could stay far enough above the surface to permit a reasonable life expectancy for any onboard electronics.

In one sense, a balloon rover on Venus is more practical than on Jupiter. The atmosphere of Venus is dense enough that a light gas could be used as the lifting medium. The gas would have to be chosen with care, since gases frequently diffuse through the skin of a balloon rather quickly. However, since there is no free oxygen in the Venusian atmosphere and hence little danger of flammability, there are more choices available for a Venus balloon than for an earth equivalent.

## NEEDED TO AVOID ERRORS

The need to develop such rovers is important. Data from a simple lander can be highly misleading—if it happens to land at the wrong spot. A nonroving lander reaching earth in prehistoric times would have reached a wholly erroneous idea of the composition of earth if it had landed in the La Brea tar pits in California. Data from the moon suggests that lunar composition is not homogenous, and it is important to remember that landing sites were chosen at different parts of the moon precisely so that a variety of different samples could be taken. In the same vein, we have no way of knowing if the rocky plains shown in the Viking photos of Mars are typical of Martian terrain.

Satellite photographs of Mars show quite different topographies across the surface of the planet. A rover would help bring some sort of relationship to the different areas—something that could only be achieved oth-

erwise by blanketing the surface of the planet with landers.

Such instrumented exploration may not take the place of manned exploration, but it generally will precede and augment the efforts of astronauts. It would be foolish indeed to dispatch a manned expedition to even our nearest neighbors without first having a very good idea of what the manned expedition would need for survival. So far from home, only our robots can tell us what the odds are.

### Robot Vehicles: Soon A Reality?

Our search for extraterrestrial knowledge has led to the development of increasingly sophisticated unmanned probes. The Surveyors on the moon and the twin Vikings that landed on Mars have probed terrain and automatically performed highly complex experiments. Yet they lacked one significant capacity—mobility. They could only examine material within a meter or two (a few feet) from where they landed. Investigation of terrain farther afield was impossible with-

An artist's concept of a balloon-type robot probe that would float over the surface of a celestial object being explored.

Small computers, similar to the one shown (right) that is used on the Voyager spacecraft, could make unmanned space probes "intelligent"—able to make certain decisions and act on its own according to its programming.

Jet Propulsion Laboratory

out moving vehicles, but control of such vehicles was out of the question as long as radio signals to and from earth were delayed by many seconds or minutes.

To circumvent this control-time phenomenon, scientists at the Jet Propulsion Laboratory (JPL) in Pasadena, California, under a U.S. National Aeronautics and Space Administration (NASA) contract, are currently using a large scale computer to investigate the requirements of unmanned, remote controlled, roving vehicles (RV).

While earthbound controllers assign goals, monitor progress, and solve problems beyond the capability of the vehicle, the rover will act to fulfill the commands while adjusting to unforeseen local circumstances. When the machine cannot accomplish the task, it will recognize that fact, stop, and call for help.

Dr. Donald S. Williams is responsible for the development of the prototype system. "Although the *initial* concept here relates to an unmanned Mars lander," Williams said, "a more practical and earlier application will be landing on the back side of the moon or, here on Earth, deep water exploration with sonar communications and their associated communications delays.

"Surface manipulators," Williams explained, "such as used in hostile environments here on Earth to handle hazardous materials, are usually controlled in a *tele-operator* mode. The operator watches the action through a protective window or on a television monitor and controls the manipulator via a 'joy stick'. The operator responds to what he sees in *real time*—not seconds to a half hour later.

"On a remote vehicle, the flight computer replaces the joy stick and partially replaces decision making functions of the human operator. The overall program is controlled from Earth, but the immediate, real time movements of the vehicle and robot are controlled by the on-board computer."

The experimental JPL vehicle has locomotive, manipulative, and sensory capabilities, which will be under control of a flight computer. The computer will issue forward, reverse, and steering commands to the vehicle's wheel drives, and will control a robot arm with six-degrees-of-freedom-reach, panning, and elevation.

From various inputs, the computer will recognize potential hazards such as a large rock or deep hole in the path of the vehicle. It will stop the vehicle and issue an alarm to human controllers.

Of primary concern in the JPL development of remote vehicle control are two computer systems: one on-board the remote vehicle, and the other at the control site. Functioning TV and robot and sensor hardware are in operation on a test vehicle.

In future, real life situations, the executive programs in the vehicle's on-board computer will be duplicated in the control site computer. This will permit the controller to try out a command for a unique situation before actually transmitting it to the vehicle□

SELECTED READINGS

"Robots don't just handle things; they do things" by J. Mattox. *Automation*, November 1976.

"Robot systems" by J. S. Albus and J. M. Evans, Jr. *Scientific American*, February 1976.

*Search for the Solar System: Role of Unmanned Probes* by James Strong. Beekman Pub. 1973.

*The Robot Explorers* by Kenneth Gatland. Macmillan 1972.

*The Next Fifty Years in Space* by Patrick Moore. Taplinger 1976.

The two Voyager spacecrafts are scheduled to fly by Jupiter and Saturn, and then one—Voyager 2—may fly on to Uranus in man's first attempt to reach and study the outer solar system.

# VOYAGE TO THE OUTER PLANETS

ON August 20, 1977, soon after the sun rose off Florida's coast, manmade fire and thunder rattled the palmetto shrub as the first of two Voyager spacecraft was launched on its Titan-Centaur vehicle. After a fitful start, the craft steadied on its course and began the first leg of its journey to Jupiter, Saturn, and beyond—a voyage to the outer planets.

On September 5, the early morning scenario was repeated. After a flawless start, this second-launched craft, Voyager 1, overtook and passed its earlier companion. It will arrive at Jupiter four months before its mate, and at Saturn nine months ahead. The slower, first-launched craft, Voyager 2, may be targeted on past Saturn to explore Uranus, if its predecessor Voyager 1 has performed well.

After exploring the planets, both spacecraft will continue farther out from the sun, probing, studying, and searching as they go. Far from earth, they will penetrate galactic space, beyond the influence of the sun, where they will cruise for eternity.

## IN THE JOVIAN SYSTEM

More than 16 months after launch—about December 15, 1978—Voyager 1 will begin transmitting photos of the brilliant disk of Jupiter. The craft will continue its approach to the planet, focusing on particular features, such as the Great Red Spot and other storms, as it gets closer.

Near-encounter will occur during the first days of March 1979. By then, high-energy radiation in Jupiter's magnetosphere will be bombarding the spacecraft and its intricate electronics. Activity on board the Voyager and back at earth will reach a peak. Shortly before Voyager 1's closest approach to Jupiter—early on March 5, 1979—the spacecraft will pass tiny Amalthea, innermost of Jupiter's satellites, and will photograph it from a distance of 415,000 kilo-

<small>NASA</small>

As the Voyager craft approaches Jupiter, its cameras will focus on particular features such as the Great Red Spot.

meters (260,000 miles). The pictures that flash toward earth will give scientists their first-ever close look at Amalthea.

Voyager 1 will whip by Jupiter about 280,000 kilometers (175,000 miles) from the visible surface of the planet. Now the radiation bombardment will reach its peak, but Voyager 1 will bore ahead. Then . . . nothing. No word from the Voyager for almost two hours as it slips behind Jupiter. Its computers will direct the flight, the data collection by its instruments, and the recording for later playback to earth. As Voyager 1 disappears behind Jupiter, scientists will obtain valuable measurements of the atmosphere of the planet as sunlight and the radio links pass through and are affected by the atmosphere.

As Voyager 1 soars away from Jupiter, boosted into its new flight path toward Saturn, it will examine all four of the big Galilean satellites of Jupiter. It will examine Io from about 22,000 kilometers (14,000 miles) at +3 hours after closest approach; Europa from 733,000 kilometers (460,000 miles) at +5 hours; Ganymede from 120,000 kilometers (75,000 miles) at +14 hours; and Callisto

from 120,000 kilometers (75,000 miles) at +29 hours.

Jupiter's gravity will slingshot Voyager 1 toward Saturn, 800,000,000 kilometers (500,000,000 miles) farther from the sun. As Jupiter grows smaller and smaller in the instruments' fields of view, Voyager 1 will continue to examine the planet and its satellites until mid-April 1979, about six weeks after closest approach.

The second craft, Voyager 2, will now move within range of Jupiter. Its "observatory phase" will begin about April 20, 1979, and will last for approximately five weeks. Voyager 2 will continue the long-term observations, making what amounts to a motion picture of atmospheric movement of the largest planet in the solar system.

Voyager 2 will navigate a more cautious course. To avoid much of the intense radiation near the planet, it will fly much farther from Jupiter than its predecessor—no closer than 645,000 kilometers (about 400,000 miles). It will not repeat the close flyby of Io, but before Jupiter encounter it will survey Callisto from 220,000 kilometers (138,000 miles) and Ganymede from 55,000 kilometers (35,000 miles). It will fly within 201,000 kilometers (125,000 miles) of Europa and will take a flashing glance at Amalthea from 550,000 kilometers (350,000 miles).

Voyager 2 will make its closest approach to Jupiter on July 9, 1979. As it heads on toward Saturn, the craft will spend the rest of July and early August looking back over its shoulder at the receding Jupiter.

### EXPLORING SATURN

About one year after the Jupiter mission has ended, Voyager 1 will begin studying Saturn, in August 1980. Instruments will begin continuous high-rate monitoring of data about Saturn's magnetosphere about one month before the craft makes its closest approach to the planet's surface—about November 13.

On its inbound journey, Voyager 1 will closely examine an object of intense interest to scientists: Saturn's satellite Titan. Titan is 5,800 kilometers (3,600 miles) in diameter, only slightly smaller than Mars. It is the only satellite known to have a dense atmosphere.

Artist's conception of how Voyager will fly behind the rings of Saturn to use its cameras and other equipment to take photographs and measurements of the planet's light and radiation.

NASA

The methane that surrounds Titan may be as dense as earth's atmosphere. Titan's mass is about twice that of the moon. Some scientists have speculated that complex organic compounds could have formed in the atmosphere of Titan and now reside on the surface, leading to further speculation that it might even harbor some primitive form of life. Voyager 1 will sail a course only 4,000 kilometers (2,500 miles) from the surface of Titan. Then it will fly behind the satellite, analyzing its atmosphere.

Saturn has other satellites: ten have been discovered, so Voyager 1 will not be satisfied by its brush with Titan. It will survey Tethys during its approach to Saturn and will survey Mimas, Enceladus, Dione, and Rhea as it leaves the planet's closest areas.

Voyager 1 is planned to pass about 140,-000 kilometers (87,500 miles) below Saturn's south pole, snapping hundreds of pictures, measuring ultraviolet and infrared radiations, and charting the magnetosphere and accompanying regions of charged particles.

As it flies away from Saturn, its instrument scan-platform will look back at the north polar region, the lighted crescent, and the tilted rings, collecting long-range information for another month.

## A SECOND LOOK AT SATURN

Six months after the first encounter ends, Voyager 2 will cruise into range in June 1981. While the course of Voyager 1 has been carefully charted, mission planners have left their options open for Voyager 2.

There are two choices. The second spacecraft could repeat the mission of its predecessor, complete with close Titan pass and flight beneath Saturn's south pole. But, if all has gone well with the first encounter with Saturn, its rings, and Titan, and if the trailing craft is healthy, controllers and scientists might pick a new path, using Saturn's gravity to boost Voyager 2 toward distant Uranus. This plan calls for another close pass by Saturn, brushing near the outer edge of the rings. Voyager 2 would whip past the ring plane about 38,000 kilometers (24,000 miles) beyond the outer edge visible from earth. It would forego a repeat of the close Titan pass, instead passing about 353,000 kilometers (220,000 miles) from Titan. Rhea would

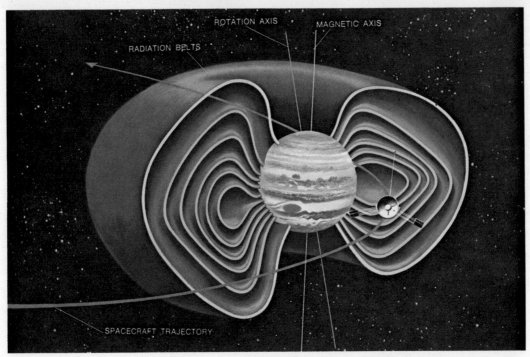

As the Voyager craft flies by Jupiter, it will collect data on the planet's variable magnetic field and radiation zones and on its interactions with its satellites and with other planets.

come within 254,000 kilometers (159,000 miles) of Voyager; Tethys, 159,000 kilometers (99,000 miles); Enceladus, 94,000 kilometers (59,000 miles); Mimas, 33,000 kilometers (21,000 miles); and finally Dione, 196,000 kilometers (122,000 miles) distant.

Voyager 2 will flash past Saturn on August 27, 1981, heading ever outward from the sun, looking back toward Saturn until late September.

## BEYOND SATURN

If the option to journey on to Uranus is exercised, Voyager 2 will sail within range of Uranus in January 1986, more than four years after leaving Saturn.

Uranus is markedly different from Jupiter and Saturn. It is tilted so far on its axis that the poles lie almost in the plane of the ecliptic. Thus, in contrast to the other planets, Uranus lies on its side. It circles the sun once in 84 years. Once in each orbit the sun shines directly down on the north pole; 42 years later the south pole is lighted. In 1986, the orientation of Uranus will allow Voyager 2 to fly almost perpendicular to the equatorial and satellite plane. Voyager 2 will get a good look at any magnetosphere and plasma cloud that may be present, and could photograph the sunlit hemisphere of Uranus

and all of its satellites. The spacecraft will also provide a first close observation of the newly discovered rings of Uranus. Voyager 2 would then sail out through the planet's wake, looking back at the dark southern hemisphere.

Years after launch, perhaps 30 times farther from the sun than earth is, their attitude control gas spent, the two Voyagers will be unable to respond to attitude correction commands from earth, and communications will fade and disappear as the spacecraft drift out of range. Their mission of discovery and exploration complete, the two craft will sail on forever.

## VOYAGER SCIENCE OPERATIONS

The scientific investigations of the Voyager mission are multipurpose. Most are intended to obtain data in a variety of environments. One family of experiments involves optical scanners. They are mounted on the spacecraft's scan platform, have narrow fields of view, and must be accurately pointed. They collect radiant energy—light, for example—from their targets and create images or spectral information that permit scientists to understand the physical form or chemical composition of the planets and satellites.

A second family of experiments senses magnetic fields and fluxes of charged particles as the spacecraft passes through them. These instruments, fixed to the body of the spacecraft, have various fields of view. Their data taken together will provide information on planetary magnetic fields and trapped radiation zones (and indirectly, on interior structures), on sun-planet and planet-satellite interactions, and on cosmic rays and the outer reaches of the solar plasma.

In a third family of experiments, antennas will listen for radio emissions and will measure waves in the plasma surrounding the planets. A radio experiment will use radio links between the spacecraft and earth to gather information on planetary and satellite ionospheres and atmospheres, and spacecraft tracking data to chart gravitational fields that affect Voyager's course.

NASA

Antennas such as this one near Madrid, Spain, are part of a worldwide Deep-Space Network that will receive radio signals from the Voyager probes.

### WHAT WE HOPE TO LEARN

A major objective of the space program is to acquire a basic understanding of the solar system and its origin and evolution. Most theoretical models state simply that the solar system started with a gaseous nebula. Temperature, pressure, and density of the gas decrease with distance from the sun. Formation of the planets is believed to have resulted from accretion of the nebular material. Observed differences in the planets are accounted for by variations in the material and conditions at formation. Knowledge gained at each planet or satellite can be related to others and contributes to overall understanding.

Missions to Mars, Venus, Mercury, and the moon have contributed greatly to this body of knowledge. Each of these planets has its own personality, significantly different from others because of its unique composition and relationship to the sun. Individual as they are, however, they are generally related as bodies that originated near the sun and are composed mainly of heavier elements. They are classified as "terrestrial" planets.

Scientists have known for a long time that Jupiter, Saturn, and the other outer planets differ significantly from the terrestrial planets. They have low average densi-

ties; only hydrogen and helium among all the elements are light enough to comprise the bulk of these planets. Jupiter and Saturn are sufficiently massive to indicate that they have retained almost all of their original material. They are, however, only relatively pristine examples of the material from which the solar system formed because, while little or no planetary material has been lost, the planets have evolved during almost 5,000,-000,000 years. If that evolution can be traced, scientists could obtain an understanding of the early state of that region of the solar system.

### THE INTERIORS: CLUES TO THE UNIVERSE

Any discussion of interior temperatures of the outer planets is impossible without knowing how much energy flows from those interiors. Discussion of their evolution requires knowledge of whether the energy is caused by primordial heat, gravitational contraction, or perhaps just energy from a short-period storage mechanism. An understanding of a planet's atmospheric structure and dynamics requires accurate knowledge of the magnitude and location of sources heating that atmosphere.

Jupiter and Saturn, unlike the dense, rocky planets Mercury, Venus, Earth, and Mars, are composed mostly of hydrogen and helium—but how much of each? The Voyager craft will, it is hoped, be able to make precise determinations. The answers will re-

NASA

Television cameras mounted on the Voyager crafts' scan platforms will provide photographs of Jupiter and Saturn and of their satellites.

A systematic study of the dynamics and composition of the clouds of Jupiter and Saturn will provide information on the cloud layers and physical mechanisms causing movement. The information, when compared to planets like earth, Mars, and Venus, will permit scientists to test general theories of climatology over widely varying conditions. The studies will be made over several months at each planet.

## EVOLUTION OF THE SATELLITES

The many satellites of Jupiter and Saturn and Saturn's spectacular rings present opportunities to understand condensed material in the outer solar system. The studies will test theories that predict the chemical composition of condensed material according to its distance from the sun, given assumed conditions in the solar nebula. The chemical histories and surface evolution, including records of meteorite impacts, of the satellites will be entirely different from the planets of the inner solar system. They are, therefore, of primary interest for detailed study.

The small satellites of Jupiter are similar to asteroids in size. Presumably, they have been pulled from the asteroid belt and captured by the planet. Because they are so small, they rapidly dissipate any heat produced by radioactive decay and should not have changed significantly since formation.

Saturn's rings are often explained as remnants of a gaseous disk that once surrounded Saturn and from which its major satellites formed. Since that description loosely compares with the formation of the planets themselves, detailed study of the rings may provide clues to the behavior of the gaseous disks that might have evolved into the satellites and, indeed, the entire solar system □

veal the general structure of the interior of the planets. If the ratio of hydrogen to helium is the same as for the sun, differences in observed properties of Jupiter and Saturn can be explained by differences in their mass and in the amount of condensed rock-forming material in the planetary cores—very small for Jupiter and perhaps slightly more for Saturn. If the ratio of hydrogen to helium varies from that of the sun's composition, and is lower at Saturn than at Jupiter, then planetary interiors without rocky cores can be inferred.

The magnetic field of a planet is an externally measurable indication of conditions deep in the interior. Jupiter has a magnetic field more than ten times stronger than earth's. The planet's radio bursts are related to radiation belts that are in turn related to the existence of the strong magnetic field. A variety of related phenomena can be directly measured by instruments near the planet. The detailed study of these phenomena and their interaction with the solar field surrounding the planet will reveal much of what lies at various depths below the clouds.

Direct evidence of a magnetic field and related phenomena is not available for Saturn. Only recently have indirect observations, from earth-orbiting satellites, indicated the presence of a magnetic field. A close-up comparison of Saturn with Jupiter will be of great interest.

 SELECTED READINGS

"Project Voyager to Jupiter, Saturn, and Beyond" by J. Schefter. *Popular Science,* August 1977.

"Voyager mission" by P. H. Abelson. *Science,* September 9, 1977.

"Voyager: multiplanet mission has message." *Science News,* August 6, 1977.

"Voyagers set for planet encounters" by J. M. Lenorovitz. *Aviation Week,* July 4, 1977.

Primate researchers have found that chimpanzees are capable of premeditated murder. It has previously been believed that only humans are capable of such crimes.

Russ Kinne, Photo Researchers

# BEHAVIORAL SCIENCES

## contents

# BEHAVIORAL SCIENCES
## review of
## the year

YLLA, Photo Researchers

A chimpanzee shows signs of recognizing its mirror image. Studies suggest that man is not the only one with a sense of self.

Senility and presenile dementia are two of the most troublesome problems of old age.

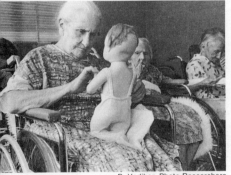

B. Vedibor, Photo Researchers

**Self-Awareness.** Until about 1970 only humans were thought to possess self-awareness. Since then, however, several researchers, notably Gordon G. Gallup, Jr., of the State University of New York at Albany, have found evidence that chimpanzees and orangutans also possess a sense of self. This finding is significant, altering previously held ideas about the evolution of mental processes. It also places chimpanzees and orangutans much closer to humans and further from other primates than previously thought.

Gallup and his associates exposed chimpanzees and orangutans to mirrors and found that within two or three days the animals exhibited signs of recognizing themselves. The animals then went on to use the mirrors—to make faces, to see and pick at food caught between their teeth, and to help them see and groom parts of their bodies that they could not otherwise view. To provide further proof that the animals were indeed recognizing themselves as the source of the reflection, Gallup went on with another experiment. He anesthetized chimpanzees and while they were anesthetized painted areas around their eyebrows and ears with a bright red, odorless, and nonirritating dye. When they awakened, the animals were observed in cages without mirrors and in cages with mirrors. In the presence of a mirror the chimpanzees tried to touch the marked parts of their bodies 25 times more than they did without the mirror. They also watched themselves more often and after touching the affected areas tried to smell and examine their fingers.

In contrasting studies Gallup and his associates found that macaque monkeys do not possess an awareness of themselves. Exposed to a mirror for some 2,400 hours for a period of five months, they exhibited no signs that they recognized themselves in the mirror images.

This and related research has led Gallup and others to conclude that there is a great gap between the great apes, the group that includes chimpanzees, orangutans, and gorillas (who have not yet been tested for self awareness), and other primates, such as the macaque monkey, and that "man may not be evolution's only experiment in self-awareness."

**New treatment approach for senility.** As the percentage of the population that is aged increases, there is more and more research on the problems specific to that age group. Senility and presenile dementia are two of the commonest and most troublesome of these problems. During 1977 Arthur C. Walsh, a practicing psychiatrist and assistant clinical professor of psychiatry at the University of Pennsylvania, reported a new treatment approach for senility. The approach involves the use of anticoagulant drugs and psychotherapy.

Walsh believes that the major cause of senility is blood sludging, or redcell aggregation that renders the cells nonfunctional. He got this idea from the work of M. H. Knisely of the Medical University of South Carolina who pointed out that blood-vessel restriction in the aged can cause red-cell aggregation and impaired blood flow. Other reports showed that anticoagulant therapy was valuable in treating blood-cell sludging among diabetics and alcoholics. Walsh then proposed to try it on senile patients.

After tests in the late 1960s revealed that the treatment had potential value, Walsh undertook a two-year study of 49 dementia patients, many of whom had been treated unsuccessfully with other methods and many of whom showed signs of severe deterioration. After treatment with the anticoagulant Coumadin and some psychotherapy, 70 per cent of the patients improved, 15 per cent dramatically so. Later 50 per cent of the patients who had improved regressed when taken off the anticoagulant.

Walsh acknowledges that serious complications are possible with anticoagulant treatment. Nevertheless he hopes that his work will pave the way for treatments that will "extend a person's usable life" and perhaps eventually make senility and presenile dementia preventable diseases.

**IQ, Genes, and Environment.** The long-standing debate concerning whether intelligence is primarily inherited or learned took a somewhat surprising twist in 1977 when University of California at Berkeley psychologist Arthur R. Jensen backed away a bit from his controversial assertion that intelligence is almost totally determined by hereditary factors. In the late 1960s Jensen published a research report arguing that genetic factors are more important than environmental ones in determining IQ. The report, which revealed average IQs among blacks to be lower than average IQs among whites, was attacked as racist and greatly fueled the debate concerning IQ determination. Now, in a report on a study of 653 youngsters in a rural Georgia town, Jensen concludes that environment is a factor in IQ. He found an apparent steady decline in IQ among rural Georgia black students as they got older and said that this "cumulative deficit in IQ" among 5-to-18-year olds is almost totally due to environmental factors of living in depressed, disadvantaged conditions that are worse than those of whites in the same area. This finding does not reverse Jensen's previous conclusion that genetic factors may play a major role in determining original IQ at a young age but does show that IQ discrepancies between whites and blacks "can't be attributed only to genetics." He said that "this means that the black-white difference at least in certain parts of the country does have an environmental cause." Commenting on the report, Harvard University psychologist R. J. Hernstein agreed that Jensen's findings strongly suggest environmental factors but he warned about the reliability and usefulness of standardized IQ tests that were designed toward the white norm.

**Crowding and human death rates.** For some years now there have been animal studies and some human studies revealing possible links between crowding and stress, crime, and other social problems, but the first report providing a concrete link between crowding and human death rates appeared in 1977. Garvin McCain and associates at the University of Texas at Arlington conducted studies of institutional death rates over a total of 26 years in which crowding conditions varied. The subjects were primarily 45 years of age or older and inmates of state prisons or maximum-security psychiatric hospitals. The study found more than a doubling of the death rate in years of highly crowded conditions over years of less crowding. They also found a significant rise in blood pressure among males in crowded conditions. These results should not be surprising, McCain states, since "there is a precedent for this in the animal literature," and "since crowding has [previously] been shown to increase illness complaints and elevate blood pressure."

Bruce Roberts, Photo Researchers

The environment appears to be an important determining factor of intelligence.

Life in overcrowded institutions appears to be associated with significant increases in crime, illness, and death rate.

Wide World

We don't know what they're saying, but we do know they are friendly, open to each other. Her arm encloses his place on the bench; they bend toward each other, hands about to touch.

Barbara Pfeffer, Photo Researchers

# HOW WELL DO YOU READ BODY LANGUAGE?

by Dane Archer and
Robin M. Akert

"THAT was terrific!" We can all transmit that message in a variety of ways. We can say it enthusiastically, praising a friend for a job well done. Or we can say it in a way that makes it clear that we are being sarcastic and that we really don't think it was terrific at all. We can raise both eyebrows in an exaggerated manner, or say the sentence very slowly, or perhaps change the tone of our voice and place unusual emphasis on the word "terrific." In other words, we can perform one or more nonverbal acts that are a "script" for sarcasm.

Even the most ordinary conversations take place in the context of a nonverbal script—facial expressions, gestures, and tones of voice that modify the meanings of the words we speak. Most of us seem able to follow and use such scripts, although few of us are capable of describing them.

## NONVERBAL ILLITERATES

The extraordinary thing is that most of us are nonverbally "illiterate." We are able to read and perform many nonverbal scripts, even though we would be hard-pressed or even unable to explain how we know their meaning. Without our fluency in nonverbal communication, however, even the simplest everyday interaction—like knowing when it is our turn to speak in a conversation—would be awkward or even impossible.

Since verbal and nonverbal behavior generally occur together, one of the key things researchers have tried to determine is the relative contribution of each. For example, psychologist Albert Mehrabian and his colleagues at the University of California at Los Angeles have tape-recorded people reading single words in different tones of voice, and have concluded that the tone of voice outweighs the word itself. But this laboratory technique may be inappropriate for the kinds of interpretations we make in real life. When we form an impression of other people, for example, are we aided more by verbal or by nonverbal clues? Before this question could be answered, we needed a new method for studying how both types of clues are actually used in natural situations.

## HOW WE INTERPRET SCENES

Since 1975 at the University of California at Santa Cruz, we have been developing a naturalistic method of studying the process of interpretation. This new method is a 30-minute videotape called the Social Interpretations Task—SIT—consisting of 20 different scenes, each 30 to 60 seconds in length, that are natural, unrehearsed interactions involving from one to four people. Each scene was edited from longer tapes of from five to 15 minutes.

We developed a multiple-choice interpretative question for each scene. In one scene, for example, viewers are asked to identify which of three men is not married. In another, viewers are asked to guess whether a young woman on the telephone is talking to her mother, her father, or a friend. One unique feature of the SIT is that all the questions have objective, unambiguous answers. In the two scenes described above, one of the men is unmarried and the woman is talking to one of the three people mentioned. In most other studies of nonverbal communication, researchers have asked people to judge emotions, attitudes, and other qualities that are difficult to verify.

First we transcribed the dialogue—the verbal information—in 16 of the scenes (four SIT scenes are completely nonverbal and could not be transcribed). We gave the written transcripts to 76 university students, without showing them the videotape, and asked them to answer the multiple-choice

questions. We showed the complete videotape to another 370 students. We then compared the accuracy of the two groups.

What follows are sample transcripts from five of the scenes, along with the questions about each. We have included photographs from each scene, which yield some nonverbal clues but, obviously, far fewer than those given by the videotapes. Try to answer the questions in two ways: first cover the photographs and answer the questions using only the transcripts. Next, see if looking at the nonverbal clues in the photographs changes your answers.

SCENE 1

## WHO IS THE BABY'S MOTHER?

### TRANSCRIPT

PERSON 1
(*woman at left*)

PERSON 2
(*woman at right*)

(*baby*)

PERSON 2 (*woman*):
Oh, who's got you? . . . Who's got you? Huh?
(*Baby makes noise.*)
PERSON 2 (*woman*):
Oh, there are more flowers on that side. . . . More flowers on that side.
PERSON 1 (*woman*):
Ahh . . . Oh, look at that boy.
(*Baby makes noise.*)
PERSON 2 (*woman*):
Whatcha doin'? . . . What are you doing? Huh?

PERSON 1 (*woman*):
Hello . . . Look at that smile.

PERSON 2 (*woman*):
Ah, can you hold that big smile?

*At the same time:*

PERSON 2 (*woman*):
That's a boy.

PERSON 1 (*woman*):
Who are you laughing at?

PERSON 2 (*woman*):
Where's your big smile? . . . Come here, ahh, umm.

PERSON 1 (*woman*):
Zachary, she's eating you!

PERSON 2 (*woman*):
Umm.

## QUESTION

Which one of these two women is the mother of the baby?

    a. The woman on the left.
    b. The woman on the right.
    c. Neither woman.

In this scene, only 50 per cent of the people reading the transcript were able to identify the child's mother—the woman on the right—while 64 per cent of the videotape watchers did so. Students reading the transcript had to guess which comments a mother would be likely to make. Those who guessed correctly often cited specific phrases; for example, many thought that "Who's got you?" was the kind of playful rhetorical question parents often ask their children. "Where's your big smile?" was also cited as the sort of comment only a mother would make: she knows the baby will produce a smile for her.

The students who saw the videotape of the same scene, however, had a banquet of potential clues. One person wrote, "The mother's voice is low and extremely sensitive to the child." Another said, "The woman on the left acted as if she had not held the baby before." A third wrote, "The woman on the right . . . wasn't afraid to touch the child." Some people commented on the baby's response to the women. One wrote, "The baby

seemed to try to get to her by reaching out his hand."

The photograph, while certainly not as rich a source as a videotape, also yields some clues to the mother's identity. The woman on the left holds the baby gingerly and tentatively, as if he were made of porcelain. The child's mother, however, leans toward the baby, trying to establish eye contact, in a proprietary yet affectionate way.

SCENE 2

## IS SHE TALKING TO A MAN?
## OR TO A WOMAN?

### TRANSCRIPT

PERSON 1
(*woman*)

PERSON 1 (*woman*):
Oh, well, you can't go because I have . . . You know. . . . So . . . Well, 'cause . . . Yeah . . . Yeah . . . Oh, you know. . . . Just awhile . . . Well, because I just had to, you know. . . . Yeah, yeah . . . I think you can do it.

## QUESTION

In this scene, the woman is talking to someone on the telephone. Is she speaking to a man or a woman?

    a. A man.
    b. A woman.

The students' comments about this scene show how nonverbal clues can sometimes prevent words from being misunderstood by modifying and clarifying their meaning. The woman on the telephone is talking to a man, yet many people reading the transcript were misled by the fact that she said, "Oh, well, you can't go."

One female student who guessed incorrectly wrote, "The woman is too assertive to be talking to a man. . . . Women aren't conditioned to talk like that to a man and if she was [talking to a man] all of her other words would have been more carefully chosen."

In fact, the words in this scene were so misleading that only 51 per cent of those reading the transcript chose the right answer, just 1 per cent more than the number who would have guessed correctly by chance, without even reading the transcript.

The students who saw the videotape interpreted the conversation very differently, and 87 per cent chose the right answer. One wrote, "She is saying 'No' with an intensely fond smile—it's probably a man she likes."

Some people noticed other nonverbal clues: "Her tone of voice was very affectionate." "She laughed like she was talking to a man." Another said confidently, "She's talking to a man—the casting down of her eyes, a coy courting mannerism." Some of these nonverbal clues—the woman's radiant smile, her fond expression, downcast eyes, and perhaps even the way she is holding the telephone—are evident in the photograph.

SCENE 3

# STRANGERS? ACQUAINTANCES? FRIENDS?

## TRANSCRIPT

| PERSON 1 | PERSON 2 |
| --- | --- |
| (*woman*) | (*man*) |

PERSON 2 (*man*):
The day we get out, I head off to Tahoe to go skiing.
PERSON 1 (*woman*):
Oh, really?
PERSON 2 (*man*):
Yeah.
PERSON 1 (*woman*):
Yeah. Some friends were up last weekend and said it was really nice. Had a really good time.
PERSON 2 (*man*):
Yeah, I've heard there was a lot of snow up there. It should be good. Hopefully, it will be.
PERSON 1 (*woman*):
Yeah.
PERSON 2 (*man*):
If everything keeps running.
PERSON 1 (*woman*):
I was . . . I was going to go to Aspen, but I think I'm going to Mexico now.
PERSON 2 (*man*):
You're going to go to Mexico?
PERSON 1 (*woman*):
Yeah, I think I could do with a change of climate . . . could be really nice.
PERSON 2 (*man*):
When are you going to go down?

## QUESTION

Are these two people:
   a. Friends who have known each other for at least six months?
   b. Acquaintances who have had several conversations?
   c. Strangers who have never talked before?

The man and the woman are strangers. This scene should have been one of the easier ones to interpret from the transcript. The two people simply do not sound as though they know each other. Neither knows where the other is going for vacation, and the woman mentions "some friends" without naming them. They are exchanging information rather formally and are telling each other things that friends would probably already know. Despite these verbal clues, only 20 per cent of the transcript readers chose the right answer, many fewer than should have gotten it by chance alone.

By contrast, an impressive 62 per cent of the videotape watchers guessed correctly. After watching the tape, with its rich array of nonverbal clues, one person wrote, "They were strangers—there was no eye contact on the part of the woman, while the man has an appraising gaze, watching her and the impression he's making." Another said simply, "They were strangers, because they didn't move around much." Their awkwardness and lack of intimacy were obvious in the videotape, by the way they sat and looked at and spoke to each other. Not all of that is visible in the photograph, of course, but the man and woman do convey the sense that they are not well acquainted. They are sitting rather stiffly; the woman is not looking at the man, and they do not have the familiar, relaxed postures characteristic of friends.

SCENE 4

WHO WON THE GAME?

## TRANSCRIPT

| PERSON 1 | PERSON 2 |
|---|---|
| (*man at left*) | (*man at right*) |

PERSON 1 (*man*):
I, uh, used too much muscle. And, uh, there's one time in particular when I hit Jack in the stomach with my elbow, which, uh, could have been avoided. Other times, I hit him, but it wasn't quite as uh . . . I, I guess, intentional as that, as that, that one was. Uh, I would try to work on layups if I did it again, so I, I could practice breaking through, see if I could get under the basket instead of relying on outside shots.

PERSON 2 (*man*):
Well, my mistake was before the game. I spent half an hour working out and I, uh, could hardly keep up with David some of the time. But on the other hand, I hit some nice long ones. So . . .

## QUESTION

The two men in this scene have just played a game of basketball. Who won?
    a. The man on the left.
    b. The man on the right.
    c. The game was tied.

In this scene, the man on the left, holding the microphone, was the winner in a one-on-one basketball game with his friend. Fifty-four per cent of the transcript readers correctly identified the winner. Some readers guessed the loser by his first statement: "Well, my mistake was before the game. . . ." The winner, on the other hand, is humble—as winners often are. Many readers correctly interpreted his almost apologetic statements as the polite humility of the victor.

Those who saw the videotape had several more clues, and 64 per cent picked the winner correctly. One watcher explained his correct answer: "The one on the left stands fairly still, while the other shows much movement, suggesting he is replaying the game he lost." The photograph, of course, does not indicate this movement, but the winner does have a relaxed, confident stance, one hand on his hip as he holds the microphone.

## SCENE 5

### WHO WON AT POKER?

### TRANSCRIPT

PERSON 1
(*man*)

PERSON 1 (*man*):
I played poker so well, like, you know, these guys just were not a match for me. I cleaned up. It was . . . What, ten minutes?
(*Voice off camera:* It was a very short game. Short game. That's too bad, Ralph.)
PERSON 1 (*man*):
So, like, you know, next time I'll give them another chance, but . . .

## SCENE 5

PERSON 2
(*man*)

PERSON 2 (*man*):
But, actually, these guys, they all think they can play poker.
(*Voice off camera:* Yeah, but they're wrong, huh?)
PERSON 2 (*man*):
But they're wrong.
(*Voice:* Yeah, well . . .)
PERSON 2 (*man*):
Actually, actually I won. . . .
(*Voice:* And his palms sweat and . . .)
PERSON 2 (*man*):
Right. Well . . .
(*Voice:* . . . hands shake. Those cards, by the time they got to me . . .)
PERSON 2 (*man*):
Yeah, actually, though I won the game . . .
(*Voice:* . . . all stuck together.)
PERSON 2 (*man*):
It was too bad, though. I didn't want to steal all their chips away. They're nicely colored and all. . . .

## SCENE 5

PERSON 3
(*man*)

PERSON 3 (*man*):
I won all the money. These hamburgers didn't have a chance.
(*Voice:* Jesus.)
PERSON 3 (*man*):
It's the truth.

## QUESTION

All three of these men claim to have won the poker game. Who really won the game?

    a. First man.

    b. Second man.

    c. Third man.

In the final scene, all three men claim to have won the poker game. The actual winner is the third man. Despite the fact that players of the game all take pride in their ability to bluff, 48 per cent of the transcript readers were able to identify the winner. People watching the videotape did even better, with 63 per cent able to pick him out.

Transcript readers who guessed correctly felt that the simplicity of the third man's statement marked him as the winner; the other two players lost credibility with their more elaborate, rambling speeches. Hearing the dialogue on videotape strengthened this impression. Referring to the third poker player, one viewer said, "He didn't need to qualify himself; he made the only definite statement." When another viewer referred to the third player's "exclamation of victory," he was being influenced by nonverbal language—the player's triumphant expression and assured, superior tone of voice.

Some of these nonverbal clues are evident in the photographs. For example, the two bluffers' hands are raised expressively, as if they are telling a story or making a point. The winner, by contrast, leans back laughing and triumphant, not trying to convince anyone of anything.

### WORDS CAN MISLEAD

The results of these five sample SIT scenes are representative of the differences in performance between transcript readers and videotape watchers on almost all the questions. People who saw the videotape did better than transcript readers on 15 of the 16 questions. Transcript readers averaged 5.50 correct answers—fewer than the six correct answers one would expect by chance guessing alone. This suggests that the transcript readers were systematically misled and not just uninformed by the words they read. By contrast, the videotape watchers had a mean

Father and son discuss politics and student activism. With crossed arms and legs, son seems to be closing himself off from his father's remarks.

Robert Houser, Rapho/PR

Is this young man feeling confident that he will get the bank loan he is requesting? What do the position of his hands and his crossed leg tell you?

of 8.85 correct answers. The added advantage of nonverbal over purely verbal clues is, therefore, beyond question.

The immense power of nonverbal clues is particularly striking in view of their fleeting, ephemeral nature. Words in a transcript can be read again and again in a careful search for meaning, but gestures, facial expressions, movements, and tones of voice vanish beyond recall—on the videotape screen as in real life—as soon as they have occurred.

Research with the Social Interpretations Task shows that most people possess remarkable interpretative powers. We are able to detect and "read" dozens or even hundreds of subtle nonverbal clues, even though they stream by us and disappear so rapidly that most of us are unable to remember more than a few of them. Our research shows that words alone provide a poor basis for making judgments about other people. The person who attends primarily to what others say, therefore, may miss the much richer revelations found in the nonverbal exchanges of everyday life. The most accurate judges of

other people attend to their nonverbal performances and not merely to what they say.

It is possible that our understanding of nonverbal clues could be improved, although it has not been tried on a wide scale. Our society places a great emphasis on words, with early and intensive training in spelling, vocabulary, writing, reading, and even foreign languages. Nonverbal communication, by contrast, appears less frequently in school curricula than even a vanished language like Latin. Since we now know that an understanding of nonverbal clues is indispensable to understanding other people, perhaps we need to explore new ways of cultivating our latent ability to read these rich, unspoken languages☐

## SELECTED READINGS

"The Language Without Words" by Robert Rosenthal, Dane Archer, J. H. Kolvumaki, M. R. Matteo, and R. Rogers. *Psychology Today*, September 1974.

*A Dictionary of Gestures* by Betty J. Bauml and Franz H. Bauml. Scarecrow, 1975.

# LEBOYER'S BABIES

## by Robert J. Trotter

FREDERICK LEBOYER, the self-styled poet of the delivery room, started a minor revolution in obstetrics in the early 1970s with the publication of *Birth Without Violence*. The Leboyer method began as an exercise in making birth as painless as possible for infants. It has been praised for its humane approach to birth, but until now there has been no solid evidence that it offers any lasting positive effects. A first follow-up study of children delivered by the Leboyer method, however, suggests that it may provide both physical and psychological benefits.

In his book Leboyer, a French obstetrician, describes in somewhat emotional and passionate terms the trauma infants go through during birth. He then goes on to offer an alternative type of delivery and describes a peaceful birth that takes place in a darkened, quiet environment. The infant, immediately after emerging from the womb, is gently lifted onto its mother's abdomen so that she can caress and fondle it for several minutes. During this process and later, as the infant is rinsed in a warm bath, the newborn gradually opens its eyes and appears to awaken to the world with a smile on its face. This kind of delivery avoids what Leboyer calls the screams of terror often heard from infants delivered in the typical sterile, brightly lighted delivery rooms of the western world.

### BORN WITH A SMILE

*Birth Without Violence* was not greeted with smiles from all of Leboyer's colleagues. Even though he made no extravagant claims for the method, other than that it is a compassionate way to treat a delicate newcomer to society, the "Leboyer circus" has been criticized for its minimal use of modern technology. The dark, shadowy delivery room, for instance, might present a hazard to both mother and child in the case of an emergency. One critic commenting on Leboyer's smiling newborns said, "The village idiot also smiles." Some of this criticism is now mellowing in the face of a study of children delivered the Leboyer way, and one hospital in France has even institutionalized Leboyer-type deliveries.

### FIRST FOLLOW-UP STUDY

The first follow-up study of children born by the Leboyer method was conducted by Danièle Rapoport of the French National Center for Scientific Research and reported in October 1976.

At a hospital in a middle-class Paris neighborhood 120 women were randomly assigned to Leboyer-type delivery rooms over a period of three years. None of the women had requested the process, but all had it thoroughly explained to them at the time their labor began. Their children born through this process—three groups of 40, now ages one, two and three years—were given standardized psychomotor examinations and have been observed by the researchers. Parents were also interviewed.

The developmental quotient, or DQ, of these children was found to be higher than average. Their mean score was 106 on a scale of 129 (100 is average). This indicates that their physical development is slightly advanced over children delivered the more conventional way. Although Leboyer's intention was not to enhance psychomotor development, such results suggest that the method does more than produce smiles on the faces of the infants.

Observations of the children show that they are exceptionally adroit and clever with both hands. This ambidextrous faculty, notable in the oldest children, has facilitated to a great extent their behavior at play. These children also began walking at an earlier age—13 months on the average, compared with the usual 14 or 15 months. They have displayed less than the normal amount of difficulty in toilet training and self-feeding and seem to be protected from manifestations of colic and shortness of breath sometimes seen during the first months of life.

## PARENTS AFFECTED TOO

The parents, too, seem to have been affected by the delivery process. Except for six women (three of whom had been anesthetized) all described the birth as a profound experience. They spoke of it as being extraordinary, moving, remarkable, and said they felt privileged. They liked all aspects of the delivery and expressed a desire to have any future children in the same way. The usual sensation of emptiness that follows birth was compensated for by placing the infant on the mother's stomach. "He was on the inside and I found him again on the outside," said one. "There was time," said another. "They let me have the time. It was unheard of."

Interestingly, the fathers seemed to take an exceptional interest in their children, especially those who came into the delivery room (after the child had been put into the bath). The women were invited to the interviews, but 80 per cent of the fathers came with them and expressed their interest. "You get more interested in a baby when you have to deal with it so soon," said one father. So, in addition to possibly enhancing physical development, the Leboyer method may strengthen the parent-child attachment

Baby, moments after birth, resting on its mother's abdomen. According to Leboyer and other researchers, such immediate body contact is important for a child's subsequent development.

Science News

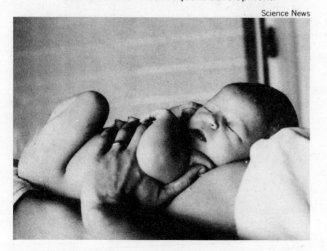

bond. This, in turn, can have lasting effects on parents' relationships with their children.

## NEED FOR TOUCHING

In a more recent book Leboyer has extended his theory. In *Loving Hands* he stresses the importance of tactile stimulation and contact between mother and child. Mothers should not only caress and massage their infants immediately after birth, he says, but should continue such treatment on a daily basis for weeks or even months, at least until the child is mobile enough to turn itself over from back to stomach. The massaging of infants with warm oil is a long-standing tradition in India, where Leboyer has recently spent several years.

This massage technique, which may seem an exotic curiosity to some, is supported by research findings. Developmental psychologists have long been aware of the fact that children who receive a minimum of tactile stimulation tend to be physically retarded, though they do often catch up with their age mates within several years. In one orphanage, for instance, researchers found that children who were severely restricted in their movements and received almost no physical stimulation did not begin to walk until three years of age. The chances they miss for exercise and exploration because of this could have lasting negative effects on development.

Leboyer further extends his theories with another import from India—hatha yoga for pregnant women. Whether these latest attempts to change our attitudes and practices toward birth will catch on remains to be seen□

📖 SELECTED READINGS

*Birth Without Violence* by Frederick Leboyer. Knopf, 1975.

"Easing a baby's way into the world: Danièle Rapoport's follow-up study on children developed by the Leboyer method" by J. Horn. *Psychology Today*, March 1977.

"Giving birth gently: the Leboyer method" by H. Higdon. *Family Health*, May 1976.

*Loving Hands* by Frederick Leboyer. Knopf, 1976.

President Lyndon Johnson died one day after plans for the dismantling of his Great Society program were announced. Were frustration and disappointment factors in his sudden death?

Johnson Library

# SUDDEN DEATH

## by George Engel

THE late U.S. President Lyndon Johnson's last years, as described in the book by political scientist Doris Kearns, were filled with disappointment and frustration. Deprived of power and influence, the retired President was judged harshly for his Vietnam policy even by former associates and admirers. Discussing the Nixon administration's efforts to cut off funds for his domestic programs, Johnson compared his Great Society to a starving woman. "And when she dies," said Johnson, who had served as President despite a heart attack in 1955, "I too will die."

Nixon was inaugurated for a second term on January 20, 1973, and the next day his administration announced plans for a complete dismantling of the Great Society. The following day—January 22—Lyndon Johnson died of a heart attack.

A coincidence? Perhaps. Still, one can't help wondering whether the demise of a man of Johnson's political passions might have been brought on by this final blow.

### BIBLICAL REFERENCES

The notion that sudden death can be traced to emotional trauma has a long and persistent history. As far back as written records exist, people are described as dying suddenly while in the throes of fear, rage, grief, humiliation, or joy.

In ancient times, the devout were prepared to believe that such deaths were at times divinely ordered. The New Testament tells us that when Ananias lied about having given up his possessions, as was required of early Christians, he was told by Peter, "Thou hast not lied unto men but unto God"— whereupon Ananias fell dead. Roman writings tell us that in the first century A.D., the emperor Nerva died suddenly of "a violent excess of anger" against a senator who had offended him.

Physicians writing before 1900 ascribed sudden deaths to intense grief, fear, rage, or triumph. But with the coming of the germ theory of disease in the late nineteenth century, which cast doubts on much folklore about medical matters, such notions fell into disrepute. Thereafter, consideration of the relationship between emotion and sudden death virtually disappeared from medical literature, although from time to time reports appeared attributing death during minor surgical procedures to "fright." Yet, with a little encouragement, physicians in private conversations were willing to recount examples of patients who they thought had died suddenly due to an overwhelming emotion.

## HELPLESSNESS

Scientific interest in the problem of sudden death did not cease altogether. For instance, the noted Harvard physiologist Walter Cannon wrote a paper in 1942, which aroused much interest, that discussed possible physiological mechanisms in "voodoo death." In 1957, Curt Richter, a psychologist at Johns Hopkins University, described an experiment in which healthy wild rats placed in a helpless situation quickly gave up struggling and died. The rats were confined in a bag, so they could not move, their whiskers clipped, and then dropped into a tank of water. Instead of struggling to keep afloat as long as possible, as most rats would, they soon stopped swimming and sank to the bottom. Autopsies showed that the rats' hearts were engorged with blood and their lungs dry, suggesting that they had died of cardiac arrest rather than drowning.

During the late 1960s, a number of clinicians began to describe patients with heart disease who had died suddenly after coming to what was described as an "impasse" in their lives or being "at the end of their rope." These reports were in accord with work being done by Arthur Schmale, William Greene, and myself at the University of Rochester in New York. Our studies suggested that illness is more likely to develop at those times when people are having difficulty coping with changes in their lives, especially when they feel overwhelmed by their problems and are inclined to give up. We had even encountered instances of people who had died suddenly, or at least unexpectedly under such circumstances.

My own interest in the sudden-death syndrome gained impetus from a traumatic event in my own life: the unexpected death of my identical-twin brother from a heart attack in 1963. Exactly 11 months later—less one day—the last day of mourning according to the Jewish faith, I, too, suffered a heart attack. This occurred during the emotional strain of anticipating the first anniversary of my twin's death.

## STUDY BEGUN

Soon afterward, I began collecting newspaper clippings on sudden death. With the aid of colleagues and medical examiners around the world, I compiled a total of 275 cases since 1965. Of these, 172 were men, 89 women, and 14 were not identified by gender in the reports. The 275 deaths generally occurred within minutes or hours of a major event in the person's life. For the most part, the victims were not considered ill at the time, or, if they were ill, they were not thought to be in imminent danger of dying.

Some of the victims were said to have had prior heart conditions or heart attacks. Though "heart attack" was given as the cause of death in many of the clippings, this diagnosis could be verified for only a small number of cases. But while the cause of death remained unclear in some cases, the circumstances surrounding death reported in the newspapers seemed to be accurate. For one thing, the kinds of events that preceded deaths corresponded with the circumstances that we had noted in our earlier studies to precede illness in general. Further, we were able to obtain independent data on 35 of the cases that elaborated upon the basic information reported in the press, and these revealed no fundamental contradictions.

Many of the clippings were reports of sudden deaths that, because of the place or the circumstances, made news. Since such newspaper reports tend to emphasize the dramatic, we also reviewed the obituaries of prominent people, to see whether we would encounter reference to some noteworthy life circumstance surrounding the death. For example, the obituary noting the sudden death, at 51, of the newly appointed president of CBS stated that he was on his way to attend

At a memorial concert honoring the late Louis Armstrong, his widow, Lucille, had a fatal heart attack as she played "St. Louis Blues." The loss of her loved one and the stress of remembering happier times such as that pictured at right were, it is believed, at least partly responsible for her sudden death.

UPI

the funeral of his father, who had died the day before. A prominent British tycoon, prematurely forced into retirement after a bitter dispute with his company, was reported to have collapsed and died at the airport as he was leaving the country for a "well-earned rest." At a memorial concert honoring the late Louis "Satchmo" Armstrong, his widow was stricken with a fatal heart attack as she played the final chord of "St. Louis Blues."

## FOUR TYPES OF EVENTS

When we analyzed the life circumstances surrounding the 275 deaths, four main categories emerged. The most common (135 deaths) was an exceptionally traumatic disruption of a close human relationship or the anniversary of the loss of a loved one. The second category (103 deaths) involved situations of danger, struggle, or attack. Loss of status, self-esteem, or valued possessions, as well as disappointment, failure, defeat, or humiliation, accounted for the third group of deaths (21 in all). And the fourth category (16 deaths) consisted of people who died suddenly at moments of triumph, public recognition, reunion, or "happy ending."

## LOSS OF A LOVED ONE

Fifty-seven deaths in the first category were immediately preceded by the collapse or death—often abrupt—of a loved one. Some survivors were reported to have cried out that they could not go on without the deceased. Many were in the midst of some frantic activity—attempting to revive the loved one, get help, or rush the person to the hospital when they, too, collapsed and died.

Two examples: a 38-year-old father collapsed and died when his efforts to revive his two-year-old daughter, who had fallen into a wading pool, failed. The clipping suggested that the girl fell into the pool while the father's attention had wandered. A 49-year-old man died two hours after hearing the news that his 22-year-old daughter had been killed and his two grandchildren seriously injured in a traffic accident.

Fifty out of the 135 cases died within the first two weeks of a loss. It was usually a spouse, but in three instances it was a twin.

Twenty deaths occurred when the survival of someone close was in jeopardy, including a 56-year-old woman who saw the wreckage of her husband's milk truck and raced more than 135 meters (150 yards) to the policeman at the accident scene. There she collapsed and died. Her husband had escaped uninjured.

In eight news items in the first category, death took place on the anniversary of a loss or during memorial services. A particularly poignant case is that of a 70-year-old man who died during the opening bars of a concert held to mark the fifth anniversary of the death of his wife, a well-known piano teacher.

## DANGEROUS SITUATIONS

The second most common circumstance preceding death—cited in 103 cases—was a situation of personal danger with threat of injury or loss of life, including fights, quarrels, struggles, or attacks. Men were victims three times as often as women. An elderly man, for example, locked accidentally in a public lavatory, died while struggling to free himself. In another case, two men who were close friends had a violent argument. No blows were struck, but one man suddenly collapsed and died. The second, who had a history of heart disease, became acutely short of breath and died soon afterward.

Situations also included natural and man-made disasters, such as earthquakes, storms, explosions, fires, shipwrecks, riots, and floods. Occasionally, the minor repetition of an earlier incident was responsible for death, causing, for example, a 50-year-old man who had survived a major earthquake to die sitting at his desk during a minor tremor a few months later.

Some victims were merely observers. A news photographer died while taking pictures of attempts to rescue a boy from an ice floe upstream from Niagara Falls. The boy was saved.

Twenty-one men and four women died shortly after danger had passed. For example, several collapsed minutes or a few hours after being in automobile accidents without suffering any injuries.

## DISAPPOINTMENT

Sudden death in the wake of disappointment, failure, defeat, loss of status, self-esteem, or valued possessions, the third category, accounted for 21 news items, all involving men. In our male-oriented culture, men are more likely to be in the public eye, while for women, the lethal events in this category may be more personal and hence less likely to be newsworthy. Lyndon Johnson's fatal heart attack after hearing the Nixon ad-

Both, UPI

Happy events can also lead to sudden death. Apparently any intense emotion, particularly if preceded by anxious waiting, can overload the body's ability to adapt and affect the heart. In the photos above, Dr. Maurice Sage takes part in a ceremony at a bicentennial dinner of the Jewish National Fund and moments later collapses, the victim of a sudden and fatal heart attack.

ministration's plan to scuttle his domestic programs might be one example. Another is the case of a 59-year-old college president who was obliged to relinquish his post under

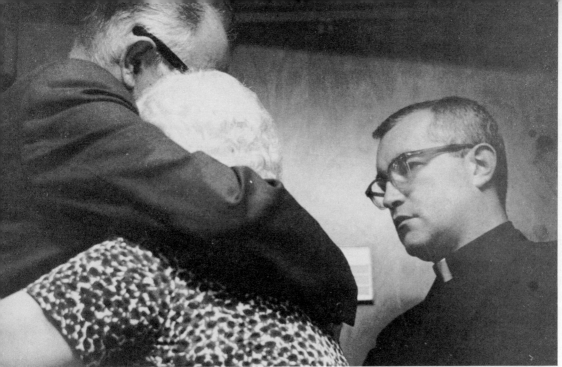

Deep grief over the loss of a loved spouse, parent, or child can lead to serious adverse physical reactions.

pressure from his Board of Trustees and was stricken at the inauguration of his successor.

Six prominent citizens died while involved in criminal proceedings or facing charges themselves. Particularly striking is the story of one witness and two defendants who turned state's evidence in the extortion trial of the mayor of a large city. All three died suddenly of heart attacks while awaiting the trial.

### "HAPPY ENDINGS"

Twelve men and four women were in the fourth and final broad category of cases. While death under circumstances described above such as grief, mourning, or fright may not be particularly astonishing, in this category people died at times of triumph, after achieving some long-sought goal—public recognition, triumphant success, or after joyous reunions and "happy endings." Some examples: a 55-year-old man died as he met his 88-year-old father after a 20-year separation. The father then dropped dead. A 75-year-old woman died suddenly after a happy week of renewing ties with her family, which she had left behind 60 years earlier. A 75-year-old man, who hit the twin double for $1,683 on a $2 bet, died as he was about to cash in his winning ticket.

### ALL WITH INTENSE EMOTION

One common denominator emerges from the medical literature and the 275 press reports on sudden death. For the most part, the victims are confronted with events that are impossible to ignore, either because of their abrupt, unexpected, or dramatic quality or because of their intensity, irreversibility, or persistence. The individual experiences or is threatened with overwhelming excitation. Implicit, also, is the idea that he no longer has, or no longer believes that he has, mastery or control over the situation or himself, or fears that he may lose what control he has. While many different emotions may be exhibited immediately before sudden death, the most frequently seen emotions seem to be those of giving up, helplessness, and hopelessness.

At first glance, situations associated with joy and triumph seem to contradict this formulation. Yet such events often involve sudden intense excitement, and others, particularly reunions after long separations, are often preceded by periods of anxious and painful waiting and anticipation. When reunion finally occurs, the joy may become mixed with intense feelings of sadness and disappointment for all the time lost during

BEHAVIORAL SCIENCES

the prolonged separation. Other instances involve pursuit of long-sought goals, upon achievement of which the person actually feels spent.

## ANIMALS REACT SIMILARLY

Sudden death in situations of psychological stress is by no means confined to humans. Trappers and zoo keepers know that animals may die when escape becomes impossible or when they are transferred to an unfamiliar locale, immobilized, or exposed to abrupt or excessive stimulation. Deaths also occur after fights without injury and after the deaths of mates.

## BODY'S EMERGENCY SYSTEMS

In the laboratory, dangerous and lethal cardiac irregularities may develop when animals are placed in situations with which they cannot contend. This is especially likely to occur among animals with already-damaged hearts, but may also develop in animals whose hearts were normal to begin with. Not much is known about just how such physiological changes are brought about, but the mechanism may involve two basic emergency systems employed by both animals and humans to cope with danger. The first, the so-called flight-fight mechanism, originally described by Walter Cannon, mobilizes the body's resources for massive and quick motor activity. The other, described as a conservation-withdrawal mechanism, prepares the body for disengagement and inactivity, sometimes livesaving when there is nothing the animal can do to cope with a threatening or depriving environment.

Each system is mediated by its own nervous-system organizations. The two are usually finely balanced in a reciprocal relationship, but sometimes, when one system is overactivated, the other may be totally inhibited. Reciprocity may break down under extreme or conflicting stimulation—for example, whenever overriding psychological uncertainty exists.

## THE HEART—TARGET ORGAN

Many animal studies have shown that even minor uncertainty may be associated with momentary cessation of motor activity and cardiac deceleration. A frightened animal's physiological reaction may begin with arousal and anticipation, but enough psychic conflict and uncertainty may invoke the inhibitory conservation-withdrawal response as well. We postulate that rapid shifts from one response to the other may have serious consequences for maintenance of effective functioning of the heart and circulation.

Laboratory animals die suddenly under psychological circumstances that are very similar to those that often accompany such deaths in humans. Further, the immediate cause of death is frequently derangement of cardiac rhythm—which considerable evidence suggests is the most frequent cause in humans. For humans and other animals, certain hormonal substances secreted in excess quantities during stress are known to predispose the heart to just such lethal arrhythmias. In the laboratory, animals can be saved from heart attacks with drugs that block nerve pathways to the heart and stabilize heart rhythm.

## PREVENTABLE?

Future experiments on animals may one day illuminate the complex sequence of events that links stress from various causes with death—and perhaps suggest ways of reversing the process. Physicians would be well advised, when dealing with patients with pre-exising heart disease or chronic illness, to try to anticipate events that might trigger sudden emotional reactions. Perhaps routine annual checkups could be scheduled before, not after, significant events such as retirement or the anniversary of a loved one's death. A physician might consider use of an anti-arrhythmic drug before a potentially traumatic event. Meanwhile, more exhaustive case studies of sudden death in humans and reserach with animal models may yield useful information for physicians and people who may be most in danger□

 SELECTED READINGS

*Psychology of Death* by Robert Kastenbaum and Ruth Aisenberg. Springer, 1976.
*Sudden Cardiac Death* by Borys Surawicz and E. Pellegrino, eds. Greene & Stratton, 1964.

Eric Hilgerdt

# AGORAPHOBIA

## by Fraser Kent

"I can go to the corner store if I have to, but it makes me uncomfortable. I feel I'm going to faint or pass out before I get back home. It's not so bad when I can go with somebody, because they could take care of me if anything happened."

Martha K. is a housewife in a small town in central Kentucky, a former teacher and mother of three grown children. She and her husband live in a large house—a house she seldom leaves except to work in the garden.

"I don't even like to go to church anymore, unless I can sit in the back row, on the aisle, in case something happens," she says. "I mean, I'd feel so awful having to run out of the church in front of everybody, or passing out where they'd all see me!"

Martha can't remember ever actually having fainted in a public place, "but I've had advance warnings. I can tell that I would pass out, just from the fluttering feeling I get."

She can no longer go to the church social events she used to enjoy, although she likes having members of the Women's Auxiliary meet at her home. She would never see her grandchildren if they were not brought to her. Mostly, she maintains contact with the outside world via telephone and television.

In short, Martha has agoraphobia.

That is the word coined in 1871 by a German psychologist, Dr. C. Westphal, to describe the fear of walking through streets or public squares. He took the Greek word for meeting place, *agora,* and combined it with the *phobia* suffix.

### COMMONEST PHOBIA

Agoraphobia is the commonest phobia. It covers a cluster of fears that involves being away from home: the fear of open spaces, of lakes and oceans, of bridges and tunnels, of crowds, of stores and theaters, of being lost, and so on. The term generally refers to various groupings of these fears as well as to any one of them alone.

It's impossible to determine just how many people have this problem because agoraphobics are usually hidden away within their own homes. Sometimes a trained observer can spot agoraphobics when they go out by their habit of walking close to walls and fences, often touching store fronts or railings as if for reassurance. Many feel most uncomfortable when crossing a wide street and would avoid walking through a park or open square.

Most agoraphobics seen by psychiatrists are female, and their symptoms usually develop between 15 and 35 years of age. These patients may also have other emotional problems, such as recurring depression, a feeling of being "outside the body" (depersonalization), obsessions, and generalized tension.

## WIDE RANGE OF SYMPTOMS

The agoraphobic's range of fears may appear at different times in different combinations and with varying degrees of intensity. A San Diego, California, psychologist said this creates one of the main difficulties in treating such patients: sometimes it is hard to tell if true progress is being made when improvement is noted, or if some of the phobic's symptoms are giving way to others. Or, on the other hand, if conditions do worsen, does it really mean that the treatment is not successful?

If one thinks of agoraphobia only as a fear of open spaces, it is hard to see why this type of person is also afraid of closed spaces, of crowds, of being lost, of losing control, and so on. Perhaps it should be defined as the fear of being at a distance from familiar and supportive surroundings. Or it can be considered as the fear of public places, if we remember that this may be only the dominant fear that ties together a group of phobias that would otherwise seem unrelated.

One group of fears centers around doing something "embarrassing" that will draw public attention, such as trembling, blushing, or vomiting. Others hinge on doing unremarkable things, such as eating, drinking, or writing, in front of people.

## ATTACKS OF HELPLESSNESS

There is a remarkable similarity in the terms agoraphobics use to describe their "attacks"—weakness, nausea, palpitations, breathing difficulties ("as though the air was being sucked out of me"), a feeling of being light-headed or dizzy, and of the ground giving way beneath them. There is a helpless certainty that they will faint, have a heart attack, or die. There is an urge to run or scream or both. There may also be a sense of unreality, of being cut off from one's safe surroundings.

In some cases the fear is apparently uniform: it peaks as soon as the person leaves home, and he or she remains in a state of panic until home is safely reached again. In other cases, the fear grows as the distance increases from home base.

In nearly all cases, there is a period during which agoraphobics can develop what may be the most painful part of their problem: the endless anticipation of disaster. They begin to plan every step of even a simple walk, and then invest every step with vague terror. Sometimes the phobic can go outside only if a sudden need arises, without a chance to build up a reservoir of foreboding about the possible calamities. For example, the phobia may vanish temporarily if the person is faced with a real and acute danger, such as a fire or accident. Of course, the phobia returns once the crisis is over.

## HOW IT BEGINS

In a study of people whose agoraphobia first appeared in adult life—by far the commonest group of such patients—Dr. Leslie Solyom of Allan Memorial Institute in Montreal, Canada, found that an anxiety-producing situation usually precipitated the initial attack. This might be a frightening or dangerous episode or a domestic conflict or crisis. In fact, agoraphobia has been called the "calamity syndrome" because it so often follows an accident or severe illness, the breakup of a marriage or family, or the loss of a spouse or child. But a phobia may also start without any marked change in a person's life or surroundings.

Agoraphobia is one disorder that can grow worse when ignored. Dr. Isaac Marks, a London psychiatrist, says: "In rare instances, the patient becomes bedridden for a while, as bed is the only place where [he or] she finds the anxiety bearable."

A fear of bridges is one way in which agoraphobia manifests itself. The agoraphobiac fears being away from home and familiar surroundings.

Not surprisingly, the agoraphobic may be depressed by the new pattern of his or her life. Obsessions and compulsions may also develop, fluctuating independently of the phobia. According to Dr. Marks, "These mostly play a small role, but at times they are as crippling as the phobia."

## DIFFICULTY IN EXPRESSING EMOTION

Several psychiatrists have observed the difficulty that agoraphobics have in expressing any feeling openly, and this often contributes to a sexual dysfunction that further complicates the basic phobia. Sexual problems can also create stress that may contribute to the onset of agoraphobia.

For example, Anne L. was engaged to marry a young Chicago architect. A few weeks before the wedding, they went to a football game where Anne suddenly felt dizzy and faint. This was quickly followed by a panic so severe she could barely "escape" from the seat high in the football stadium.

This was the first sign of a phobia that grew increasingly worse, starting with the fear of crowds and ending with her isolation at home, afraid to go out except after dark, and then only with one of her parents. The wedding was postponed, and then the engagement was broken off.

In therapy, Anne was found to have a deep-seated fear of sexual activity. Her therapist suggested she was not escaping from the football crowd but from marriage. She was not able to resolve either her sexual conflicts or her agoraphobia despite extensive treatment. She now lives with her mother, writing children's books.

It should not be assumed that the phobia grew from a sexual conflict, her therapist said. Both may have grown from the same hidden seed, to appear in different forms.

There is another sexual aspect to agoraphobia: many of its victims are afraid they will be vulnerable to irresistible sexual temptation or attack, or that they will expose themselves in a public place.

## FEARS CAN DESTROY FAMILIES

Relatively few agoraphobics live alone, so their various fears almost always affect their families.

"As the patient's restrictions increase, her family inevitably becomes involved,"

Marks observes. "She may require an escort to and from work, or give up her work. Her husband and children have to do her shopping. Social activities are restricted or abandoned. Sometimes a constant companion is required when the patient cannot remain alone at home without anxiety.

The fluctuating nature of agoraphobia makes it difficult for families and friends to accept that it is an illness and not the result of laziness, lack of willpower, or a way of getting out of awkward situations.

Agoraphobics may try to overcome their fears by deliberately facing the situations they dread, or they may be pressured into doing so by well-meaning family and friends. If these efforts fail, the phobia may be worse because it is now more difficult than ever to meet a situation that has proved to be disastrous.

## GRADUAL DESENSITIZATION

When the agoraphobic seeks professional treatment, the therapist will make certain that there is little chance of failure in confrontation. The patient learns how to relax in the presence of the phobic stimulus—the things, places, or activities that produce the most fear—and to associate that relaxation with carefully prepared "steps" away from the basic fear.

Dr. Joseph Wolpe of Temple University School of Medicine developed "systematic desensitization," the most commonly used treatment of all phobias today. It is a step-by-step process of exposing the victim in his or her imagination to whatever is feared—in the agoraphobic's case, a multitude of fears—while simultaneously providing a pleasant, or at least non-traumatic, relaxation of tension. There is no attempt to find out why a person fears such and such. The object of this therapy is to get rid of the phobia rather than to examine it. Psychologists do not usually consider the phobia to be symptomatic of a more serious emotional problem, and if they encountered more serious problems, he or she would probably be referred to a psychiatrist.

In a desensitization process, the phobic is aware of how much a feared object can be tolerated without anxiety. It is hoped he or she will calmly continue to experience the phobic stimulus without tension and anxiety as the mental image of it becomes more and more threatening. The test of therapeutic success, though, is repeating the imaginary encounter in real life with little or no psychic

Many agoraphobiacs first experience an attack of helplessness when traveling and confronted with stressful situations such as those that visits to different cities and countries can present.

Many agoraphobiacs fear tunnels. In desensitization programs, these people may be shown films of people walking through tunnels and may be accompanied on walks through tunnels in an attempt to help them overcome their irrational fear.

F. B. Grunzweig, Photo Researchers

discomfort. In a great many cases, that is exactly what does happen. In fact, it is claimed that systematic desensitization is the most effective method of treating phobia now available.

Dr. Wolpe says of the technique he originated that it is "clearly indicated for the patient who expresses a single fear or a few well defined fears, rather than multiple or vague fears." It does not work well in the person who doesn't really know what he or she is afraid of, or whose phobic stimulus changes from day to day.

### SUDDEN CONFRONTATIONS

If systematic desensitization is a careful step-by-step process of building up the phobic's ability to face whatever is feared, then "flooding" and "implosive therapy" can be described as a series of dramatic head-on encounters that are designed to tear down the phobic's anxiety reactions.

The processes sound destructive and cruel, but the phobic emerges safely after facing the worst possible outcome of the confrontation, and thus learns that there is nothing to fear.

Flooding consists of directly confronting the patient with the situation or object that is feared. Instead of simply imagining the stimulus (as in desensitization), the phobic is safely exposed to it. As with desensitization, the stimuli are carefully graded and presented in a systematic way, with the patient relaxing between encounters.

This is the technique used by Fraidy-cats, an organization that helps people combat the fear of airplane travel. They begin with lectures and slide illustrations of plane exteriors and interiors, and then they visit airports (perhaps to see someone off or just to make a group tour) and see planes moving along the runways. Then the group goes on board a grounded plane, visits the cockpit and sits down for a sociable half hour. Ultimately, they are able to go on a brief flight without discomfort and find they have pretty well overcome their phobia.

Dr. George C. Curtis, a University of Michigan psychiatrist, has described flooding as "an intense, rapid and simple" technique. He noted that "the patients know beforehand everything that is going to happen; there are no surprises. They are not forced to progress faster than they can tolerate, but are constantly urged to push themselves to the limit, maintaining anxiety at the maximum tolerable level."

Implosion therapy is more abrupt and dramatic. The patient is urged to experience the phobic stimulus as vividly and as long as possible, instead of relaxing between exposures, until he or she is "finally unable to feel fear any longer," Marks says. Instead of pushing aside each wave of tension, the patient is urged to increase it, augment it, experience it even more vividly than before until he or she simply learns to bear it.

## ROLE PLAYING

Another approach to treatment is Gestalt therapy. This behavior-oriented treatment uses various forms of role playing, sometimes as a form of group therapy. The therapist considers everything a person is doing bodily, emotionally, vocally, and so on. Dr. Carmi Harami, director of the Humanistic Psychology Center in New York City, described how this works: "The first step would be to look for the heart of the problem. If a person has an elevator phobia, what is the major inconvenience? The phobic wants to be free to go anywhere, but is confined by the fear of going up into tall buildings.

"In role playing, the therapist might ask the patient to experience being the elevator; speak in the first person as the elevator goes up and down, as its buttons are pushed, as its doors open and close. There is an integration of the self and the problem: I am my experience, my fear. As the elevator, I ask what doors I am closing on myself, for example. There is a human tendency to deal with a problem as though it is alien to oneself; we disown what we cannot accept, and the Gestalt therapist insists that you 'own' your fear. This demands a direct confrontation."

In short, this is a type of treatment in which all of the phobic's usual escape routes are blocked; the problem must be faced head on without illusions or excuses.

## MANY OTHER TREATMENTS

Hypnosis has also been used as a treatment for phobias. Dr. Theodore X. Barber of the Medfield Foundation in Massachusetts, a leading clinical hypnotist in the psychological field, says: "Hypnosis works best when used in stages, rather than trying it as a one-step cure. . . ." Hypnosis is particularly

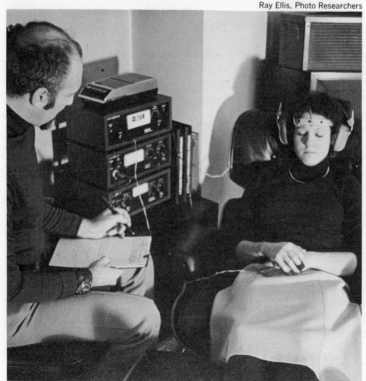

Biofeedback techniques are sometimes used to help determine which exercises might help an agoraphobiac overcome his or her fears.

For this agoraphobiac a trip outdoors looms as an impossible task.

Bob Combs, Photo Researchers

useful for those tense people who have trouble with mental imagery, and it may also speed up desensitization.

Meditation and biofeedback are also seen as aids in treating agoraphobia because they can help the patient relax.

### WHERE TO FIND ANSWERS

All of this may sound like there is a bewildering array of techniques for the treatment of phobia, but perhaps such a choice must be available because of the widely differing needs of people who really share only a symptom: the fear of something. If you or someone you know suffers from phobic symptoms, it is important to get help.

Where do you begin to look for help? Your family physician may be able to refer you to a suitable therapist. Community health centers can often provide help or guide you to a good source of assistance. You might contact the nearest university and ask for the chairman of its psychology department to tell you of psychologists involved in agoraphobia treatment in your area. Or you might write professional associations of psychologists asking for information.

You are going to invest both time and money in therapy; so once a psychologist or psychiatrist is recommended, it's fair and reasonable for you to check credentials and ask about his or her general approach to therapy. By proceeding cautiously, you can minimize the danger of ending up with the wrong kind of therapist and the wrong kind of treatment.

Above all, as you enter treatment, remember that you have nothing to fear: you may be on your way to losing the chains of phobia that have restricted your life for far too long □

 SELECTED READINGS

"Agoraphobia: Life Ruled by Panic" by Julie Baumgold. *The New York Times Magazine,* December 4, 1977.

*Nothing to Fear: Coping with Phobias* by Fraser Kent. Doubleday, 1977.

A. W. Ambler, Audubon/PR

The fennec fox is the smallest fox in the world; it also has the largest ears of any fox. It lives in desert regions in Africa and the Arabian and Sinai Peninsulas. Of all the carnivores in the Sahara, it is the only one that does not seem to need water.

# BIOLOGY

## contents

# BIOLOGY

## review of the year

National Institutes of Health

Special laboratories, known as P-4 labs, have been designed for recombinant DNA research. In these labs the research is carried out inside a system of enclosed gas-tight cabinets and strict precautions against any possible accidents are taken.

Cloning—the production of an organism from a single cell—hit the news in early 1978. Here scientists examine a vial used to store animal cells that may be used in cloning experiments.

UPI

**Ups and downs for recombinant DNA.** The power of recombinant DNA research techniques was firmly established in 1977. These techniques involve the addition of the DNA (deoxyribonucleic acid) of one organism to the DNA of another organism of a different species, producing a combination that does not normally exist in nature. There are normally barriers preventing breeding between members of different species. During 1977 the recombinant DNA procedure was routinely used in a large number of laboratories to produce large quantities of a wide variety of genes, the functional units of DNA. In May scientists at the University of California in San Francisco announced the first successful transplantation of a mammalian gene into bacteria. The gene that controls the production of insulin in a rat, joined to a small ring of DNA (plasmids), was inserted into bacteria. The bacteria did not then produce insulin, but did produce abundant copies of the insulin gene.

In November another group of scientists succeeded in forcing bacteria to actually produce a mammalian product, the human brain hormone somatostatin, which is believed to play a role in the production of insulin and of a growth hormone. The researchers tricked the bacteria into production by providing them with a hybrid DNA blueprint, or set of instructions, for the production. They chemically synthesized the gene for somatostatin production and inserted it into the bacteria along with instructions for the bacteria to "turn on" the foreign gene and start production. Somatostatin has no known medical uses, but its production in bacteria proved that there are no fundamental differences between bacterial and animal genes that would prevent bacteria from being used to produce useful animal products.

While the possibilities for recombinant DNA research blossomed, attempts to regulate research bogged down. Despite copious discussion, the U.S. Congress failed to pass any legislation regulating DNA research. ■ There was an acknowledged violation of the DNA research guidelines issued by the National Institutes of Health—NIH—by the researchers involved in the rat insulin experiments. They say they stopped earlier experiments when they realized they were in violation of the guidelines. They contend that there was considerable confusion about the guidelines and about obtaining NIH approval of research projects. ■ Meanwhile, NIH proceeded with plans to open special recombinant DNA research laboratories that would provide rigid precautions against accidental release of an experimental material into the environment.

**Gene interruptions.** Detailed analyses of bacterial genes have shown an uninterrupted linear relationship between DNA and its protein products. In 1977 analyses of the genes of yeast, fruit flies, mice, and two animal viruses, SV40 and adenovirus, presented an unexpected contrast. Sections of DNA containing no coding information were found to interrupt sequences that dictate protein structure. The question then arose whether the divided genes actually work or whether the interruption silences them. Benjamin Hall and colleagues at the University of Washington in Seattle found that in yeast the interrupted gene is functional. Scientists have suggested that the intervening DNA sequences may have some role in evolution or in controlling the expression of genes.

**Spelling out viruses.** The complete genetic information for two viruses was unraveled in 1977. Fred Sanger and coworkers at the Medical Research Council in Cambridge, England, determined the exact sequence of the 5,375 nucleotides making up the nine genes of bacterial virus phiX174. Sherman Weissman and colleagues at Yale University reported the 5,200 nucleotide sequence of animal tumor virus SV40. Both solutions contained surprises. In two regions of phiX174, a stretch of DNA codes for two completely different proteins. The overlapping genes begin at different "start" signals so they group nucleotide "letters" into different three-letter "words" and thus code for different amino acid parts of a protein. The surprise in the SV40 sequence was a silent intervening DNA segment containing a "stop" signal in the middle of a gene.

**New branch on the tree of life.** Evolution, it has long been thought, forked once from its main trunk. One branch contains simple, single-celled organisms: bacteria and blue-green algae. The other branch includes all higher plants and animals. Studies during 1977 revealed that a group of methane-producers, previously thought to be bacteria, may be a separate, third, branch of evolution. Carl R. Woese and colleagues at the University of Illinois found, through analysis of nucleic-acid sequences, that the "methanogens" are no more closely related to bacteria than they are to higher organisms. The members of the newly-proposed evolutionary line resemble the ancestral life form that gave rise to both bacteria and higher organisms, Woese suggests. The methanogens thrive on hydrogen and carbon dioxide in oxygen-free niches, such as the hot springs in Yellowstone Park and the mud under San Francisco Bay. The door is now open for the discovery, through further genealogies, of yet other evolutionary lines. See also "Methanogens" on page 68.

**A sulfide-based, underwater clambake.** Large clusters of animals, common in shallow water, were found for the first time deep in the ocean by researchers of the Woods Hole Oceanographic Institution who were studying geologic processes at the site of the Galápagos Rift in the Pacific Ocean. Since there is no light and therefore no plant synthesis of food at the 2,700-meter (9,000-foot) depth at which the animal community, nicknamed "clambake," was found, the researchers searched for a food source. They found warm water vents containing hydrogen sulfide emerging from bulbous lava on the ocean floor. Bacteria that thrive on the hydrogen sulfide serve as the lowest link in the food chain that supports the animals. See also "The Galápagos Rift" on page 134.

**Other discoveries.** The adaptability and wide dispersal of life forms was reaffirmed in 1977 when a cold, largely uninhabited plateau in northern Tibet, long thought to be arid and deficient even in plant life, was found by Chinese scientists to be filled with life—some 300 different specimens of plants as well as antelope, sheep, wild asses, hares, foxes, bears, waterfowl, and fish in mountain brooks. ■ The success of some forms of life over long periods of time was demonstrated when green elm leaves buried in volcanic ash in Oregon some 30,000,000 years ago were found upon analysis by New York Botanical Garden researchers to be surprisingly similar to elm leaves today.

Julie Miller

Woods Hole

Scientists exploring the geology of the Galápagos Rift area were surprised to find large clusters of animals living in the area's warm-water vent areas.

New York Botanical Garden

Green elm leaves buried in volcanic ash in Oregon some 30,000,000 years ago (left) were found to be very similar to elm leaves today (right).

The newly discovered organism—termed a methanogen—is dividing into four new cells. Discovery of this new microorganism may open a "third kingdom" of living material, not plant or animal.

J. G. Zeikus, U. of Wisc.

# METHANOGENS

## by Richard D. Lyons

SCIENTISTS studying the evolution of primitive organisms reported in late 1977 the existence of a separate form of life that is hard to find in nature. They described it as a "third kingdom" of living material, not plant or animal. The organisms in this third kingdom are composed of ancestral cells that abhor oxygen, digest carbon dioxide, and produce methane.

The research group working at the University of Illinois in Urbana reported that this third form of life on earth is genetically distinct from the higher organisms that evolved from it—bacteria and, finally, the plant and animal world. Bacteria, with their own distinct form of cells, are more primitive than plant and animal life, which have vastly more complicated cellular structures.

Believed to have evolved 3,500,000,000 to 4,000,000,000 years ago, these organisms have yet to be named but are being referred to informally as either archaebacteria or methanogens. Before this discovery, the oldest form of life, bacteria, was believed to have evolved about 3,400,000,000 years ago.

"We have shown that they are genetically distinct from the higher organisms," said Dr. Carl R. Woese, the leader of the group investigating the evolution of microorganisms.

The genetic tracking efforts of the scientific group, which spanned five years, were made public by two of the U.S. government agencies that supported the research, the National Aeronautics and Space Administration and the National Science Foundation.

### IMPORTANT FIND

Asked for their evaluation of the results of the team at the University of Illinois, two other scientists familiar with the genetics of microbiology described the reports as "important" and "exciting," adding that it would further what is known of the basic processes of evolution.

Dr. Woese and his colleagues conclude that before the emergence on the earth of bacteria, usually regarded as the simplest form of life as we know it, at least one and perhaps several earlier forms of primitive organisms had evolved from the primordial ooze that developed after the crust of the earth had been solidified from a gaseous cloud.

Dr. Woese, whose name is pronounced "woes," said in an interview that the practical value of the research probably was nil.

But he added that, if the efforts of his group were confirmed by other researchers, the findings would enhance knowledge of human genetics and perhaps explain some of the mysteries of evolution and puzzles of the solar system.

## WHY EARTH

One flight of fancy advanced by Dr. Woese, is that the presence of this class of organisms might explain why life evolved here and not on earth's sister planet, Venus.

The rationale goes as follows: clouds of carbon dioxide originally enveloped both planets, but methanogens developed on earth and digested much of the cloud and in turn produced the hydrocarbons that developed into higher forms of life. But on Venus, according to this line of speculation, the lack of methanogens allowed the carbon dioxide to accumulate to the point that the so-called "greenhouse effect" took over the Venusian surface, making it too hot for life to evolve.

Dr. Woese, a slightly built biophysicist who has an unruly shock of graying hair, expounded on the research of his group in a three-hour interview in his sparsely furnished office. Nearby rooms are filled with such gadgets as electron microscopes and X-ray machines that are the basic tools used in deciphering the genetics of microorganisms.

"For years I've wanted to understand how life evolved," he said, "and five years ago my colleagues and I set about looking into the genealogy of organisms."

Dr. Woese, who is 49 years old, said that only in the last 10 years had it been feasible to explore the genetics of such rudimentary organisms. Elaborating, he cited the existence of only an elementary knowledge of molecular genetics a decade ago, the development of more powerful electron microscopes, and the discovery of more sophisticated techniques for examining the molecular structures of microorganisms.

## STARTED STUDYING BACTERIA

At first the group examined the deoxyribonucleic acid (DNA) of bacteria molecules. These molecules contain the coded information needed for the function and development of the cell. The team also studied bacterial ribosomal RNA, the ribonucleic

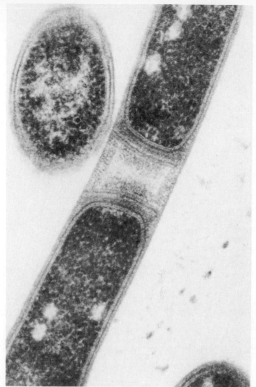

J. G. Zeikus, U. of Wisc.

Left: a cross section of the new microorganism. Right: a chain of two of the microorganisms, each 0.001 millimeter long. Scientists hope that continued study of these microorganisms will lead them to a better understanding of the basic processes of evolution.

acid that is a major constituent of the ribosomes. These are the units within cells where the messages from the genes are received and read in order to make the proteins the cell needs.

The ribosomal RNAs are believed to be extremely old and represent parts of the ancestral replicating, or duplicating, systems of both primitive and advanced organisms.

Examining the parts of either an animal cell or a plant cell is relatively easy as compared with examining the parts of a bacterial cell, which is perhaps 1,000 times smaller. Also, the bacterial cell does not have a clearly defined structure that the higher forms of life possess.

According to Dr. Woese, the early research on the evolution of microorganisms focused on their structural differences, rather than their genetic differences.

By examining ever simpler forms of bacteria, the University of Illinois scientists arrived at what then were believed to be the simplest forms, which the scientists have now found not to be bacteria at all.

University of Illinois

Dr. Carl. R. Woese was the leader of the research team at the University of Illinois at Urbana that reported that the methanogens are genetically distinct from the higher forms of life that evolved from them.

"The methanogens themselves are not new to science," Dr. Woese said. He noted that ten different forms had been examined in the course of the research and that their total number was unknown because "scientists have just begun to isolate them in earnest and there could be millions of them."

To be examined, the methanogens must be cultured under extremely difficult conditions since they will not exist in the presence of oxygen.

NO OXYGEN FOR THEM

Various forms of methanogens have been found in mud at the bottoms of San Francisco Bay and the Black Sea, in deposits in Carioco Bay off the coast of Venezuela, and in deep, hot spring waters such as those at Yellowstone National Park.

They generally are found in what are called anaerobic niches, or areas free of the presence of oxygen, which are relatively uncommon on the earth's surface.

The technique used here cultured the methanogens in the presence of radioactive phosphorus, which in turn made the RNA radioactive and traceable. The radioactive RNA then was separated from the genes and digested with enzymes into smaller pieces. The RNA molecular sequences, or messages, as they are called, were then compared with the RNA messages of either higher or lower organisms.

"Somewhere along the line in evolution a mistake is made and a mutation results," Dr. Woese said, adding that by studying these mutations it was possible to compare the ages of different RNAs. By deciphering the mutations of the genetic material, the scientists were able to identify methanogens as being distinctly different from bacteria.

Dr. Woese credited the name "methanogen" as having been coined by a colleague on the project, Dr. Ralph S. Wolfe, a professor of microbiology. Other collaborators included Linda J. Magrum, a research assistant; William E. Balch, a graduate student; and Dr. George E. Fox, now an assistant professor of biophysical sciences at the University of Houston.

Asked for comment about the work, Dr. Sol Spiegelman, now a professor of genetics at Columbia University, said that "the research results look O.K.

"Dr. Woese is a substantial scientist of international reputation who has contributed a number of ingenious ideas to science," he added.

Dr. Cyril Ponnamperuma, director of the laboratory of chemical evolution at the University of Maryland who has reported on extraterrestrial organic molecules, described the work as "very exciting, even fantastic.

"It fits into the general idea of evolution under nonoxygen conditions," he said □

📖 SELECTED READINGS

"Methanogens: third branch of life." *Science News,* November 12, 1977.

"Phylogeny: Are methanogens a third class of life?" by Thomas H. Maugh II. *Science,* November 25, 1977.

"Third form of life." *Chemistry,* January 1978.

"4 billion year old form of life is new discovery: methanogens." *Science Digest,* February 1978.

Irvin L. Oakes, Photo Researchers

In nature's last fling before winter, the leaves of many trees turn various shades of yellow, orange, red, and brown, presenting a fiery burst of color.

# WHY DO LEAVES TURN COLOR IN THE FALL?

## by Kenneth V. Thimann

FALL in North America can be a fiery burst of glorious color, nature's last fling before the trees huddle into their dark winter garb. The birches, elms, and poplars content themselves with yellows and light browns, but the red maples go in for crimson, the sugar maples for scarlet, and the sumacs for orange to red. In a good season the foliage colors can be as brilliant as the flowers in a summer garden, and the comparison is valid, because the bright pigments of autumn leaves are indeed of the same type as the pigments of flowers.

### UNMASKING OF YELLOW

In the coloring of autumn leaves two types of changes are involved. The simpler change is the fading of the green color of the chemical chlorophyll contained in the leaves.

This fading lets the yellow pigment, which is present in the leaves all the time, show. The leaves begin to lose their protein, which breaks down into its constituent amino acids, and these are carried back into the roots. As a result the chlorophyll, which is stable only when it is combined with protein, becomes bleached by the bright autumn sunlight. In the same way old people begin to lose their protein too, and doctors speak of their going into "negative nitrogen balance." It is a typical reaction of aging.

The yellow pigments of leaves do not bleach so readily. We only notice them when the chlorophyll is gone, because otherwise their color is masked by the green. The yellow pigments are related to the orange pigment of carrots and hence are called carotenoids. To understand why this is we

American aspens, *Populus tremuloides,* lose their green coloring and take on a brilliant yellow as shorter days and cooler temperatures herald the start of fall.

need to consider what happens when color is generated.

When white light, consisting of all wavelengths of the spectrum from about 400 to 710 millionths of a millimeter, falls on a surface that contains pigments, the pigments absorb some wavelengths more than others. The shortest wavelengths appear to the eye as violet, the longest as red, with the others in between. If a pigment absorbs only the violet, and perhaps a little of the adjacent blue region, our eyes receive the remainder: a mixture of red, yellow, green, and some blue. This mixture does not add up to white but to yellow. In other words, white minus violet equals yellow.

Every pigment has its own range of wavelengths absorbed and reflected, and these can be shown as an "absorption spectrum," a curve plotting the percentage of absorption at each wavelength. The curve on page 73 shows the absorption spectra of a complete leaf (in this case a spinach leaf) and of some of its constituent pigments, the green chlorophylls *a* and *b* and the yellow carotene. The plot shows that the chlorophylls absorb light mainly in the blue and the red, some in the violet, but almost none in the green. Thus our eyes, looking at a leaf, receive mainly the

green light, with some yellow and part of the violet. The result is a sensation of green.

The absorption spectrum of the carotene shows that it absorbs only blue and violet light, which are largely absorbed anyway by the chlorophylls. As a result, the yellow pigments (there are several others besides carotene) do not much change the visible color of the leaf, and hence their presence goes largely unnoticed. The absorption spectrum of the complete leaf is essentially the sum of the absorptions of the individual pigments, so that the unabsorbed light, which we see, is mainly a yellowish-green. With the onset of autumn and the bleaching of the chlorophyll, the yellows are unmasked.

## APPEARANCE OF RED

The second type of color change, however, and the one that gives the North American fall its special glory, is the appearance of red. Normally no red is present in the typical summer leaf, so it is evident that here a new pigment enters the scene. Only a few leaves, including the copper beech and some varieties of corn, have red pigment during the summer. In the red pigment of these and autumn leaves, one of the primary families of chemical compounds in nature declares its presence. But how? How does the green of a summer leaf become the red of an autumn leaf?

## TWO DIFFERENT TYPES OF CHEMICALS

As is now so well known, the green pigment chlorophyll presides at the capture of the sun's energy and its fixation in the starch compounds formed by leaves in the process of photosynthesis. From this simple starting material life processes build up all the diversity of molecules in the tissues of plants and animals. Chlorophyll, itself derived from the original starch molecule, belongs to the family of fats and sugars called "aliphatics" by the 19th century founders of organic chemistry. In the plant kingdom the most abundant member of this family is cellulose. This compound, consisting of a chain of glucose molecules joined end to end, supplies the structural fibers of plants, constituting about half their weight and bulk, and has supplied technology with such commodities as cotton and paper and the rayon, cellophane, and plastics reconstituted from cellulose by the chemical industry.

The red pigment in leaves and flowers, however, belongs to that other primary family of organic chemicals called "aromatics" by the 19th century chemists. The name comes from the odorous benzene and phenol

compounds those pioneers isolated from coal tar. To the plant kingdom the family of aromatics supplies lignin, a brownish plastic that binds the fibers of cellulose together in woody plants, giving wood its brown color and constituting the other half of its weight and bulk. Lignin has so far defied the efforts of technology to capture it intact. On the degraded products of lignin in coal, however, 19th century technology founded the organic chemical industry, with its dyes, drugs, and plastics.

It was the search for the origin of red pigment that helped to establish one of the pathways of synthesis that tie together the aliphatics and the aromatics in the family tree of organic chemicals.

Closely related to the red pigments of autumn leaves are the red, blue, and mauve pigments of flower petals. The first of these to be known was extracted from blue cornflowers (*Centaurea cyanus* or "bachelor's buttons") by the Frenchman F.S. Morot over 100 years ago. He gave it the name anthocyanin which means, in Greek, flower-blue, and the name has later come to designate the whole family of pigments. The studies that have now so nearly explained the origin of the anthocyanins—and so of the family of aromatic compounds—started with flowers, for so many of our garden flowers come in red,

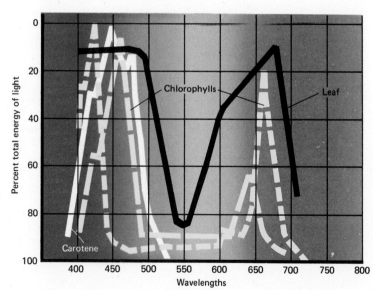

Colors in the spectrum of sunlight, corresponding to its wavelength (horizontal coordinate), are differently absorbed and reflected (vertical coordinate) by leaf pigments. Chlorophylls absorb violet and red wavelengths and reflect green and yellow. Bleaching of chlorophylls in autumn unmasks the yellow-reflecting pigment carotene and so leaves turn yellow.

William M. Harlow, Photo Researchers

A sugar-maple leaf showing three colors: green, yellow, and red. Triggered by changes in light, enzymes control the gradual change of the leaf's color.

pink, and white varieties of the same species. Sometimes one species offers red, blue, and violet shades, like African violets. The plants with the different colors are usually quite alike in other characters so they can be readily hybridized and selected. By doing this over the years with such groups as primulas

and impatiens, geneticists, especially at the John Innes Institute in England, discovered that there were relatively straightforward inheritance patterns. A typical plant would have one gene which controls anthocyanin formation in general, another gene controlling intensification of the color, and additional genes for modifying it—turning the red towards mauve, for instance, or adding a touch of yellow.

This was, however, far from telling how the plant applies its chemical ingenuity to making the red pigment. The task was to discover how the aromatic structure of anthocyanins could be derived from the aliphatic structure of the sugars from which they are made.

## HOW CAN ONE BE CONVERTED TO THE OTHER?

The difference between the two families is profound but subtle. The simple sugar glucose consists of a hexagonal, or six-cornered, ring of five atoms of carbon and one of oxygen, with an additional carbon atom attached to one corner. Each carbon atom

John J. Smith

The eastern larch, or tamarack, is one of the few pine trees to turn color and shed its leaves in the fall.

bears hydrogen atoms and OH groups (i.e. oxygen and hydrogen, paired). The hexagonal benzene ring, with six carbon atoms, one at each corner, looks superficially similar but differs in an important respect. It has three double bonds that give it and many of the compounds built on it a special stability. So the problem was: how do plants convert one type of ring into the other?

The structure of anthocyanin contains two benzene rings. Surprisingly, it was found that the two rings, A and B, are formed in quite different ways. Ring B comes ready-made from one of the amino acids. The benzene ring A comes, however, from the breakdown and reconstitution of the glucose ring. The six-sided glucose ring is first split into two halves, as it is in most reactions involving glucose. Each of the fragments, containing three carbon atoms, is seized by a versatile catalyst—coenzyme A—found in the cells of all plants and of all animals as well. A catalyst is a substance that affects a chemical reaction, usually increasing its rate, without itself becoming affected by the reaction. An enzyme is a type of catalyst.

One of the three carbon atoms is lost in this reaction. The combination of the remainder with coenzyme A makes the molecule very reactive, as when an energetic youngster on a family walk takes his father by the hand. Three of these excited combinations now assemble in a ring facing one another. A chemical reaction takes place in which the coenzymes, along with the surplus atoms of hydrogen, carbon, and oxygen, depart, and a new benzene ring is formed. Finally, rings A and B come together, and, with some additional minor chemical adjustments, we have anthocyanin.

## CONTROLLING THE CHANGE

As might be imagined, a great many enzymes have to take part in this sequence. It is a general rule, in these intricate molecular dances, that enzymes are highly specialized. They control only a single step of a complex routine. We came upon the trail of the enzymes in our study of the reddening of duckweeds, tiny plants that float on the surface of ponds.

It had long ago been observed that some aquatic plants, if floated in sugar solutions

Kent and Donna Dannen, Photo Researchers

Closeup of some yellow aspen leaves. The yellow pigment is always present but becomes apparent only when the leaves begin to age and the chlorophyll becomes bleached.

and exposed to bright light, would turn red or purple. We chose a duckweed (*Spirodela oligorrhiza*) that turned purplish-red in this way and cultured it in the artificial-light growth chambers at Harvard University. When the little plants had grown we took them out of the nutrient solution and floated them on pure water or pure sugar solution, so that they could grow no more but would form anthocyanin if the conditions were right. They could thus be compared to autumn leaves, which have long finished growing but are still carrying out photosynthesis. Sugar promoted the reddening, but a more interesting fact was that some substances prevented it, and powerfully.

Chief among these inhibitors were compounds that interfere with the formation of nucleic acid, the molecule that governs the expression as well as the transmission of hereditary characteristics in the cell. Some of these compounds are active as pigment inhibitors in minute amounts, such as 20 parts per 1,000,000,000 of water or a teaspoonful in 100 tons. Each compound resembles, and therefore interferes with, one particular part of the molecule of nucleic acid. Its action can be offset, therefore, by adding small amounts of exactly that part of the nucleic acid with which it interferes. In the presence of both

George Bakacs, APF

The northern red oaks (genus *Quercus*) are spectacularly colorful parts of the autumn scene in North America.

substances the duckweeds color up normally again. It is thus evident that to make anthocyanin the plants have first to make nucleic acids. Thus what really controls and limits the formation of anthocyanin is the formation of the necessary nucleic acids. And each nucleic acid leads to the synthesis of a single enzyme.

## ROLE OF LIGHT

For this formation of nucleic acids there is probably a reaction controlled by light. Both red and white light play parts in this. A small amount of red suffices, but bright white light is needed even if sugars are provided. As yet we do not know just how the special light reaction works. We do know that when duckweeds are first transferred out of the nutrient solution and put in bright light no anthocyanin is formed for 18 to 20 hours. Then it begins and continues at a steady rate for several days. The 18 to 20 hours lag may well be the time needed to synthesize first the nucleic acids and then, from them, the necessary enzymes.

## WHY COLORS CHANGE

In autumn leaves the same controlling factors operate. From the duckweed experiments we can see how it is that in some seasons the colors are brighter than others. Sunny days are needed both to accumulate plenty of sugars in the leaves and for the light reaction mentioned above. Cold temperatures, especially at night, are needed to slow down the export of the sugars out of the leaves into the trunk. Probably the low temperature also promotes conversion of stored starch in the leaves into glucose. The aging of the leaves also means that proteins are being broken down and so the amino acid is being set free for the production of ring B of anthocyanin.

When North American red or sugar maples are planted in the cool and cloudy climate of Europe, where the autumn days are not so bright as ours nor the autumn nights so cold, the fall colors are weak. Europe's woods in the late fall are yellow and brown, not red, though there will be just an occasional red leaf. Shelley wrote:

". . . the leaves dead
Are driven like ghosts from an
  enchanter fleeing,
Yellow and black, and pale, and hectic
  red,
Pestilence-stricken multitudes."

It is curious that a majority of the trees that bear red leaves in the fall also have red, or at least pinkish, leaves in the spring, when they are very young. This shows that the tendency to form the needed enzymes is there, though only in small amount. When the useful life of the leaves is drawing to a close and they are beginning to become old, we can think of them, like some of our aged relatives, as entering their second childhood□

 SELECTED READINGS

"Harvest of color" by J. P. Jackson. *American Forest,* November 1976.

*Leaves: Their Amazing Lives and Strange Behavior* by James Poling. Harper, 1971.

"Roses are red, white, yellow, pink: plant pigments responsible for color" by P. W. Spencer. *Natural History,* June 1976.

"To see the autumn in a single leaf" by D. Farber. *Horticulture,* October 1976.

A diver swims toward an underwater forest of kelp. These giant treelike plants, sometimes 15 meters tall, form a beautiful sanctuary for a wide variety of marine life.

Peter Capen

# THROUGH A KELP FOREST

## by Peter D. Capen

AT some time in our lives many of us have walked in a grove of towering redwoods and been captivated by the beauty of the environment over which they preside. Yet few of us have explored another kind of forest, a forest not of the land, but of the sea. Instead of trees, it has giant underwater plants, called kelp, which rise up more than 15 meters (50 feet) from the ocean floor.

For most people, kelp is that tangled, foul-smelling, fly-ridden mess that occasionally blankets the Pacific coast's beaches. Underwater, though, it becomes an incomparably beautiful sanctuary for a dazzling array of marine life. Attached to the rocky substrate by a conical, rootlike holdfast, the lofty kelp *Macrocystis* reaches up towards the light above with one or more slender, stemlike stipes. The stipes are buoyed up by gas-filled bladders, off of which grow long, leafy fronds. On the surface the plant spreads out, forming a dense canopy. In this canopy the fronds take in the nutrients of the water and, with energy from the sun, produce foodstuffs through the process of photosynthesis. The food is then passed downward to nourish the rest of the plant in the twilight world below.

To the diver on the bottom looking up at the canopy, the scene is breathtaking. Shafts of light beam through and radiate out, delicately highlighting the floating fronds. As gentle ocean swells undulate through the forest, the shafts break and dance across the canopy. The variegated pattern of kelp and light is a kaleidoscope of subtle changes.

### WELL CONCEALED CRABS

Life in the kelp forest is abundant. Found at every level, it is often so varied and unusual that many of its forms are completely overlooked by the casual observer. The concealment of the masking crab, *Loxorhynchus crispatus,* is so perfect that, unless it moves, one can look right at it and never know it is there. While several crab species tolerate or encourage natural growths only on their shells, *L. crispatus* completely covers itself with pieces of algae, hydroids, sponges, and anything else available.

### CONSPICUOUS CORALS AND SPONGES

In contrast to the animals that employ elaborate techniques of camouflage are many others that revel in the conspicuousness of their beautiful coloration. Pink and purple variations of the hydrocoral, *Allopora,* form small, dense, branched colonies in the ledges and on the ridges of the rocks. Masses of red and yellow sponges, like splashes of paint randomly thrown around, brighten their surfaces. Among the sponges are delicate, feath-

Peter Capen

The giant green anemone, one of the most striking inhabitants of kelp beds, is home to single-celled algae.

ery-shaped, colonial hydroids, and orange and beige bryozoans, some of which look like delicate lacework.

Sprinkled liberally about is the solitary coral, *Balanophyllia elegans.* Seldom more than one centimeter (0.5 inch) across, it is very short, round, and also bright orange. Peeking out from the nooks and crannies are the clustered, multi-hued gills of the sabellid feather-duster worm. So sensitive is this worm to a sudden change in light that even a passing shadow will cause it to withdraw its gills dramatically into the safety of its tube-shaped home.

### UNMATCHED ANEMONES

While many of the attached animals living among the kelp are beautifully colored, none can match the anemones. Named for the windflowers of the mountains and woodlands, sea anemones display a multitude of variations. The large *Anthopleura xanthogrammica* is emerald green. Its vividness is produced by the single-celled algae, *Zoochlorella,* living within its tissues in a symbiotic relationship with it. Smaller, but no less alluring, are the several species of *Tealia* that dot the seascape. One form has tapering, white tentacles surrounding an oral disk of deep yellow etched in orange lines. Another is bright cherry-red. *Corynactis californica* is one of the smallest of the anemones. Yet, what it lacks in size it more than compensates for in sheer abundance. Whole sections of rock are carpeted by dense aggregates of this little, white club-tentacled, red-bodied anthozoan.

Far less profuse than *Corynactis,* but fascinating for its behavior, is the plumose anemone, *Metridium.* Frequently pure white, it rises up on a long muscular column, the top of which is fringed with hundreds of tiny tentacles. While this animal seems to be stationary, it is not. In seeking food, the *Metridium* exhibits a highly complex pattern of movement which can be observed only through the use of specialized movie-camera techniques.

So pervasive are the anemones that their presence extends even to the sandy areas bordering the forest and stretching between the boulders. In the soft bottom *Cerianthus* builds a narrow tube. From the shelter of this tube it reaches out into the surrounding water with long, slender tentacles. Rhythmically it rakes them back and forth in beautiful arching motions. As tasty morsels are caught, they are passed off to very short tentacles massed inside the tube which carry the tidbits down to the animal's mouth.

### INTRIGUING SEA SLUGS

Living with the fixed communities are a host of invertebrates that slide, crawl, and scurry about. Many of them are as colorful and interesting as the forms that are attached. Some are predators, others scavengers. A number of species are herbivores, which graze on the kelp or scrape the rocks for their algae covering. Easily the most captivating animals in this melange of life are nudibranchs — the sea slugs.

Despite their name, sea slugs show little resemblance to their terrestrial counterparts. On their backs are delicate protuberances through which they breathe. These append-

A delicate sea slug moving along a bright red sponge mass, feeding as it goes along.

Peter Capen

Peter Capen

A large beautifully colored sea star, or starfish, lies on a rock substrate with many small brittle stars.

ages are either in the form of a retractable rosette of gills, surrounding the anus, or fingerlike projections, called cerata, which extend all along the body.

## AND EVERYWHERE—SEA STARS

Less intriguing than nudibranchs, but more easily found, are the sea stars. The red, webbed-rayed sea bat, *Patiria miniata,* is everywhere apparent, as are the several species of *Pisaster*. Not uncommon, too, is *Pycnopodia helianthoides,* the sunflower star. This huge, many-rayed asteroid is a lively pink or purple shade and sometimes has a spread of over 60 centimeters (2 feet). Its body is relatively soft and when roughly handled will often shed an arm or two. Brittle stars, as their name implies, are even more masterful at discarding limbs. When disturbed they will crumble their arms to pieces, then later regenerate them again. Although these tiny, frail creatures generally live under rocks, they occasionally can be seen out in the open in great numbers, with their arms all extending upwards gathering in the steady rain of food matter from above.

Related to sea stars are sea cucumbers and the spiny urchins. Sea urchins are voracious grazers and will wreak havoc on the kelp when their numbers go unchecked by their natural enemies. One of their chief enemies is the sunflower star, which is such a thorough eater that it leaves nothing of the urchin but a beautifully cleaned outer hard covering.

## AND MANY MANY MORE

Other invertebrates usually seen moving about the kelp habitat are a bewildering as-

sortment of worms, crabs, limpets, chitons, and snails. The worms live beneath the rocks or in the holdfasts of the kelp. Many of the crabs hide down in the crevices of the rocks during the day, but at night come out in the open to feed. Some other types have found unique forms of shelter. The tiny pea crabs live in commensal relationships inside such hosts as sea cucumbers, giant keyhole limpets, and *Cryptochitons,* the world's largest chiton. The gregarious hermit crabs choose snail shells for homes, which, once obtained, they carry about with them.

## FISHES TOO

In addition to the hordes of invertebrates, the kelp forest is an indispensable sanctuary for a large fish population. These fish are usually found mingling in disarranged schools just under the canopy or foraging over the rocks below. The bottom dwellers make up a motley group who often have bizarre color combinations and weird, grotesque, appendaged shapes. Their distinct designs and coloration, however, greatly enhance their ability to blend into their environment. Not a few of them lead solitary lives. Most show little inclination to move around. Commonly encountered are rockfish, sculpins, and greenlings. Sometimes seen, too, are sizeable eels, who despite their ugly appearance and fearsome reputations are really quite docile.

## TEMPORARY VISITORS

Seaward of the kelp is the void of the open ocean. A few of its creatures visit the forest from time to time on their unceasing

A hermit crab peers out of its snail shell home in the midst of a brilliantly colored kelp bed

Peter Capen

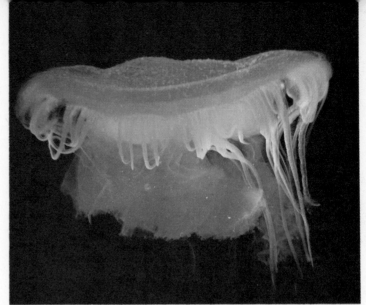

Jellyfish are frequent kelp visitors, carried to the kelp beds
by the ocean currents.

odysseys. A hungry blue shark quickly passes through, then returns to the blue depths beyond. Occasional seals and sea lions playfully dash in and out among the seaweed. Jellyfish and salps become involuntary visitors due to fickle winds and currents. Even if brief, their presence lends a beautiful dimension to the many other forms of life among the giant *Macrocystis*. Their fragile opaque and transparent bodies float or gently pulsate through the water near the surface. Many of them have luminescent organs, which show up after dark like distant, twinkling lights. The small, spherical comb jellies not only luminesce, but during the day also give off a shimmering iridescence. Their electric colors are caused by light reflecting off the rows of tiny paddles with which they propel themselves.

Frequently mistaken for jellyfish are the salps, whose clear, hollow bodies and bioluminescent organs are like something out of a science-fiction writer's imagination. The individuals of one remarkable species link together side by side to form beautiful, long chains. At the base of each animal in the chain glows a yellow-orange organ. The organs clearly stand out against the blue-green water, but unless one is close to them the transparent bodies do not. What one sees is often just an eerie glowing row of lights. The impact of seeing these lights is further heightened by the unique way in which the salp chain moves. It spirals up, then spirals out, forming and reforming a series of curling loops, some of which look like backwards sixes.

## MUST BE SAFEGUARDED

A visit to the kelp forest always ends too soon. Restricted to the air supply carried, the diver must eventually return to the world above. Yet, if only for a brief period of time, the diver has had the experience of exploring an environment few could guess at. He or she has been witness to a myriad of delicate interrelations: between one animal and another, and between the animals and their home of kelp. For the diver a matted pile of *Macrocystis* washed up on the beach, or a thick canopy of it gently rising and falling on the offshore swells, will never again mean quite the same thing. Inevitably the diver will look at it and see the forest in its entirety, with its great treelike plants, its patterns of suffused, dancing light, and its rich and varied fauna. And he or she will hope that those who have not been there will have the foresight to help protect and preserve this most captivating of environments from people's perennial indifference and neglect. For only by its rational management and protection will those explorers of succeeding generations have the chance to take a journey through the kelp forest□

### 📖 SELECTED READINGS

*Biology of the Giant Kelp Beds: Macrocystis in California,* edited by W. J. North and others. Stechert, 1971.

"Farming giant kelp" by L. Wood. *Sea Frontiers,* May 1977.

"Seaweed: resource of the 21st century" by E. M. Leeper. *Bioscience,* May 1976.

Many common garden plants, such as the azalea are poisonous. Most, however, are not sufficiently dangerous to warrant their removal from your garden.

John J. Smith

# POISONOUS GARDEN PLANTS

## by Guy Hartman, M.D.

"MY wife has uprooted the azaleas," an alarmed Sacramento, California, homeowner recently told me. "She's thrown the poinsettias over the fence and is ready to rip out the iris! Help!" The cause of all this was a local newspaper article describing what's known as the Sinister Garden, a collection of poisonous plants located just outside the Pediatric Clinic of the Kaiser/Permanente Medical Center in Fontana, California. The Sacramento woman's reaction was typical of those who discover some of the same plants growing in their backyards. I hastened to offer reassurance. "Replant your azaleas," I said. "Rescue the poinsettias and defend the iris. I will personally guarantee that none of them will kill any of your progeny."

I feel perfectly safe in making such a guarantee. It would require 10 to 20 grams of azalea vegetation to seriously poison a 12-kilogram (25-pound) child. Although the poinsettia is not entirely harmless, the myth of its fatal toxicity has been thoroughly debunked by recent research, and I cannot imagine any toddler digging up the iris rhizome for an afternoon snack. Chewing on the flower stalk could produce blisters of the lips and mouth, but this need not cause you to sacrifice this lovely garden flower.

Most plants are entirely harmless, but there are more than 700 plants in the United States alone known to produce harmful effects. Of these, probably only the castor bean and the oleander are sufficiently toxic to require their removal from the range of young children. The Sinister Garden was planted to educate the public to potential dangers lurking unsuspected in their backyards. My purpose here is similar. I do not intend to present an encyclopedic coverage of all plants, but only to increase the awareness of the gardening public and to present some interesting and curious facts.

### MANY UNREPORTED POISONING CASES

There are distinct advantages to being informed in this area. James Hardin and James Arena, in their book *Human Poisoning from Native and Cultivated Plants,* state that 12,000 poisonings are recorded annually in the United States, but they point out that this probably represents less than 5 per cent of the total. The Poison Information Center at Los Angeles Children's Hospital alone reported 2,845 cases in 1976. But reporting plant poisonings to poison centers or to county health agencies is not mandatory and it is therefore safe to assume that many more

Castor bean (top photo) and oleander (lower photo) are sufficiently toxic that they should be removed from gardens where children may wander. Both plants can, if ingested in sufficient amounts, cause serious illness and even death.

cases never reach the files of those who compile statistics. No figures are available on the number of deaths that result from plant ingestions.

Identifying plants that can cause poisoning depends upon the geographic region, as well as the season. For example, house plants are more commonly eaten during the winter months when small children spend most of their time indoors. Castor beans and oleander produce poisoning in the warmer areas of the country where they grow best, and the rosary pea produces its deadly effect where it grows in tropical areas or from seeds used in the manufacture of souvenirs sold to tourists.

In my own experience in one year, the plants that produced harmful effects were:

aralia (2), spotted clover (2), philodendron (4), castor bean (2), mushroom (4), and 30 miscellaneous cases which included eucalyptus, dieffenbachia, sweet-potato leaves, donkeytail, iris, sorrel, tiger lily, English ivy, and primrose. I also know of ten patients admitted to the hospital for intensive observation and treatment; six had eaten Jimson weed, and one each castor bean, mistletoe, oleander, and mushrooms. At Los Angeles Children's Hospital Poison Information Center, the 2,845 cases for 1976 break down as follows:

| | |
|---|---:|
| Hallucinogens (nutmeg, morning glory, peyote, etc.) | 89 |
| Mushrooms and toadstools | 419 |
| Castor beans | 31 |
| Oleander | 124 |
| Miscellaneous | 2,182 |

The questions I am asked most frequently are, "How poisonous is this plant? How much would have to be eaten to produce symptoms? Could it be fatal? Would chewing one leaf be dangerous?" Unfortunately, reasonable as the questions are, they do not have simple answers. The quantitative effects of plant poisoning in humans are difficult to ascertain, and most of the available information deals strictly with animal poisoning.

## DIFFERENT PLANT PARTS POISONOUS

Some plants, such as azaleas, caladiums, delphiniums, flax, tobacco, and Jimson weed, carry toxin in all of their parts, while others, such as agave, avocado, ranunculus, and foxglove, concentrate it only in their leaves. Holly, ivy, and mistletoe have poison in their berries, while elder, cherries, apricots, peaches, plums, eggplants, and tomatoes produce edible fruits on plants which are otherwise generally noxious.

Toxins in plants such as pokeweed and oak can be inactivated by heating or leaching, making the plant edible. Other plants (foxglove, lobelia, vinca) are valuable as medicinals but are dangerous if eaten indiscriminately. The rhubarb plant has an edible stalk but poisonous leaves. The wisteria has flowers which are dipped in batter and fried for a treat in China but the leguminous seeds cause severe vomiting and diarrhea.

Some plants, such as the poison oak, are harmful if touched, producing moderate to severe skin irritation.

Euphorbias have extremely irritating sap, while other look-alikes, the cacti, have sustained human life on the desert with their juice. The cultivated lima bean is a good source of vegetable protein in the human diet, but its close relative, the Java bean, produces cyanide poisoning. Another cousin, the fava bean, while tasty and nourishing to most people, produces severe hemolytic anemia in people who have a hereditary deficiency of a certain enzyme. This genetic deficiency affects 15 per cent of all blacks and is also found in caucasians of Mediterranean ancestry. The husk of some seeds, like the cashew, can be extremely irritating, while the seed coat of seeds such as *Prunus*, castor bean, or rosary pea, if swallowed intact, will prevent poisoning from the toxic material contained within.

## SOME HARMFUL IF TOUCHED

Many plants are poisonous in contact with the skin. The most common are the *Toxicodendron* siblings, usually known as poison oak, poison ivy, and poison sumac. Poison sumac often is but should not be confused with the non-poisonous sumacs, *Rhus* species. About half of all people are sensitive to these plants, some so much so that they claim just passing near the plant will make them break out. This is a myth. Reaction requires actual contact, though this can be in the form of smoke from the burning plants. Other skin irritants include stinging nettle, spotted spurge, and trumpet creeper. Anyone with an inherited allergic potential can become sensitized to any plant or its pollen, a fact that is particularly noticeable in the case of ragweed. This is a case of individual sensitivity rather than a strictly poisonous plant.

## CHRISTMAS PLANTS MAY BE DANGEROUS

The traditional plants of Christmas may disturb the peace and happiness of the season. All plant toxicology references list *Euphorbia pulcherrima,* or poinsettia, as one of the worst, citing a 1919 case report in which a child in Hawaii died after eating one leaf. Severe skin irritation and blindness reportedly occur following contact with the juice. Subsequent animal experiments, however, have failed to confirm the information, and further investigation has cast serious doubts upon the accuracy of the Hawaiian report. We must conclude, therefore, that the most popular of the Christmas flowers, if toxic at all, must be of a very low order of magnitude.

Mistletoe berries, however, must be included on any caution list. I know one young woman who, one hour after eating 24 berries in a salad, developed vomiting and diarrhea severe enough to necessitate hospitalization. Holly berries contain an alkaloid which causes gastrointestinal irritation as well as central nervous system depression.

Jerusalem cherry, often used in Christmas decorations, belongs to the family of nightshades. Its berry, resembling a cran-

Several of the plants commonly used for Christmas decorations are poisonous. Holly berries, for example, can produce digestive and nervous system disorders.

Derek Fell

The Jerusalem cherry is another common Yuletide plant that is poisonous.

berry or small cherry tomato, produces the same effects as the holly berry, the unripe berry containing a greater concentration of the solanine alkaloids. The black seed in the red "berry" of the yew, a plant also often used for Yuletide color, causes vomiting, diarrhea, dilated pupils, muscular weakness, and convulsions if cracked and swallowed. The leaves and twigs are also poisonous.

## SPRING PLANTS TOO

The flowers that bloom in the spring have their menacing aspects also. Tulip, laurel, lily-of-the-valley, jonquil, narcissus, daffodil, and ranunculus all have toxic potential. One fledgling cook in my practice learned an important but painful lesson by mistakenly dicing her mother's gift Holland tulip bulb into the Spanish rice. She and her brother had a generous serving before their mother came home from work. Both can testify that eating tulip bulbs causes severe vomiting and diarrhea. Spring bulbs taken out of the ground for the winter and left in garages and gardening areas often prove to be most attractive to toddlers, and should be kept out of their reach.

## SPURGES

The *Euphorbiaceae,* or spurge family, is an interesting group that contains several potentially dangerous plants. The tung-oil tree (*Aleurites fordii* Hemsl.) is a native of China but is planted extensively along the Gulf Coast, not only as an ornamental and for shade but also in groves for its commer-

cially valuable oil. All parts of the tree are poisonous but the nutlike seed especially so.

The castor bean (*Ricinus communis*), which is also grown for its commercially important oil, is grown domestically as well for the attractiveness of its tropical foliage and ease of cultivation. Its toxin, ricin, is concentrated in the seed and is a very common source of poisoning in the warm areas where the plant is found. Its pretty seeds are often made into necklaces.

Almost all of the euphorbias contain a milky sap which is irritating to skin and eyes. Commonly cultivated specimens include *E. milii* (crown-of-thorns), *E. tirucalli* (pencil tree), *E. hermentiana* (milk bush) and *E. mammillaris* (corncob). Snow-on-the-mountain (*E. marginatum* Pursh.) has a sap so caustic that it is said to have been used to brand cattle in the early days of the U.S. West. The pencil tree, which grows to a height of 3 to 5 meters (10 to 15 feet) in North Africa, was responsible for delaying Mussolini's conquest of Ethiopia. Many of the invading Italians, attempting to construct a road through a grove of tirucalli trees, were blinded when they wiped sweat from face and eyes with sap-covered hands.

Some of the euphorbias are equipped with spines and resemble members of the cactus family. They can be differentiated by their sap, the juice of the cactus being watery and non-toxic. The cassava, from which we get tapioca and whose starchy tuber is used as food in tropical areas, contains a large amount of prussic acid in its uncooked root.

Daffodils are a welcome sign of spring, but they too must be treated with care. Daffodil bulbs, if ingested, can cause vomiting and diarrhea.

George Bakacs, APF

## POTATO FAMILY—BOON AND BANE

The potato family, *Solanaceae,* is both a boon and a bane to humans. The family contains many of our most important foods as well as some of our serious toxins, often in the same species. This is the family of nightshades and it is here that the deadly nightshade (*Atropa belladonna*) and its cousin the Jimson weed (*Datura stramonium*) belong. Atropine is found in all parts of these plants but the berry of atropa is the part most frequently eaten. Drinking tea brewed from the leaves or chewing the seeds of Datura has become a popular pastime among drug-oriented people pursuing a new hallucinogenic high. With this plant, however, hallucinations are a symptom of atropine poisoning and many users end up in the hospital critically ill.

Other noxious plants belonging to the *Solanaceae* include the tomato, the leaves of which can be poisonous; Jerusalem cherry; potato, all parts of which are poisonous except the tuber itself; and eggplant, of which only the fruit is edible.

## SOME CAUSE CYANIDE POISONING

The rose family (*Rosaceae*) includes many surprising members. The genus *Prunus,* including such familiar staples as cherry, peach, apricot, and plum, contains in all parts, except the drupe fruit itself, a substance which becomes cyanide within the body. I know a man who became seriously ill after eating 48 apricot seeds. Similarly, seeds

Jimson weed is one of the most poisonous of plants. Atropine, found in all parts of the plant, can produce hallucinations and many other symptoms.

W. H. Hodge

John J. Smith

The bark, leaves, and seeds of the black locust contain a substance that produces vomiting and weakness.

of the common apple (*Malus* spp.) also contain this cyanogenic glycoside. All of us have swallowed apple seeds with no apparent ill effects—the body can metabolize small amounts of cyanide—but there is a case report of a man who roasted and ate a whole cupful, after which he died.

Bad actors in the pea family (*Fabaceae*) include the rosary pea (*Abrus precatorius*), one of the most poisonous plants known. Its small scarlet berry with one black end is used extensively in jewelry made in tropical areas where the plant is native. Because of its appearance, it is often used as eyes in carved animals; it is in this manner that it acquired one of its other common names, crab's eye. The plant's powerful toxin has an effect similar to snake venom.

Other malevolent members of the family are sweet pea, golden chain (*Laburnum anagyroides* Medic.), the java and the fava beans mentioned earlier, bird of paradise shrub (*Poinciana* or *Caesalpinia gilliesii*), black locust (*Robinia pseudoacacia*), mescal bean, and wisteria. In all of these plants the leguminous seeds carry toxins.

The arum family (*Araceae*) contains many plants cherished by American gardeners, plants which pose some threat to their children. Dumbcane (*Dieffenbachia*), philodendrons of all species, elephant ears (*Colocasia*), anthurium, and caladium all contain oxalate crystals and asparagine, substances which cause extreme irritation of the mouth, throat, stomach, and intestines. Paralysis of the throat that can be one effect of these sub-

W. H. Hodge

The death cup, or fly amanita, is a highly poisonous mushroom, hard to distinguish from its edible relatives.

stances has given dumbcane its name. The undomesticated cousin Jack-in-the-pulpit possesses all of the same endearing characteristics.

## MUSHROOMS

There are about 40,000 species of mushrooms in the United States; of these, 10,000 are poisonous. The most serious danger with wild mushrooms is that the ones that are poisonous are very, very poisonous. Only a small portion of the plant is required to produce severe, even fatal effects and it often requires the services of an expert to tell the difference between edible and poisonous mushrooms.

Symptoms from mushroom poisoning usually fall into two general categories: those that develop after six hours and those that develop after eighteen hours. In either case, it is impossible to retrieve any of the substance from the stomach and there are no specific antidotes to the toxin. One can take some small comfort from the knowledge that the earlier the symptoms develop, the more likely the victim is to survive. Many do not.

## MANY OTHERS

There are hundreds of other plants capable of causing mild to severe symptoms in the unwary ingestor. Many of them are rich in folklore which may or may not be true.

The chart on pages 86–87 lists some of these plants and indicates the symptoms they cause.

## IF POISONING OCCURS

Treatment in all cases of plant poisoning consists of inducing vomiting as soon as possible after ingestion and then seeking medical attention. Every household with small children should keep handy in the medicine cupboard some Syrup of Ipecac, a substance that induces vomiting. When you seek medical attention, take a sample of the plant with you for purposes of identification. If the physician is unfamiliar with the plant, he or she should contact the nearest Poison Information Center or member unit of the National Poison Control Center Network where resources for plant identification and information concerning toxicity are very readily available.

## PREVENTION IS BEST

Some rules suggest themselves:
• Become familiar with the toxic potential of all the plants in your garden and, if you have small children, consider removing some of the more dangerous and attractive plants such as castor bean and Jerusalem cherry or at least rendering them inaccessible.
• Keep all jewelry made from seeds away from small children. Many of the seeds are lethal.
• Do not eat either raw in salad or cooked as greens any plant unless you know absolutely that it is edible.
• Do not absent-mindedly chew on unfamiliar stems and grasses plucked while hiking in the woods or sitting in the meadow.
• Buy your mushrooms at the market. If you can't resist harvesting them in the wild, take an expert mycologist along with you □

### SELECTED READINGS

"Beautiful but Dangerous" by Marcia Opp. *Medical World News*, May 16, 1977.

"Burgeoning cult of wild food nourishes fatal misconceptions" by Robert E. Arnold and Laer Pearce. *Smithsonian*, February 1977.

"Herbal intoxication" by Ronald K. Siegel. *Journal of the American Medical Association*, August 2, 1976.

# COMMON POISONOUS GARDEN PLANTS.

| PLANT | TOXIC AGENT | POISONOUS PART | SYMPTOMS |
|---|---|---|---|
| Aesculus<br>Buckeye | Esculin glycoside | Leaves, flowers, sprouts, nuts | Vomiting, diarrhea, weakness, twitching, dilated pupils, depressions, paralysis |
| Colocasia antiquorum<br>Elephant's ear | Asparagine, calcium oxalate crystals | All parts | Burning of mouth and throat with swelling, salivation, vomiting and diarrhea |
| Consolida ambigua<br>Delphinium, Larkspur | Alkaloids | All parts, especially seeds and young plants | Burning of mouth and skin, vomiting, low blood pressure, weak pulse, convulsions |
| Convallaria majalis<br>Lily of the Valley | Convallotoxin and other alkaloids | Leaves and flowers | Vomiting, irregular heartbeat |
| Convolvulus cneorum<br>Morning glory shrub | Amides of lysergic acid | Seeds | Psychotic reaction, nausea, hallucinations |
| Daphne spp.<br>Daphne | Daphnin | All parts, especially seeds | Vomiting, abdominal pain, bloody diarrhea, weakness, convulsions |
| Digitalis purpurea<br>Foxglove | Digitalis glycosides | Leaves | Vomiting, diarrhea, abdominal pain, headache, irregular heartbeat, tremors convulsions |
| Datura stramonium<br>Jimson weed | Atropine and related alkaloids | All parts | Thirst, dilated pupils, flushing, hallucinations, headache, nausea, elevated blood pressure |
| Euphorbia pulcherrima<br>Poinsettia | Probably not significantly poisonous; too pretty to remove from the garden | | |
| E. trigona (hermentiana)<br>Milkbush<br>E. mammillaris<br>Corncob<br>E. milii splendens<br>Crown of thorns<br>E. tirucalli<br>Pencil tree | Unknown irritant | Sap | Skin and eye irritation, swelling of tongue, mouth and throat, vomiting |
| Gelsemium sempervirens<br>Carolina jessamine | Gelsemine and gelseminine alkaloids | All parts | Profuse sweating, muscular weakness, convulsion, respiratory depression |
| Hyacinthus orientalis<br>Hyacinth | Alkaloids | Bulb | Severe vomiting and diarrhea |
| Hydrangea spp.<br>Hydrangea | Hydrangin-cyanogenic glycoside | Leaves and buds | Vomiting, diarrhea, gasping, rapid breathing |
| Ilex spp.<br>Holly | Ilicin | Berries | Vomiting and diarrhea, central nervous system depression |
| Ipomoea violacea<br>Morning glory | Amides of lysergic acid | Seeds | Psychotic reaction, nausea, hallucinations |
| Iris spp.<br>Iris | Unknown | Rhizome, flower stalk, leaves | Vomiting and diarrhea, blisters of lips and mouth |
| Lantana camara<br>Lantana | Lantanin alkaloid | Green berries | Vomiting and diarrhea, muscular weakness, circulatory collapse |
| Lathyrus spp.<br>Sweet pea | Aminoproprionitrile | Seeds | Slow and weak pulse, shallow breathing, paralysis, convulsions |
| Ligustrum spp.<br>Privet | Unknown | Leaves and berries | Vomiting, diarrhea, low blood pressure, kidney damage |
| Lobelia | Lobeline, lobelamine alkaloids | All parts | Vomiting, weakness, prostration, tremors, convulsions, coma, death |
| Mirabilis jalapa L.<br>Four o'clock | Unidentified | Roots, seeds | Vomiting, diarrhea, abdominal pain |

| PLANT | TOXIC AGENT | POISONOUS PART | SYMPTOMS |
|---|---|---|---|
| Narcissus pseudonarcissus Daffodil Narcissus spp. Narcissus, jonquil | Alkaloids | Bulb | Vomiting, diarrhea |
| Nerium oleander Oleander | Oleandrin, Nereoside | All parts | Vomiting, abdominal pain, dizziness, slow and irregular heart beat, dilation of pupils, bloody diarrhea, respiratory paralysis |
| Nicotiana glauca Tree tobacco N. trigonophylla Wild tobacco | Nicotine | All parts | Vomiting, diarrhea, slow pulse, dizziness, collapse, respiratory failure |
| Parthenocissus quinquefolia Virginia creeper | Unidentified | Berries | Vomiting, diarrhea (two deaths reported) |
| Philodendron pertusum Monstera | Calcium oxalate | Leaves | Burning of mouth, vomiting, diarrhea |
| Phytolacca americana Pokeweed | Unidentified | All parts | Vomiting, diarrhea, abdominal pain, respiratory depression, convulsions, death |
| Ranunculus spp. | Protoanemonin | Leaves | Vomiting, diarrhea, weakness, weak pulse, respiratory paralysis, convulsions |
| Rhododendron occidentale Azalea | Andromedotoxin, arbutin glucoside | All parts | Nausea, salivation, vomiting, weakness, dizziness, difficulty breathing, loss of balance |
| Rheum rhaponticum Rhubarb | Calcium oxalate | Leaves | Burning of mouth and throat, vomiting, diarrhea |
| Rhus diversiloba Poison oak | 3-n-pentdecylcatechol | Sap from all parts | Blisters, itching |
| Ricinus communis Castor bean | Ricin | Seed | Severe vomiting, diarrhea, convulsions, kidney damage, death |
| Robinia pseudoacacia Black locust | Robin | Bark, leaves, seeds | Vomiting, weakness, depression |
| Sedum acre Sedum S. morganianum Donkey tail | Unidentified glucosides | All parts | Vomiting, diarrhea, weakness, respiratory depression |
| Solanum melongena Eggplant S. pseudocapsicum Jerusalem cherry S. rantonnetii Nightshade | Solanine alkaloids | All parts except fruit / Leaves and unripe fruit / All parts | Vomiting, diarrhea, convulsions, respiratory and nervous system depression |
| Tanacetum vulgare Tansy | Tanacetin oil | Leaves, flower heads | Vomiting, rapid and weak pulse, convulsions |
| Taxus cuspidata Japanese yew | Taxine alkaloid | All parts, especially berries | Vomiting, diarrhea, dilated pupils, weakness, convulsions |
| Thevetia peruviana Yellow oleander | Thevetin alkaloid, cardiac glycoside | All parts, especially fruits | Vomiting, diarrhea, weakness, collapse, slow and irregular heart beat |
| Tulipa spp. Tulip | Tulipene | Bulb | Vomiting, diarrhea |
| Wisteria sinensis Wisteria | Resin and wisterin glycoside | Seeds and pods | Severe vomiting, diarrhea, collapse |
| Zantedeschia aethiopica Calla | Calcium oxalate | Leaves and rhizome | Burning of mouth and throat with swelling, vomiting |

Leonard Lee Rue, III, Photo Researchers

The Southern Fence Lizard is one of many species capable of regrowing lost appendages. The shorter tail was most likely damaged by a predator. It was eventually replaced by the longer, regenerated tail.

# BIOELECTRICITY AND LIMB REGENERATION

## by Richard B. Borgens

LOSING a limb would be disastrous for most animals. But a large number of species—worms, fish, lizards, and cockroaches, to name but a few—are able to replace certain parts of their bodies if they are lost. Some animals have even evolved the regeneration of a lost appendage as a defense mechanism. The tails of some lizards, for example, have built-in breaking points; when seized by a predator, the lizard's tail separates from its body. The predator is left with a small meal, while the lizard is usually able to scamper off and eventually regrow what the predator took.

For several years, I have studied the remarkable regenerative abilities of newts and other salamanders. When certain species of salamanders lose a limb, they grow a replace-

ment that will be a nearly perfect copy of the original. This capability, common to most tailed amphibians, has been a puzzle to scientists because there are no obvious differences between the tissues of these animals and those of vertebrates that are unable to regenerate lost body parts.

The same types of structural and functional tissues make up the limbs of salamanders and those of humans. Yet, the regenerative power of newts and salamanders is virtually limitless.

### SEQUENCE OF EVENTS

The changes that take place after the amputation of a salamander's limb serve to characterize the sequence of events during regeneration. After amputation, the tip of the

Lewis Walker, Photo Researchers

The Gecko has a tail with a built-in breaking point. When seized by a predator, the tail easily separates from the lizard's body. The lizard is then able to scamper off and regenerate the lost appendage.

stump quickly becomes covered with a thin, transparent wound epithelium, which seals off the lesion from the external environment. Internally, the damaged tissues of the appendage are removed by the body's natural "cleanup" mechanism, and the remaining healthy cells begin a process called dedifferentiation. This means that many of the tissues just beneath the surface of the stump tip begin to lose the characteristics that distinguish them from each other. Cartilage, bone, and muscle tissues regress to an unspecialized cell type. The resultant homogeneous mass of cells, with its epithelial covering, is called a blastema.

The blastema, after reaching a certain size, then redifferentiates. It reorganizes and develops back into a replica of the severed portion of the limb. The length of time needed for this body repair is variable, depending on the season of the year, and the age and particular species of salamander. In general, a fine forelimb, with only minor differentiation still in progress, is produced in two to four months.

## CONTROLLING FACTORS

Experimental limb amputations in salamanders and adult grass frogs, a related but nonregenerating species, have provided clues to the factors controlling the power of regeneration. A classic example is the pioneering work of biologist-anatomist Marcus Singer, who deciphered the relationship between nerve supply to the limbs of salamanders and grass frogs and their ability to regenerate.

Singer has shown that a critical relationship must exist between the cross-sectional surface area of nerve tissue at the stump tip and the total area of the amputation surface. In salamanders, if enough nerves leading to the stump are cut away so that this ratio is lowered to a certain point, the limb will not regenerate.

Adult grass frogs, like other nonregenerating vertebrates, are naturally low in this ratio. However, if an extra large nerve, such as the sciatic nerve of the leg, is surgically rerouted to the stump of a grass frog's amputated limb, the appendage will begin to regenerate. (The limb does not regrow fully, however, and what does regenerate is deficient in internal structure and atypical in outward appearance.)

Other experimental methods have been successful in promoting regeneration in grass frogs—namely, immersion of an amputated stump in aqueous solutions of sodium chloride (table salt), the surgical implantation of extra adrenal glands, and electrically stimulating the nerves servicing the forearm stump.

## INDUCING REGENERATION

One of the most provocative recent experiments dealing with ways of bringing about regeneration in frogs was performed by Stephen D. Smith of the University of

Kentucky Medical School. Smith implanted (for experimental convenience) small electrical stimulation units, made from hearing-aid batteries, into the backs of adult frogs (*Rana pipiens*). With an insulated wire, he directed minuscule levels of current to the amputated forearm stumps of the frogs. In four weeks, the batteries were removed and the forearms began to regenerate.

This experiment caught the attention of Lionel Jaffe, a scientist whose major research has demonstrated how naturally produced electricity helps shape the development and modify the growth of a variety of plant and animal cells. His laboratory at Purdue University developed a remarkable tool, the vibrating probe, to measure the tiny, naturally produced electricity. Jaffe, developmental biologist Joseph Vanable, Jr., and I felt that the startling results of battery implants on frogs provided evidence for a direct connection between self-produced electricity and regeneration.

## ROLE OF ELECTRICITY

The first step was to demonstrate that the regeneration promoted in adult frogs was, in fact, caused by electricity and not by any electrode byproducts.

Having eliminated the chance of electrode byproduct contamination, we achieved results comparable to Smith's: organized extension of the forearm bone, abundant new muscle, large quantities of new nerve tissue, and development of cartilage masses resembling the bones of the forelimb. In all cases where the stimulating electrode (lead) was negative, regeneration was initiated. (Interestingly, if the positive lead was used, the opposite effect occurred—severe tissue destruction of the forelimb.)

Although perfection was not reached, the frogs certainly produced more than if left to their own devices. This, plus the amazingly low current employed, made us look more closely at salamanders. Could self-generated electrical currents account for their ability to regenerate lost body parts?

The notion that electricity plays a role in the normal replacement of salamander limbs dates back to the early twentieth century, but the idea was never fully explored. To settle the question of electric-current flow in salamander limbs, we used the vibrating probe. The flow of current was measured around the regenerating forelimbs of red-spotted newts.

In a biological sense, the current densities were enormous, often reaching 100 microamperes per square centimeter. The path of the current arced from the end of the stump and reentered the animal's body and the shank of its forelimb. These currents persisted for the first two weeks after amputation and seemed to mark the location of the budding blastema.

The measurements of current flow raised a number of questions, yet one thing was certain: from inception, the normal regeneration of appendages in salamanders is a highly electrically active event.

## SOURCE OF THE ELECTRICITY

Three major questions arose. What is the source of the animal's electricity? How necessary for regeneration are the naturally produced electrical fields? If the fields are required, what tissues do they affect? Further experiments with the salamanders helped us answer two of these questions.

The source of electricity was the simplest question to approach experimentally. Nerves are certainly electrically active and might be the source of the current we had measured. However, our measurements using the vibrating probe confirmed earlier findings that nerves were not the source of the current. No change in electrical activity was noted after nerve transection.

Amphibians possess another electrically active tissue, the skin, that operates like a battery. The skin of most amphibians possesses a sodium-specific transport system, which moves sodium from the water on the skin's surface into the body. In effect, the transport system acts as a complicated, sodium-dependent "pump" that drives strong electric currents.

The "skin battery's" sodium dependence provided us with a test of whether the skin is the source of the regeneration currents. Using red-spotted newts, we deprived their skin of sodium, and so were able to turn off their skin batteries.

Robert J. Ashworth, Photo Researchers

The tail of this salamander is at a late stage of regeneration. It has nearly reached the length of the severed limb and will soon develop into an exact replica.

By increasing sodium well above the normal levels found in pond water, we were able to increase the magnitude of the currents. With these inhibition and modulation techniques, we have been able to prove that the skin surrounding the remainder of the amputated appendage, and perhaps some of the body, is the source of this electrical activity.

## NECESSARY FOR REGENERATION

The same approach was used to test whether these currents were necessary for regeneration. The experiments are still in progress, but one thing is clear—limb regeneration can be severely disrupted by techniques that shut off the skin battery current and its associated field.

In one such experiment, a drug was applied only to the cuff of skin surrounding the forelimb stumps of tiger salamanders in such a way that the sodium channels of the outer layers of skin were blocked, and thus the skin battery turned off. Fifty per cent of the animals so treated were inhibited from regenerating or regenerated grotesque facsimiles of a forearm and hand. Preliminary evidence also shows that most animals are either inhibited from regenerating or do not regenerate normally if kept in a low-sodium medium, while those in a high-sodium medium regenerate extraordinarily fast.

We can now begin to make sense of how immersions in salt solutions are able to initiate regeneration in grass frogs: the electrical output of their skin batteries was stimulated and increased by the presence of more salt than is found in the pond water inhabited by the frogs.

We know that the natural replacement of body parts in salamanders is preceded by a period of high electrical activity, during which a naturally produced electric field is set up around the limb stump. We also have some evidence that such a field is necessary for normal regeneration in these animals and that artificially stimulating the stump of nonregenerating adult frogs will partially restore their regenerative capabilities.

## WHAT TISSUES ARE AFFECTED

We do not know what the cellular target or targets of the electric current might be, but we have some guesses. Ironically, although nerve tissue is not a source, it may prove to be the target of the current. Studies of embryonic chicken nerve bundles have shown that the direction in which new nerve processes grow can be controlled by weak electric fields. Perhaps nerves (which are also essential for regeneration) are directed by these natural fields into the region where they influence blastema formation.

## WHY MOST CAN'T REGENERATE

Another unanswered question concerns the electrical behavior of the limb stump in frogs. Adult frog skin also acts as a sodium-dependent battery, yet these animals do not regenerate. Preliminary work suggests that the current exiting from the stump of adult frogs is one-tenth the magnitude of that in salamanders—possibly frogs are "shorted out" internally. This may well prove to be true: beneath a frog's skin are large lymph pockets that do not exist in salamanders. The lymph may short circuit the flow of electricity around, and not through, the internal tissues of the stump.

Human beings, like all vertebrates, are not complete nonregenerators. Skin, bone, and parts of other organs and tissues of our bodies replace themselves as a normal part of the life process. Yet the ability to form functional tissue or to replace missing portions of the body is greatly restricted in all vertebrates except the tailed amphibians. Bioelectricity certainly seems to be one factor separating the two groups.

## ELECTRICITY TO AID HEALING

At present, some success is being achieved in healing chronic nonunions of human bone fractures by stimulating the fracture sites with low levels of current. Electricity has also been used to aid the healing of bed sores.

There is a parallel between humans and nonregenerating amphibians that also demands close scrutiny. Although adult frogs do not regenerate portions of their appendages, tadpoles do. They lose this ability during metamorphosis. Adult humans do not replace portions of their extremities; children do, though it is not well known.

Pediatricians Cynthia Illingworth of England and B. S. Douglas of Australia have demonstrated that children (up to eleven years of age) can perfectly regenerate tips of their fingers from past the first joint. The cosmetic results are remarkable, including well-formed fingernails. This extraordinary result was achieved without any experimental intervention. The fingers were simply splinted and bandaged, without surgical tampering, and nature did the rest.

Nothing is known about whether electricity plays a role in the finger regeneration of children. Interestingly enough, before the American Civil War, physiologist E. Du Bois-Reymond discovered that natural currents emanate from wounds of human skin. In light of our data, the existence of these currents suggests that they may aid in wound healing and, conceivably, finger regeneration.

George Porter, Photo Researchers

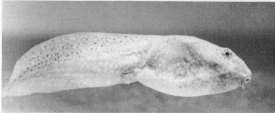
A. W. Ambler, Photo Researchers

The tadpole (above) is able to regenerate lost appendages. The adult frog (top), however, cannot regenerate. Experiments suggest that bioelectricity is the cause of regeneration. The source of this electricity is apparently lost during metamorphosis.

Humans apparently also lose their regenerative ability as they mature. Could bioelectricity be involved in regaining this ability, as it certainly is in frogs?

We may well hope that biological research in amphibian regeneration will someday deliver tools to modern medicine for making tissue-regeneration therapy a normal part of hospital procedure. This may sound more like science fiction than science fact, yet it is certainly possible that latent in human beings is the promise of whole-tissue regeneration so elegantly realized in the tailed amphibians ☐

 SELECTED READINGS

"The fascination of limb regeneration: if a newt can regrow an appendage, maybe humans can too" by Robert Bahr. *Smithsonian*, January 1977.

# THE 1977 NOBEL PRIZE WINNERS IN PHYSIOLOGY OR MEDICINE

## by David Hendin

THREE American scientists—a woman and two men—shared the 1977 Nobel Prize in Physiology or Medicine for their "formidable development" of the protein-hormone research field.

The three scientists are Dr. Rosalyn S. Yalow of the Veterans Administration Hospital in the Bronx, New York City; Andrew V. Schally of the Veterans Administration Hospital in New Orleans, Louisiana; and Dr. Roger C. L. Guillemin of the Salk Institute in La Jolla, California. Dr. Yalow was the second woman ever to win a Nobel Prize in medicine, and only the sixth woman to win the Nobel Prize in any scientific category.

### RADIOIMMUNOASSAY

Dr. Yalow was awarded half of the $145,000 prize for her key role in developing the radioimmunoassay (RIA). The RIA is a test that revolutionized the measurement of protein hormones in the body. The test is so sensitive that it is capable of detecting 1/1,000,000,000 of a gram of a material. One scientist explained that this was like locating half-a-lump of sugar in a lake some 100 kilometers (62 miles) square and 9 meters (30 feet) deep.

"It was accomplished by a spectacular combination of immunology, isotope research, mathematics, and physics," the Nobel Committee stated.

Today the RIA-technique allows physicians to detect conditions that once were missed because methods of analysis were too crude to measure the incredibly small changes in hormone levels that can affect a person's health. RIAs are being used today to measure the concentrations of various hormones, vitamins, viruses, enzymes, drugs, and other substances that can help physicians differentiate between normal and disease states. Thousands of blood banks are using RIAs to identify and remove from

Medical Media Production Service

Rosalyn S. Yalow

stock blood samples that have been contaminated with hepatitis virus.

Dr. Yalow began her work in 1950 with Dr. Solomon Berson, with whom she collaborated for 22 years until his death in 1972. "The only tragedy in today's Nobel award," she said at the ceremony, "is that Dr. Berson did not live to share it."

Dr. Yalow's work is closely linked with the work of Drs. Guillemin and Schally because RIAs have permitted their work on hypothalamic hormones to move more quickly than would have been possible with previously available and less-sensitive tests.

### HYPOTHALAMIC HORMONES

Drs. Guillemin and Schally split the second half of the Nobel Prize for research showing that the pituitary gland is not really the master hormone gland of the brain, as had long been thought. Instead the pituitary

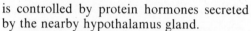
The Nobel Foundation
Roger C. L. Guillemin

The Nobel Foundation
Andrew V. Schally

is controlled by protein hormones secreted by the nearby hypothalamus gland.

When stimulated by hypothalamic hormones, the pituitary sends out hormones that govern the activities of other glands throughout the body—including the sex glands that affect sexual behavior and reproduction, the thyroid gland that regulates growth and metabolism, and the adrenal glands that affect the body's reaction to stress.

Until the early 1960s, Guillemin and Schally were research colleagues at Baylor University in Texas. Since then they have worked independently. As often occurs in pioneering scientific research, some of Dr. Guillemin's early findings were rejected in 1969 by a leading scientific journal after a preliminary reader of the paper implied that hypothalamic hormones were probably imaginary. Since then several of the hypothalamic hormones have been not only identified but also synthesized by Guillemin, Schally, and others.

The first hypothalamic hormone to be discovered is called TRH, for thyrotropin-releasing hormone. TRH causes the pituitary gland to release a substance called thyrotropin, which, in turn, causes the thyroid gland to release thyroid hormone. The research groups headed by Schally and Guillemin discovered TRH virtually simultaneously in 1969.

Research into the brain hormones has pointed toward potential new contraception, new ideas about controlling diabetes, and to a wealth of knowledge about the way the brain acts as the chemical master of the body. One group of brain hormones, only recently discovered, are the endorphins. It is believed that they may hold the key to mental illness, one of the world's major health problems. Other brain hormones have shown promise as drugs to treat Parkinson's disease, diabetes, and other illnesses.

*Rosalyn S. Yalow* was born in the south Bronx in New York City. She attended local public schools and received her Bachelor of Science Degree from New York City's Hunter College, where she graduated as the school's first physics major in 1941. She received her Ph.D. degree in Physics in 1945 from the University of Illinois. Since 1950 Dr. Yalow has worked at the Veterans Administration Hospital in the Bronx, New York, and she has been chief of nuclear medicine there since 1970. She is also on the faculty of the Mt. Sinai Hospital School of Medicine. Dr. Yalow is married to Dr. Aaron Yalow, a physics professor at Cooper Union College.

*Roger Charles Louis Guillemin* was born in 1924 in Dijon, France. He earned his Bachelor of Arts and Science degree at the University of Dijon in the early 1940s. In 1949 he received his M.D. degree from the School of Medicine in Lyon, France. Then he moved to Canada where he did post-graduate work at McGill University and the University of Montreal, where he received his Ph.D. degree in physiology and experimental medicine. In 1952 Dr. Guillemin moved to the Baylor College of Medicine in Houston, Texas, where he remained for 18 years teaching fundamental endocrinology as a professor of physiology. Dr. Guillemin became an American citizen in 1963. In 1970 he joined the Salk Institute in La Jolla, California, as a resident fellow and research professor. He also holds an appointment as a professor of medicine, adjunct, at the Medical School of the University of California in San Diego. He is a member of the National Academy of Sciences. In addition to his research work on hypothalamic hormones, Dr. Guillemin writes extensively on the history of medicine and, as a hobby, collects pre-Columbian art.

*Andrew Victor Schally* was born in 1926 in Wilno, Poland. He left war-ravaged Poland in 1939, studied chemistry in London during the late 1940s, and earned both his B.Sc. (1955) and Ph.D. (1957) degrees in biochemistry from McGill University in Montreal. From 1957 to 1962 he served as a research associate and assistant professor in the department of physiology at Baylor University. In 1962 he went to New Orleans to take his present post as Chief of the Endocrine and Polypeptide Laboratories in the Veterans Administration Hospital. Since 1967 Dr. Schally has also been a professor of medicine at the Tulane University School of Medicine, where he became an associate professor in 1962. Dr. Schally has spent most of his career studying the brain hormones that act on the pituitary gland □

Dr. Yalow at work on radioimmunoassay in her Bronx, N.Y. laboratory.

Medical Media Production Service

Computers are becoming more and more a part of everyday consumer life. Here a computerized supermarket checkout counter with an electronic scanner that automatically reads the prices of items as they pass over a special screen. This new system reduces the rate of error and is so far liked by both consumers and checkers.

Associated Press

# COMPUTERS AND MATHEMATICS

## contents

# COMPUTERS AND MATHEMATICS
## review
## of the year

Volkswagen of America

A computerized dashboard displays information about traffic flow and road conditions gathered by a special guidance network using roadside computers.

**Computer trends.** The year 1977 saw a continuing trend toward smaller, less expensive, and more "intelligent" computers. Although microcomputers have smaller memories, are slower, and can handle fewer terminals than can minicomputers, the differences between the two lessened. Microcomputers are now being equipped with larger memories and are being made to handle more terminals. As a result, the smaller-sized and cheaper microcomputers are seriously challenging the minicomputers. In fact, it seems to be getting harder to decide whether a microcomputer or a minicomputer is better for a specific task. ■ Microcomputers moved into a number of areas—from controlling pet-food processing to monitoring energy consumption in office buildings to operating a spray-paint assembly line that insures quality paint jobs. ■ Microprocessors, the small-scale computing units on silicon chips that serve as the processing units of microcomputers, are being used to control fuel emissions and gasoline mileage on some 1977 and 1978 automobiles. And cars may soon come equipped with microprocessor-controlled safety devices.

**Expanding consumer uses.** Computers may soon provide other conveniences for automobile drivers as well. In West Germany, engineers are developing a special computer guidance system to reroute drivers away from accidents and traffic jams. A computer installed in the car will be in communication with a system of roadside computers that will monitor traffic patterns and road and weather conditions. The driver uses a code to record his or her destination in the car's computer. This information is conveyed to the roadside computers along the way, and they, in turn, inform the driver of the best route to follow and later of any previously unexpected tieups and possible alternate routes. The system, which will cost the consumer about as much as a car radio, is to be tested in the near future and, if all goes well, is expected to be in use in about five years. ■ The home computer and TV-game unit were combined in 1977. The *Bally Library* is a TV-game center with a brain. Its computer capability is similar to that of an IBM 5100. With ten separate memories, it can be used for personal bookkeeping, as a mathematics teaching tool, and as a game center. It also has planned add-on features such as magnetic tape decks, an alpha-numeric keyboard like that of a typewriter, and a high speed printer that will turn it into a personalized home computing center. ■ A computerized burglar-alarm system triggered by motion within a certain protected area is also now available for home use.

Computerized checking accounts—the electronic transfer of funds from the consumers' checking accounts to the merchants' accounts—have brought six Long Island, New York, communities closer to the "cashless society." The Hempstead Bank instituted the system in 1975, but it is taking a while to catch on. The consumers who use the system seem quite enthusiastic about it so far. The only identification the customer needs is a special credit card issued by the bank. The merchant inserts the card into a computer terminal and punches in an identification code and the price of the item the customer is purchasing. The customer then punches in his own secret code—known only to him and the bank. Assuming that there is sufficient money in the customer's checking account, the bank transfers the amount of the purchase from the customer's account to the merchant's account.

Computers that can talk, called voice-response systems, and computers that can understand human speech, called voice-recognition systems, are coming into wider use. Banks are using some of these systems. The consumer talks to the computer by Touch-Tone telephone and the computer responds with a synthesized voice. Voice-response systems are also being used to train blind people for certain Civil Service jobs, and voice-recognition systems are currently being used for such things as taking inventory, speech research, computer games, and for computer input where it would be impractical to use a keyboard.

**Expanding use in science.** The New Jersey Institute of Technology in Newark has established an experimental computer system that, it is hoped, will eventually allow scientists throughout the United States to cummunicate with each other by computerized conferences and scientific journals. Over 200 scientists now have access to terminals linked to the central Newark computer and can send messages to each other, "publish" papers and results of experiments, and discuss their research.

Scientists are also developing specialized computer programs to help them in their research. Massachusetts Institute of Technology (MIT) geophysicists have, for example, created a computer program that simulates the motions of the earth's crust, and Theodore J. Crovello, professor of biology at the University of Notre Dame has used a computer to compile and analyze data on over 100 species of mustard plants from 35,000 individual plant collections. ■ Computer-enhanced photography is nothing new to astronomers, but its use has now expanded to bring out very faint features on photographic plates taken by earth-bound telescopes. This advance has enabled astronomers to view previously unseen structures in distant galaxies and to eliminate blurring of photos caused by turbulence in the earth's atmosphere.

**Mathematics.** The debate over the merits and failures of the "new math" continued in 1977. "New math" advocates became more vocal, arguing that problems with "new math" were due to the use of teachers not properly trained to teach the subject and to other similar problems. Critics of "new math" stressed a "back-to-basics" approach, but a number of educators warned that such an approach could leave students with certain computational skills but might deprive them of an understanding of mathematical concepts.

Catastrophe theory, widely publicized in 1976, came under sharp criticism from some mathematicians during 1977, leading to some rather heated debates on the merits of the applications to which the theory was put. See also "Catastrophe Theory" on page 100.

Jane Samz

Docutel Corporation

The use of computers in banks is increasing rapidly. Here a customer uses a Total Teller, an automated teller system, for her banking needs.

Apple II is a perfect tutor. Hooked into a TV for its display screen, the computer can be used to teach a wide variety of basic skills and to entertain with numerous games.

Regis McKenna

Could this riot have been predicted? Proponents of catastrophe theory say yes—that the probability that sudden events will occur can be forecast by plotting developments mathematically.

UPI photo by Leslie H. Sintay

# CATASTROPHE THEORY

## by Malcolm W. Browne

AN increasingly bitter debate is spreading among experts in many fields of science over "catastrophe theory"—a mathematical concept intended to explain and predict events as disparate as chemical reactions, dog bites, stock-market crashes, and the outbreak of war.

General interest in the principle has reached the point that a lecture on the subject at the University of California attracted 1,000 people, and the supply of papers on catastrophe theory is exhausted almost as soon as they are published.

Catastrophe theory is a concept that says the probability that sudden events will occur can be accurately forecast by plotting developments mathematically.

Its proponents say that catastrophe theory promises to predict all kinds of sudden events, even from very small amounts of data, and even if some of the data are wrong.

Critics of catastrophe theory contend that it is mathematically unsound, that it has little or nothing to do with the real world, and that the predictions drawn from it are so vague and general as to be worthless.

There are eminent mathematicians on both sides of the argument, although the tide seems to have turned during 1977 in favor of the critics.

The dispute among mathematicians has spread to many fields—biology, social and political science, psychology and other "soft sciences"—where "catastrophists" see potential applications of the principle.

Proponents of the catastrophe theory say that the theory represents the greatest revolution in mathematical thought since the discovery of calculus three centuries ago.

### CAN PICTURES SYMBOLIZE EVENTS?

Catastrophe theory is based on the idea that pictorial representations can symbolize real events.

One of the pictures is a simple line graph, drawn as a two-dimensional figure, which shows how something changes between one state or point and another.

More complex graphs can be drawn on three-dimensional surfaces—spheres, cylinders, and paraboloids, for example. Multi-dimensional graphs contain much more information than two-dimensional graphs, and can represent more subtle changes and relationships.

Topology, the mathematical study of the shapes of surfaces, is the science from which catastrophe theory developed in the mid-1960s, largely because of the work of René Thom, the French mathematician.

Dr. Thom's particular interest was in a kind of surface that folds on itself, changing abruptly from a smooth form to a discontinuous break of some kind. He postulated that

A symbol of the Depression era. Catastrophe theory is based on the idea that pictorial representations can symbolize real events.

there are seven basic forms of such a curve, and he called the discontinuous break characteristic of all of them a "catastrophe."

## WIDE ACCEPTANCE AT FIRST

Dr. Thom and his followers, especially E. Christopher Zeeman, an English mathematician, proposed that such surfaces, which are mathematical abstractions in themselves, might serve as suitable models for describing real events. They then set out to prove the idea.

Dr. Zeeman suggested that many real events—a sudden change in a chemical reaction, the sudden buckling of a steel girder, the sudden decision of a dog to attack, the sudden differentiation of growing cells into an embryo—could be represented as "catastrophes" on suitable mathematical surfaces.

He also asserted that if the right surface were chosen to symbolize the variable factors affecting an event, only a small amount of information would be needed to predict the shape of an entire surface, and from this the event it represented could be predicted.

Among the groups that sought applications in Dr. Zeeman's work was the British prison system. Prison authorities helped Dr. Zeeman in a study he made of the events that had led to a 1972 riot at Gartree Prison, which, he said, could have been plotted on a "catastrophe" surface.

By refining the technique it should be possible, he reasoned, to identify the times and circumstances under which a riot would be most likely and to take preventative measures.

Dr. Zeeman published other papers contending that catastrophe surfaces may represent heartbeats, the onset of certain kinds of mental illness, and social unrest. For several years, the scientific community appeared to accept these ideas without comment.

But lately, the work of Dr. Zeeman and others has come under increasingly heavy challenge.

## ATTACKED AS TOO VAGUE

A volley of scientific papers by Hector J. Sussman and Raphael S. Zahler, associate professors of mathematics at Rutgers University, was the first concerted attack on the ideas of catastrophe theory. *Science*, a respected U.S. journal, soon followed this with a strong criticism entitled "Catastrophe Theory: The Emperor Has No Clothes."

Dr. Sussman and others accused the catastrophists of trying to intimidate nonmathematicians (and even mathematicians unfamiliar with their work) with such phrases as "deep mathematics."

Could catastrophe theory be used in the future to prevent occurrences like this?

University of Minnesota

Political scientist Robert T. Holt believes that catastrophe theory provides a mathematical tool for the social sciences.

Catastrophe theory, Dr. Sussman wrote, "is tantamount to claiming that the world can be deduced from pure thought—a claim few scientists would accept."

He added: "Catastrophe theory offers to mathematicians the hope of applying mathematics without having to know anything but mathematics. An appealing dream for mathematicians, but a dream that cannot come true."

Dr. Zeeman has not replied in print to the growing criticism. In an interview with *The New York Times,* he said that his published papers spoke for themselves and that Dr. Sussman's critiques contained "many misquotations, misrepresentations, and mathematical mistakes."

Responding to the charge that catastrophe theory is too vague and general to be useful, he asked, "What would you say of numbers—one, two, three, and so forth? They are also general and vague, but would you contend they are not useful?"

He said that he was not attempting to prove the utility of catastrophe theory in any field of research, but merely to offer it to others as a tool that they might find useful. In three or four years, he said, social scientists may begin making predictions based on the theory.

But many mathematicians reject even this possibility. Among them is Dr. Stephen Smale, a professor at the University of California and winner of the Fields Medal, the highest recognition that a mathematician can receive. (There is no Nobel Prize in mathematics.)

"I've been a close friend of Chris Zeeman for years," Dr. Smale said in an interview, "and he awarded me an honorary degree at the University of Warwick in Coventry, where he is director of mathematical research.

"But in a sense I reject catastrophe theory completely. It is more philosophy than mathematics, and even as a philosophy it doesn't explain the real world. Zeeman's assertions constitute a heavy-handed argument he just cannot justify," Dr. Smale concluded.

USE AS TOOL

Despite such criticism, the number of Dr. Zeeman's supporters appears to be growing in some fields. Dr. Robert T. Holt, professor of political science at the University of Minnesota, is one of them.

"In the social sciences it is terribly difficult to obtain and use exact data of the kind produced by the natural sciences," he said in an interview, "and the catastrophe theory work of Thom and Zeeman offers us a way to get around this.

"For example," he said, "both the beginning and end of the First World War came as big surprises to everyone. Gradual processes suddenly and unexpectedly resulted in the outbreak of the war and the ending of the war. We believe these can be plotted on catastrophe curves of the types proposed by Thom and Zeeman.

"We believe, also, that it would be possible to identify times at which a war would be most probable or least probable using the theory.

"This gives us a mathematical tool which is qualitative as well as quantitative, and I think you have to appreciate the spirit of the theory. Zeeman's papers are clues, not proofs, and we should use them in that spirit"□

SELECTED READINGS

"Catastrophe model: can it see crises?" by P. P. Luedtke. *Science Digest,* February 1977.

"Catastrophe theory: the first decade" by L. A. Steen. *Science News,* April 2, 1977.

"Catastrophe theory." *Scientific American,* March 1976.

A scientist plays chess with a computer. Some computers—but not those based on artificial intelligence principles—have been programmed to play a good game.

# IF COMPUTERS COULD REASON

## by Lee Dembart

CAN machines think? Should they? The computer world is in the midst of a fundamental dispute over those questions because an eminent computer scientist wrote a book arguing that machines could never be made to reason like people and, what was more, should not be.

In the 1950s, in the infancy of the computer revolution, before problems began cropping up, the public was told that computers would be smarter than brains. Computer chess champions and machine translation, for example, were just around the corner. So far, neither has been accomplished successfully, and neither is likely to be any time soon.

Nor have computers had much success in making decisions that require judgment. They can rattle off a large city telephone directory unerringly time after time, which no human can do, but they cannot begin to distinguish one face from another, as babies can.

Computer scientists have always said, "Give us more time. The problem is more complex than we thought." Then one of them, Joseph Weizenbaum, a professor of computer science at the Massachusetts Institute of Technology, wrote a book saying that the project was fundamentally unsound and dangerous to pursue, partly, he said, because the computers' and humans' ways of thought would always be alien, and because knowledge might become limited to what a computer could understand.

### CONTINUING DEBATE

The elders of the artificial intelligence community reacted with outrage. Even those who agreed with his premises criticized the book as being too harsh in tone, too personal in its attacks. Computer journals bristled with reviews, comments, and replies provoked by Professor Weizenbaum's book,

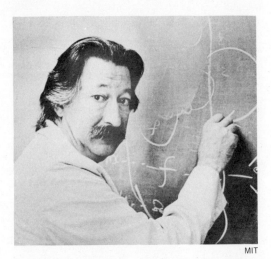

Professor Weizenbaum believes that it may be dangerous to pursue artificial intelligence.

*Computer Power and Human Reason.* Then the controversy spilled into the prestigious publication *Science.* In an article entitled "What Computers Mean for Man and Society," Professor Herbert A. Simon of the Carnegie-Mellon University in Pittsburgh argued that computers were no more or less dangerous than any other machine of the industrial revolution.

Professor Simon, who is one of the leading figures in artificial intelligence research, asserted that Professor Weizenbaum's position was that humans were not subject to natural laws and that knowledge about their ability to think was dangerous.

"I have pronounced heresy and I am a heretic," the tweedy, 54-year-old Mr. Weizenbaum said in his office in Cambridge, Massachusetts.

Professor Weizenbaum, who says he loves beautiful machinery, was not the first critic of artificial intelligence, but he was the first from inside the field.

"Weizenbaum has as much experience as almost anyone in the world with this subject," one of his opponents, Professor Bruce G. Buchanan, acknowledged. "He is a much more informed critic than we have ever had."

While machines provide the ostensible cause of the debate, the debate really encompasses some of mankind's oldest and newest questions. How do we know what we know? What does it mean for a human to know something? What does it mean for a computer? What is creativity? How do we think? What are the limits of science? What are the limits of digital computers?

There are also public policy questions involved, for the vast majority of work in artificial intelligence is supported by governments. Efforts to get computers to reason involve between 200 and 500 people in the United States alone.

## NO MAJOR BREAKTHROUGHS AS YET

At Stanford University in Palo Alto, California, one of a handful of centers researching artificial intelligence, computer scientists conceded that they have not achieved the major breakthrough of teaching machines to think rather than to simply repeat what they have been told. But they eagerly demonstrated several programs that, they said, exhibited "cleverness."

The ultimate aim of one such program, called MYCIN, is to enable a physician to type in a patient's symptoms and test results and get back a diagnosis and suggested treatment.

So far, the machine has been taught 450 rules regarding meningitis. It compares patients' histories to those rules and has given accurate diagnoses under experimental conditions. Sometimes the machine will ask for more information about a test or about the patient, if the given information does not fulfill its program, and will explain to the physician why it wants to know. It is also able to explain how it reaches its conclusion by telling which of its rules apply to the given patient.

"These are programs with very narrow limits," said Professor Buchanan, who worked on MYCIN with Dr. Joshua Lederberg, professor of genetics at Stanford and Nobel laureate in medicine. "There's no widespread intelligence here. Yet."

Professor Weizenbaum retorted from M.I.T., "My argument that it cannot be done does not rest on any particular limitation of computers, or the state of the art, or anything of that kind. It simply rests on the nature of science.

Stanford University

Dr. Joshua Lederberg disagrees. He believes that the full potential of computers should be explored but warns that computers should not be allowed to get out of control.

"How far can science see into anything, particularly man?" he said. "The artificial intelligentsia claims that the computer metaphor can somehow explicate the whole man. This strikes me as being enormously arrogant and just plain wrong—wrong in principle."

Back at Stanford, Dr. Lederberg countered, "Assertions about what will never be possible are not logically tenable. I don't know what's impossible. I prefer to work in what is possible and try to see what we can do.

"Organisms are built out of matter. I can see no place in principle by which I can believe that a brain can do a computation that a machine cannot," he said. "A brain is, however, enormously more complex and dynamically organized, built on very different principles and subject to four billion [4,000,-000,000] years of evolution. So far we're far from having a very clear picture of how that is put together. That's one of the major frontiers of biology at the present time."

## SKEPTICISM

One of the reasons Professor Weizenbaum became skeptical that parallels could be drawn between human and computer thought was the reaction to a major artificial intelligence program he wrote in 1965. Called ELIZA, it aimed to simulate a psychiatrist at work. The psychiatrist's role was chosen for this attempt at conversation because the computer could always respond with "Please go on" if it did not understand what was being said.

Otherwise, the machine had a series of canned sentences that it could generate when it encountered words or structures that it recognized.

Dr. Ken Kolby of Stanford built a program called PARRY, which responded as a paranoid would, and the "paranoid" and the "psychiatrist" were set to talking, generating a conversation that included the following circular exchange:

PARRY: In my opinion you have a one-track mind.

ELIZA: What makes you think I have a one-track mind?

PARRY: I used to go to the track every week.

ELIZA: What does that suggest to you?

PARRY: I avoid racetracks now because the races are fixed.

ELIZA: Is that the real reason?

PARRY: I'd rather not discuss it.

ELIZA: What else would you like to discuss?

PARRY: That's something I don't want to go into.

After writing the program, Professor Weizenbaum said, he was startled to find that instead of recognizing it as a parlor trick, some people thought they were talking to a person, and some computer scientists predicted that this tool would bring computer psychiatry to large numbers of people now unable to afford treatment.

"There are aspects to human life that a computer cannot understand—cannot," Mr. Weizenbaum said. "It's necessary to be a human being. Love and loneliness have to do with the deepest consequences of our biological constitution. That kind of understanding is in principle impossible for the computer."

## "WORTH INVESTIGATING"

But Dr. Lederberg of Stanford said he felt that computer psychiatry should be explored. "I don't find it at all unimaginable that it may be very useful," he said.

"I don't see anything either inappropriate or immoral in it given the framework that it's a help to an individual to help himself," Dr. Lederberg said. "The needs for mental health support are to enormous and are so impossible to meet by using people as the sole basis that some amplification by having machines as amplifiers may be worth investigating."

But with MYCIN, the program that diagnoses disease and prescribes treatment, the expects were not willing to do away with the doctor and let the computer dispense pills to each patient in the hospital.

"If a program such as MYCIN were acting independently of a physician, I think that would be inappropriate," said Professor Buchanan. "The problem is that human diseases are open-ended.

"Our goal is to build a program that can assist working scientists with reasoning problems. You wouldn't expect a tool to have all of the power of a working scientist, but you would hope that you could design a smart system to provide some of the solutions to subproblems."

## NO "HAL" IN SIGHT

But the early goal of artificial intelligence studies, to build a machine that could handle unrestricted problems within a given area, has proved more elusive with each advance of knowledge. A computer like Hal in the movie *2001*, which talks, listens, thinks, reasons, has emotions, and so forth, is nowhere within the conceivable future.

In chess, there are computers programmed to play a good game. But those which are based on artificial intelligence principles, which seek to apply strategy rather than pure memory, are not among them. The memory programs, which defeat those with artificial intelligence, do not attempt to simulate human thought. They work because of the brute force of the computer in its ability to examine many moves ahead, just as a 747 flies because of the brute force of its engines and not because it simulates a bird in flight.

In machine translation, the problem seemed simple for a computer: give it a dictionary and a grammar of each language and let it translate. But no general purpose machine has yet been devised that can figure out a sentence like "The book is in the pen." No computer can yet read a novel and write a summary of its plot, much less translate it into another language.

## "MAN IS NOT A MECHANISM"

Some of these issues were discussed in the early 1970s by Herbert L. Dreyfus, a philosopher at the University of California at Berkeley. His book *What Computers Can't Do* created a small stir then. In a recent interview Professor Dreyfus argued that human activity was understandable only as a whole and could not be described as a complex assembly of simple parts. "Man is not a mechanism," he said.

"If what they want are localized, restricted, game-like situations, they can make solutions," he said. "But if they think they can go on broadening these little solutions till they get to the big ones, I think they just haven't faced the situation.

"Unfortunately, we cannot have a science of human beings. That's what this comes down to. Even though Plato had a dream that we could and Newton had success with physical objects."

Dr. Lederberg, who has been working on building a computer program that will help plan biological experiments, disagreed at least in theory. He said that computers just have not been big enough to handle the complexity necessary for the big solutions. The researchers said that they have been able to set up programs that mimic human problem-solving strategies within limited contexts. "Efforts to keep bootstrapping to higher and higher levels of generality really are impeded by the hardware," Dr. Lederberg said. ("Hardware" is the term used by computer scientists for the computer itself; the computer program is known as "software.")

Dr. Lederberg said that he thought the computer's ability to combine and examine large numbers of alternative possibilities could theoretically enable it to use human problem-solving strategies.

"I don't know how I get 'flashes of insight,' " he said. "I'm willing to go along with Einstein's self-description that he thinks it's

A prosthetic knee joint capable of being "tuned" to a person's individual gait by signals from a microcomputer has been developed. Research is being conducted on ways that the artificial leg could retune itself automatically when the microcomputer senses a coming change in gait.

combinatorial play, that he thinks it's parsing through very large numbers of combinatorial alternatives. But it's got to be structured in some way."

The computer scientists noted that their failures in artificial intelligence have been helpful because they have helped specialists in other areas make explicit the knowledge that they have. And it has helped psychologists studying information processing in the brain.

"To the extent that you can codify human thinking may not tell you that that's exactly the way humans do it, but it may give you some insight into how humans might think about the problem to do it better," Professor Buchanan said.

## SHOULD ARTIFICIAL INTELLIGENCE BE PURSUED?

But Professor Weizenbaum said he believed that it was dangerous to pursue the goal of artificial intelligence, for machines will always be alien to humans, though they may eventually appear to be smarter.

He traces his views of machines to his experience as a small boy in Nazi Germany. In 1936, at the age of 13, he fled with his parents to the United States, settling in Detroit.

"I had an introduction to the world in formative years of the miscarriage of the ultimate form of rationality," Professor Weizenbaum said.

"What decided me to go into mathematics," he said, "was that of all the things that one could study, mathematics seemed by far the easiest. Mathematics is a game. It is entirely abstract. Hidden behind that recognition that mathematics is the easiest is the corresponding recognition that real life is the hardest. That has been with me since childhood."

Dr. Lederberg agreed, "There are things that should not be done." But, he added, "I don't see the difference between things that people shouldn't do and things that com-

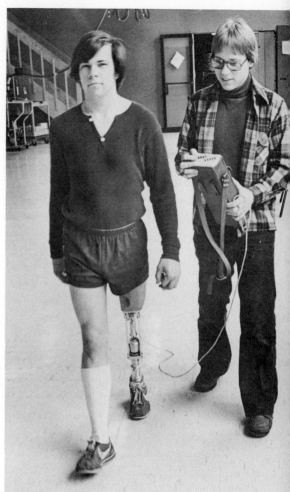

Calvin Campbell, MIT

puters shouldn't do. What should not be done is to allow computers to get out of control."

Said Dr. Buchanan: "Any tool with sufficient power to have enormous benefits also carries elements of risk if that tool is misused. Scientists who are developing that tool need to be aware of the risks as well as of the benefits" □

SELECTED READINGS

"Robots that talk, think, create—and even go crazy." *Science Digest*, September 1976.

"Post-human intelligence" by Robert Jastrow. *Natural History*, June 1977.

"When the computer procreates" by J. Bernstein. *New York Times Magazine*, February 15, 1976.

"Why can't computers be more like us?" by L. Thomas. *Saturday Evening Post*, October 1976.

In a matter of seconds, flight information requested by a passenger reservations agent appears on the screen of her CRT computer terminal.

American Airlines

# CRYPTOGRAPHY

## by Gina Bari Kolata

COMPUTERS are increasingly a central part of cheap and efficient communication systems, but a number of experts warn that computer-controlled communications networks are coming into use before problems of ensuring privacy and security have been solved. This issue is coming to the fore as these communications networks play an ever larger role in technological societies.

One way to provide security is to encode computer messages. New developments in cryptography, or coding, promise to change the age-old methodology of secret coding by the seemingly contradictory proposal to keep codes secret by making them public. This proposal may be arriving just in time to overcome the massive problems that exchanging codes will pose if computerization of communications continues as expected.

Many technological systems already involve computers that "talk" to each other. For example, electric-power companies often use computer messages to control their systems. Floodgates at major dams are controlled by computer messages. Airlines use computer networks to make passenger reservations. Many long-distance telephone calls are transmitted by computer. Electronic fund-transfer systems are becoming commonplace in the banking industry, and electronic mail systems are now being tested by some businesses and corporations. Electronic mail is also being tested in a town outside Tokyo, where 3,000 households are sending and receiving messages by means of a closed-circuit television system.

### SECURITY PROBLEMS

This growing use of computers in communication networks gives rise to a number of questions. How can a bank be assured that a computerized request to transfer funds to a particular account is legitimate? How can terrorists be prevented from tapping into computer lines used by a power system and inserting messages that cause blackouts? How can two people at different branches of a corporation who communicate by means of electronic mail be sure that a competitor does not tap their lines and intercept their messages?

Some of these problems can be solved if sensitive or private computer data is cast in secret codes to be deciphered only by authorized persons. But current cryptographic systems do not allow for computer messages to be authenticated by so-called digital signatures and are not easily used in large communications networks of the kind now under development.

## CODING SCHEME

Current cryptographic devices make use of special-purpose computers to encode and decode messages. A message, which may consist of an English sentence, a chart, a phone conversation, or even a picture, is represented in a computer as a set of numbers. A special-purpose computer encodes a message by transforming it into a different set of numbers. The numbers of the message are transformed into a different set of numbers according to a particular coding scheme in which the uncoded message-numbers and the coded message-numbers express a definite mathematical relationship. The computer decrypts, or decodes, a message by reversing the coding procedure—that is, by acting on the coded message with the mathematical inverses of the coding functions.

Each group of users of a particular coding procedure has its own coding scheme. With the encryption schemes currently available, knowledge of the coding function allows a person to encode computer messages and to decode them as well, but even a person who designed the scheme cannot decipher a group of users' messages without knowing their coding scheme.

## SECRET DECODING KEY

One problem with these cryptographic systems is that a key, or information specifying the coding function, must be sent out to all users before messages can be exchanged. The military often uses private couriers for this purpose. But sending a key involves a time delay that may not always be practical and raises the possibility that the key may fall into unauthorized hands. Sending keys may be completely infeasible in large communications networks, such as those being envisioned for electronic mail.

Recently, Whitfield Diffie and Martin Hellman of Stanford University devised an ingenious way to send and receive messages without the need for secret coding functions. Their solution also leads to a way to generate digital signatures.

The Stanford investigators' solution is to make use of enciphering functions whose inverses, which are used for deciphering, are impossible to deduce, but which are known to the users of a particular system. In current schemes, deciphering functions are easily determined from knowledge of enciphering functions. In the proposed new system, each user places its enciphering key in a public file and keeps its deciphering key secret. It is then easy to send a coded message to a particular recipient by using the recipient's pub-

Ralph Merkle, Martin Hellman, and Whitfield Diffie of Stanford University.

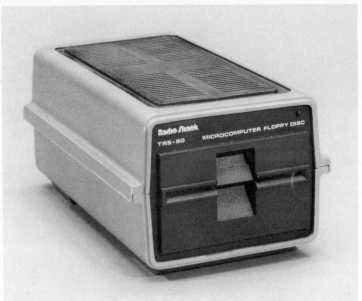

A floppy disc can store one year's correspondence for a typical businessman. The entire disc can be searched in less than one minute for a particular letter. Cryptographic devices such as these are needed to keep information confidential.

Radio Shack

lic enciphering key, but only the intended recipient can decode the message. Hellman and Diffie call their new schemes public key cryptosystems.

## MANY POSSIBLE USES

In the future, they believe, businessmen may make use of public key cryptosystems to exchange messages by electronic mail. A businessman in Atlanta, Georgia, say, would sit at his computer terminal and call an information number to obtain the public encryption key of another businessman in New York City. Then he would type a letter on his computer terminal. As he typed it, the computer would automatically encode it with the New York businessman's coding function. The encoded message would be transmitted to the man in New York, whose computer would automatically decode it. Only the New Yorker could decipher the message since only his computer would contain his secret decoding key.

The man in Atlanta could also use his computer to "sign" an order for goods that he wishes to buy from the man in New York. He first types the order for the goods into his computer and instructs the computer to encode the message with his secret deciphering key. This is his "signature." A deciphering key, like an enciphering key, is a rule for transforming computer messages. Thus it may be used to encode as well as decode. He then has the computer act on the message a second time, encoding it with the New York

man's public enciphering key. This double-coded message is sent to New York.

The New York businessman uses his secret deciphering key to reverse the second coding of the message. He then uses the Atlanta man's public enciphering key to reverse the first coding and extract the original message. This procedure works because encoding and decoding rules can be applied in either forward or reverse order. The message must have been "signed" by the Atlanta businessman since only he knows his secret deciphering key. Only the New York man could understand the message since the New York man's deciphering key is known only to him.

## TRAPDOORS

Development of public key cryptosystems was previously impeded because investigators found it impossible to derive suitable coding functions that could not be inverted. The success of the newly proposed system depends on specially developed mathematical functions known as "trapdoor one-way functions." These are functions that are easy to compute but whose inverses are impossible to derive from descriptions of the functions unless some special information is known about how the functions were constructed. The special information is the "trapdoor." The idea is for a user to construct such a one-way function and, in so doing, also construct the function's inverse. Although the function would be made public, no one who sees only the function would be able to construct its inverse.

Ronald Rivest, Adi Shamir, and Len Adleman of the Massachusetts Institute of Technology and, independently, Michael Rabin of the Hebrew University in Jerusalem recently developed a class of one-way functions that could serve as the basis of a public key cryptosystem. According to Rivest, the MIT group is now planning to implement their scheme in ways that will make it commercially available.

## COMPUTER CHIP TO DO IT ALL

The researchers made use of well-known results in number theory to design their one-way functions. A person, A, employing this system would publish two numbers, $r$ and $s$, as his key. Anyone wishing to send A an encoded message would raise the numbers that constitute the message to the $s$th power, divide that number by $r$, and determine the remainder. The remainder is the coded message. To decode the message, A would make use of a number, $t$, whose identity would be kept secret. Recipient A would raise the encoded message to the $t$th power, divide it by $r$, and determine the remainder, which would be the decoded message.

This encoding and decoding scheme hinges on the relations between $r$, $s$, and $t$. The number $r$ is the product of two very large prime numbers, and $r$ is constructed by finding two large primes and multiplying them together. The numbers $s$ and $t$ are also constructed from these two large primes, and $t$ can be determined only if the identities of the large primes are known.

To break this code, it is necessary to find $t$. But no way is known to find $t$ without first factoring $r$ into its constituent primes. This task is not easily accomplished. For example, the MIT investigators estimate that it is technically impossible to factor a 125-digit number into primes, even if the fastest computers and the most efficient factoring algorithms are used. They quote other experts on the subject who say, "In general, nothing but frustration can be expected to come from an attack on a number of 50 or more digits, even with the speeds available with modern computers."

Although it is computationally infeasible to factor a very large number into primes, it is entirely feasible to find very large primes with a computer. A number of efficient algorithms to do so have recently been developed, and Rivest says it should be possible to use a computer chip incorporating the encryption and decryption algorithms to find large primes. This may make the system easier to implement since only one chip may be necessary to encode, decode, find an encoding key ($r$ and $s$) and its corresponding decoding key ($t$). Security should also be tighter since the code would be generated in the same computer that uses it. Thus the secret deciphering function need never be taken out of the computer.

## KNAPSACKS

An alternative group of one-way functions is proposed by Ralph Merkle of Stanford University and Hellman. Their cryptographic scheme is based on the fact that it is easy to select arbitrarily and to add up a subset of numbers from a large collection of numbers. But it is very difficult to reverse this procedure—that is, to decide which subset of the collection adds up to a particular sum.

In Merkle and Hellman's scheme, a user's public encryption key is a large collection of numbers, chosen in a specific way, which is being kept secret as part of their patent application. The particular way in which it is chosen provides a "trapdoor." A person sends a message by adding up a particular subset of those numbers and transmitting the sum. Because the recipient has knowledge of the trapdoor, he can easily decide which subset of numbers was added up and can extract the original message from the enciphered one. According to Merkle and Hellman, an eavesdropper would essentially have to try out all possible ways to add up subsets of the large collection of numbers to find a subset that adds up to a particular sum. This task is computationally infeasible for large collections of numbers.

Merkle and Hellman's encryption scheme is based on a problem, known as the knapsack problem, whose solution becomes computationally infeasible as the problem

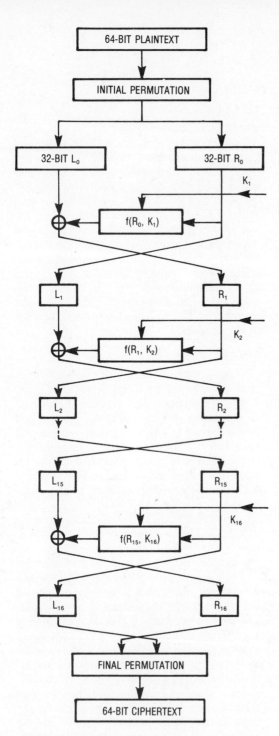

| | |
|---|---|
| **64-BIT PLAINTEXT** | |
| **INITIAL PERMUTATION** | |
| 32-BIT $L_0$ | 32-BIT $R_0$ |

$K_1$

$f(R_0, K_1)$

$L_1$ ⊕ $R_1$

$K_2$

$f(R_1, K_2)$

$L_2$ $R_2$

$L_{15}$ $R_{15}$

$K_{16}$

$f(R_{15}, K_{16})$

$L_{16}$ $R_{16}$

**FINAL PERMUTATION**

**64-BIT CIPHERTEXT**

Computer programmers use flow charts such as this one to assist them in *enciphering* codes. The original uncoded information is represented by the word "plaintext" at the top of the chart. The final coded material is represented by the word "ciphertext" at the bottom of the chart. For the reverse process of *deciphering* codes, different flow charts are required.

grows in size. The knapsack problem is one of a class of problems known as NP-complete. These problems are equivalent in that, if an efficient way to solve one were found, all could be solved efficiently. But computer scientists have been continually frustrated in their search for efficient solutions to NP-complete problems and strongly suspect that there is no easy way to solve any of these problems. This failure may be an asset to cryptographers. NP-complete problems could serve as the basis of provably "unbreakable" public key cryptosystems.

## UNBREAKABLE SYSTEMS

The development of provably unbreakable systems would represent an important step in cryptography. Before the twentieth century, cryptographers "proved" their systems were unbreakable by enumerating all the steps necessary to break them. But clever spies would continually find ways to circumvent most of those steps. Since 1900, systems have been tested by assigning cryptanalysts the task of breaking them. If the cryptanalysts failed, the systems were said to be secure. The use of NP-complete problems or other provably hard mathematical problems to design cryptographic systems, however, will result in systems whose security does not depend on this sort of experimental certification.

Although public key cryptosystems and digital signatures are not yet in use, a need for them has arisen, and, many believe, current designs for them are feasible. As societies begin to rely on computer-controlled communication networks, cryptography becomes essential to ensure privacy. Cryptography, in the eyes of Hellman and Diffie, now stands "on the brink of a revolution" □

  SELECTED READINGS

"Automated cryptography" by M. Guillen. *Science News,* September 18, 1976.

"How to decipher secret messages" by F. W. Chesson. *Radio Electronics,* December 1977.

"Cryptography—scientists puzzle over threat to open research" by D. Shapely and G. B. Kolata. *Science,* September 30, 1977.

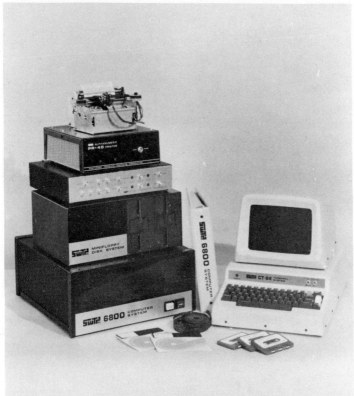

Photo at left shows parts of a typical home computer system: a basic microprocessor unit— the SWT 6800; a display window (right); an alphanumeric printer that provides written responses; and program cassettes (forefront).

Southwest Technical Products Corp.

# NEW HOME COMPUTERS

## by William J. Hawkins

UNTIL very recently, to operate a home computer you had to be part electronic engineer, part programmer, part handyman, and part lucky. Most hobby units available have been very complicated and time-consuming. Success in building and operating them has been reserved for the devoted electronic enthusiast.

But all that is changing: a new generation of home computers is beginning to emerge. With these, you take them home, plug them in, and begin using them. Costs vary widely and there is a lot of market maneuvering. But the central fact is that now— or very soon—everyone can have at his or her command affordable computing power, power that until recently has been available only to corporations and other big-money institutions. It's bound to have a major impact on the way we all live, in ways we can now only dimly imagine.

### SPREADING QUICKLY

The home-computer movement really began in the early 1970s. That's when a company called MITS began producing the first computer kit for hobbyists. The idea caught on slowly at first, but has now exploded. Computer shops and clubs are springing up across the United States, and in other countries. New magazines, books, and newsletters dealing with the subject are appearing monthly.

### EASY TO OPERATE

New brands began to emerge as well. Well known to computer hobbyists, makers such as IMSAI, SWT, PolyMorphic, Processor Technology, TDL, Cromeco, and many others have been producing products for some time. But with growing competitive pressure, changes are coming—fast. Sophis-

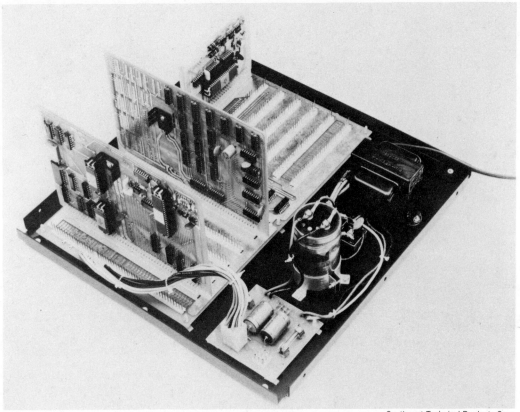

Printed circuit boards found inside a basic microprocessor computer unit such as the SWT 6800 unit shown on the previous page.

tication and ease of operation are headed up while prices are headed down. Units are not designed just for the hobbyists, but for almost anyone who can put in a plug.

MITS, for example, makes the model 680b, which is specifically designed for the beginner. IMSAI offers a computer on a board, made to do jobs around the house—everything from running model trains to controlling the heat.

The latest entries are well-known brands: Heath, Sears, and Radio Shack. They will rely heavily on both their stores and mail-order systems for sales. While the Radio Shack and Sears units come prebuilt only, the two Heathkit models are available in kit form. The long-time kit designers are sure to remove a lot of the guesswork that has been a part of a do-it-yourself computer until now.

The Commodore PET unit is a prebuilt, all-in-one device that can be programmed by almost anyone. The cassette tape that comes with it directs the computer, which then teaches you how to use it. You can become an expert in a couple of hours. It comes with enough memory to run BASIC, an easy-to-understand computer language. PET's keyboard prints standard letters or graphics on the TV screen to produce graphs, charts, or photos.

COST OF A SYSTEM

Prices for such systems vary greatly depending on exactly what you include in the "system." For instance, you can buy a microcomputer for $300 or even less—but it won't do anything but sit there and perhaps hum. You need memory for storage, peripheral equipment such as a keyboard or video screen for putting in information and taking it out again, tape systems for saving programs, and a host of special circuitry to do such things as graphics. Depending on what you need, costs can run up rapidly.

But if history is an example, the price trend will be down from here on. Over the next year or two, other brands are sure to come on the market. A few years ago, we saw hand calculators go from $400 when first introduced to a low of $10 or less now.

## BASIC LANGUAGE

If you're worried about programming, don't—you can be an expert in just a few hours learning the standard BASIC language that these machines will use.

BASIC is simply that: a basic, simple way to communicate with a computer. It is a program designed to convert your program into machine codes—a bunch of letters and numbers—that the computer can understand.

If you want the computer to print out the word "hello" on the TV screen, for example, it would take about 20 special machine instructions to do it. In BASIC, however, you simply type in: PRINT "HELLO."

Math is done just as easily since BASIC uses the normal math signs (+, −, /, *) to represent addition, subtraction, division, and multiplication. Two and two is simply: PRINT 2+2, and the computer will print out 4 on the screen. And, with most versions of BASIC, you can also use trigonometric functions, square roots, and engineering notation by simply specifying a symbol.

But BASIC is only one program, and the programs that will accompany the new computers will be just as important as the unit itself. At present, costs vary enormously: BASIC, for example, costs as much as $200 at one company and as little as $10 at another company.

Plans for the newer systems, however, look good to the pocketbook. BASIC is usually thrown in with the computer when you buy. Other special programs—for games, income-tax data, and information

Southwest Technical Products Corp.

Right: an inexpensive graphics terminal that can generate graphic displays on any monitor or standard TV set to which a special video input has been added. This terminal makes possible a pictorial play area for computer games. Bottom left: a microcomputer system that can be used in a classroom. Bottom right: line printer that can be used with this system.

Radio Shack

Radio Shack

**115**

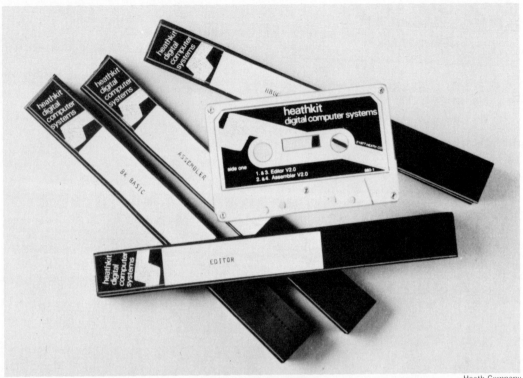

Heath Company

Most home computers use the standard BASIC language, provided in cassette or tape form as shown above, that converts what you want—your program—into machine codes.

storage, for example—will be sold at a price between $5 and $20.

## IN YOUR HOME

The prices are dropping. The computers are simple to use, and they are easily available. But what will you do with them around the house?

Are you on a diet? Tell the computer and it will plan your menu for each meal, forecast your caloric intake, and predict your weight loss for the next month.

Do you need a loan (perhaps to pay for the computer)? The computer will tell you when and where to get it, and how and when to pay it back so that it will cost you as little as possible.

Are you shopping around for a new house? If so, you will probably need a mortgage, and a home computer can be programmed to analyze the mortgage market for you.

Buying stocks and bonds? One of the most common uses of the more-advanced home computer models is in portfolio management and investment analysis.

Budgets, income taxes, mass storage (perhaps of frequently called phone numbers) for instant recall, "canned" programs to tutor your children at home, appointment reminder, or games such as chess—a computer can do those and many other jobs.

But the ultimate impact these home computers will have on our lives will be far greater than just playing games or balancing our checkbooks. Major inventions have always changed our society in ways that could not be predicted □

SELECTED READINGS

"And Now a Computer for Your Home." *Changing Times*, December 1977.

"Home, Sweet Computerized Home" by I. Berger. *Popular Mechanics*, September 1976.

"What It's Like to Build and Use Your Own Home Computer" by W. J. Hawkins. *Popular Science*, May 1977.

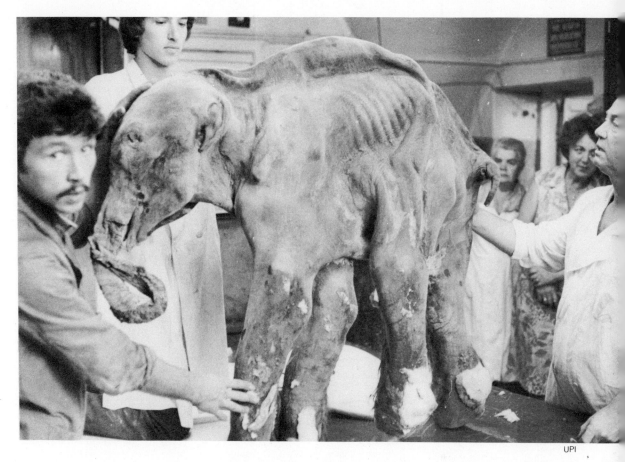

UPI

The intact body of a 10,000-year-old baby woolly mammoth was found in the Siberian permafrost during 1977. Examination of this now extinct relative of the elephant will, it is expected, reveal clues about the animal's way of life and why it became extinct.

# EARTH SCIENCES

## contents

# EARTH SCIENCE
## review
## of the year

H. Bureau, Sygma

On March 4, 1977 a strong quake hit Bucharest, Rumania, killing many people and causing widespread destruction.

Wide World

Mt. Usu Volcano on Japan's Hokkaido island erupted violently, spewing black smoke over a nearby resort town.

**Earthquakes and seismology.** The largest earthquake to occur in 1977—and "one of the strongest in recorded history"—was an underwater quake. On August 19, a quake, assigned Richter readings varying from 7.7 to 8.9, occurred 300 kilometers (about 185 miles) south of Sumba, Indonesia, under the Indian Ocean. It was reportedly felt by people on the upper floors of tall buildings as far away as Perth, Australia, some 2,300 kilometers (1,425 miles) south of the quake's epicenter. The quake generated a large tsunami, or seismic sea wave, but the death toll was not high because of the comparatively isolated areas affected. ■ Earlier in the year, on March 4, a quake, registered at 7.2 on the Richter scale, killed an estimated 2,000 persons in Bucharest, Rumania. From its epicenter at Vrancei in the Carpathian Mountains, about 215 kilometers (135 miles) northeast of Bucharest, it was felt from northern Italy to Moscow.

The Richter scale that has been used for 40 years as a measurement of ground motion in an earthquake, and thus as one indication of an earthquake's severity, was revised during 1977. The revision, announced by a geophysics professor at the California Institute of Technology, is based on new theories and instruments that more accurately record and explain energy released by major earthquakes. The new rating system does not replace the Richter scale but rather changes the method by which higher magnitudes are computed. According to the revised scale, a few quakes now for the first time register above 9. The 1964 Alaska quake, for example, has been raised from 8.4 to 9.2 on the scale, and the 1960 Chile quake from 8.3 to 9.5.

Scientists of the U.S. Geological Survey continued to monitor California's Palmdale "bulge" for signs of an impending quake. The land centered around Palmdale, California, has risen as much as 45 centimeters (18 inches) since 1959. Studies show the elevated area to extend from Point Arguello eastward to the Arizona border, with the zone of uplift about 145 kilometers (90 miles) wide between Bakersfield and Los Angeles. The area is located over a portion of the San Andreas Fault System, where many geologists believe a major quake is due to occur. Since certain earthquakes have in the past been preceded by relatively rapid land uplifts, the Palmdale "bulge" is of continuing geologic concern.

Earthquake prediction studies continued in 1977 with investigations centered on reports that days or hours before a quake occurs there may be certain unusual phenomena, including strange animal behavior, changes in rock structure and travel time of seismic waves, and the appearance of unusual lights, that can warn of an impending quake. ■ Earthquake prevention is also being attempted. It is believed that Soviet geologists prevented a large earthquake by encouraging many smaller quakes in the Nurek Dam region of central Asia. As the dam reservoir was filled, it is believed that small tremors were induced and the buildup of a large amount of rock stress prevented by water penetrating the surrounding rock, weakening cracks, and producing very small disturbances.

**Volcanoes.** Two major eruptions occurred in the northwest Pacific during 1977: in late March Japan's Kamchatka's Bezmianny Volcano erupted more violently than it has in 20 years, sending clouds more than 15 kilometers (9 miles) in the sky; and in August the eruption of Usu Volcano on the Japanese island of Hokkaido threw rocks more than 10 kilometers (6 miles) high, breaking the window of an airliner overhead.

**Glaciers and polar geology.** The technical, economic, environmental, and legal problems associated with locating, transporting, and exploiting Antarctic icebergs were discussed at the first International Conference on Iceberg Utilization held at Iowa State University in October and attended by some 200 scientists and representatives of 18 nations. Saudi Arabia is particularly interested in the idea as a means for solving its water-shortage problems. ■ Alaska's glaciers may also have potential usefulness. Geologists with the University of Idaho's Juneau Ice Field Research Program believe that the glaciers may cover valuable ore bodies and hold large reservoirs of fresh water.

**Paleontology.** Paleontologists were delighted during the year with the discovery of the intact body of a 10,000-year-old baby woolly mammoth in the permafrost of the Kolyma gold mining district in Siberia. The specimen of this now-extinct relative of the elephant is 117 centimeters (46 inches) long and 107 centimeters (42 inches) high and has a 58-centimeter (23-inch) trunk. It is the best preserved mammoth specimen to date. Twigs, bits of willow and birch tree trunks, and grass and moss found in sediment near the body suggest that the baby mammoth probably drowned in a small lake or swamp.

Dinosaurs were again in the news in 1977. A Soviet geologist proposed that rickets might have been an important contributing factor in dinosaur extinction. He pointed out that dinosaur eggs from the Cretaceous Period, the period some 70,000,000 years ago during which dinosaurs died out, have a very thin, lime-poor shell and that dinosaur skeletons of that period were often twisted. Meanwhile two U.S. paleontologists suggested that climatic changes occurring during the same time period may have played an important role. They point out that sea advancement during that time caused the replacement of subtropical communities by temperate communities into which early mammals spread and then began to diversify and compete with the dinosaurs, eventually causing their extinction. ■ What is thought to be the largest dinosaur footprint ever discovered was found in Granby Quarry in western Massachusetts. The print is 150 centimeters (59 inches) long and 84 centimeters (33 inches) wide and appears to have been made by a 21-meter (70-foot) long reptile that had three toes on each foot and walked on its hind legs.

In late 1977 Harvard University paleontologists found the remains of a 3,400,000,000-year-old single-celled, algaelike fossil in sedimentary rock in South Africa. This fossil pushes back the age of the oldest known evidence of life by about 100,000,000 years. ■ The age of one form of life—birds—may also have to be reevaluated. A Brigham Young University scientist has discovered a fossil bird that may be older than *Archaeopteryx*, the oldest bird known to date, in Colorado.

William H. Matthews III

Polar Information Service

Interest in moving and exploiting icebergs as a source of freshwater is increasing. Here three specially equipped ships move a huge iceberg off the coast of Antarctica.

Granby Dinosaur Museum

What is thought to be the largest dinosaur footprint ever discovered was found in western Massachusetts in 1977. The print is 150 centimeters long and 84 centimeters wide.

The combustion of all fossil fuels releases carbon dioxide into the atmosphere. Will this ever increasingly release of carbon dioxide seriously alter future climate?

EPA

# FUTURE CLIMATE

## by J. Murray Mitchell, Jr.

IN recent years, books and newspaper stories have conditioned us to expect colder weather in the future. In the geological perspective of thousands, hundreds of thousands, and millions of years, the case for cooling is strong. The modern world is in an interglacial period, a relatively warm interlude—lasting perhaps 10,000 years—between much longer intervals of cold and snow. If this interglacial respite is typical and lasts no longer than a dozen earlier ones in the past million years, we may reasonably suppose that the world is about due to begin a slide into the next ice age.

Considering the much more recent past, climatologists point out that the world has been in the throes of a general cooling trend during the last 30 or 40 years. Because this cooling trend has sometimes been misinterpreted as an early sign of the approach of an ice age, it has reenforced the popular notion that our future is likely to be a cold one. In point of fact, this cooling trend is really only one of many irregular ups and downs of climate that mankind has witnessed through history, and it has, in fact, been faltering in very recent years, perhaps already starting to reverse itself.

I agree with those climatologists who say that another ice age is inevitable. I strongly disagree, however, with those who suggest that the arrival of the next ice age is imminent, and who speak of this as the proper concern of modern civilization in planning for the next few decades or centuries.

Should nature be left to her own devices, without interference, I feel confident in predicting that future climate will alternately warm and cool many times before shifting with any real authority toward the next ice age. It would be these alternate warmings and coolings, together with the same year-to-year variability of climate that has always been with us, that would be the appropriate object of our concerns about climate in the foreseeable future.

### MAN ENTERS THE PICTURE

Because of man's presence on the earth, however, what will actually happen in future decades and centuries may well follow a different scenario—imperceptibly different at first, but importantly so later on.

When speaking in general of man's impact on climate, we are concerned with not one, but many kinds of impact. There are the potentially significant climatic effects that may follow from massive alteration of the earth's surface through agriculture, irrigation, forest cutting, and urbanization. There are further climatic effects that may follow from our discharges of heat, smoke, dust, and various gaseous wastes—carbon dioxide, sulfur dioxide, chlorofluoromethanes ("Freons"), and nitrogen oxides—into the atmosphere.

It is not likely that any one of these activities has played an important role in climate fluctuations up to now. This, however, is no grounds for complacency about the future. Man has amply demonstrated that he is a socially and technologically progressive being. In the decades and centuries ahead, he is likely to increase in numbers and advance his standards of living. He will put heightened pressures on his natural resources, expand his reliance on energy, exploit new territory for agriculture, and manage his environment in many new ways. In some of these activities, he will undoubtedly impact global climate more intensively, and more extensively, than now. In other respects, however, his concern for his environment will perhaps reduce the stress on climate. Already man seems willing to check the volume

of many forms of atmospheric pollution. One pollutant, however, will not be easily controlled. I refer to carbon dioxide.

## SPECIAL ROLE OF CARBON DIOXIDE

Carbon dioxide is a gas that is a product of combustion of all carbonaceous fuels, including coal, oil, gasoline, natural gas, wood, peat, methane, propane, and a wide variety of lesser fuels.

When we burn wood for warmth or energy, we are not really adding new carbon dioxide to the atmosphere. We are simply replacing carbon dioxide that was withdrawn from the air by photosynthesis when the tree composed of the wood was growing in the forest, a relatively short time ago. Much the same is true when we burn peat or organic methane.

On the other hand, when we burn coal or a petroleum derivative, the carbon dioxide released into the atmosphere had been withdrawn from it millions of years ago. In all the years since, the carbon dioxide used in the growth of the coal- or petroleum-producing flora had ample opportunity to be replaced through very slow natural processes, such as the oxidation of exposed sedimentary rocks. Now we suddenly release that carbon dioxide back to the atmosphere, at a rate enor-

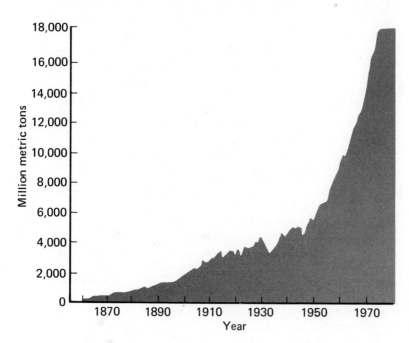

The amount of carbon dioxide in the atmosphere has increased dramatically since the Industrial Revolution and in particular since about 1950.

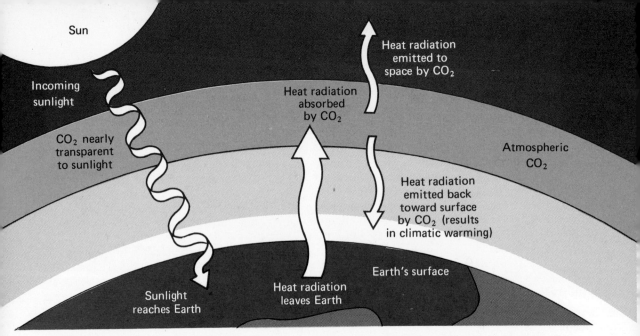

The greenhouse effect of carbon dioxide. Even in its present concentrations, carbon dioxide in the atmosphere can absorb a significant part of the heat radiated from the earth's surface and reemit it back to earth, thus increasing the earth's surface temperature. If there were less carbon dioxide, the heat would be radiated out into space.

mously faster than the rate at which other natural regulatory processes can remove it from the atmosphere again.

INCREASING IN THE ATMOSPHERE

Fuels that are withdrawn from geological formations, and contain carbon fixed from atmospheric carbon dioxide in the distant geological past, are referred to as fossil fuels. The overwhelmingly greater part of all the energy produced in the world today is derived from the combustion of fossil fuels. At the present time, nearly 20,000,000,000 tons of carbon dioxide are released in this way to the atmosphere each year. This amounts annually to about 0.7 per cent of the total carbon dioxide already in the atmosphere. Since at least 1950, the release rate of carbon dioxide to the atmosphere has been growing by an average of 4.3 per cent per year, though significantly less rapidly, since the Arab oil embargo of 1973. In all, this represents a truly enormous source of "new" carbon dioxide to the atmosphere.

To date, all the "new" carbon dioxide released to the atmosphere by fossil-fuel combustion since the dawn of the Industrial Revolution comes to more than 20 per cent of the total already in the atmosphere. Since 1958 reliable estimates of the amount of carbon dioxide in the atmosphere, and its changes from year to year, clearly reflect an accumulation of the gas. The observed rate of accumulation, however, is consistent with what we know is entering the atmosphere from fossil sources only if between 50 to 60 per cent of the fossil input has remained in the atmosphere. The remaining 40 to 50 per cent has somehow been leaking away from the atmosphere into other carbon reservoirs. Since we know that geological processes by which the gas could be removed from the atmosphere are much too slow to have accounted for the missing percentage, it is highly likely that the gas has been accumulating either in the oceans or in terrestrial vegetation.

CARBON SINK

Careful studies have shown that most of the missing carbon dioxide has probably been accumulating in the near-surface layers of the oceans. It remains to be seen if a substantial fraction also has found its way into vegetation or some other reservoir such as soil humus. Such possibilities are extremely difficult to verify. Some scientists have suggested that through human activities the total mass of carbon in vegetation may have been decreasing over the years, rather than increasing. If that turns out to be true, then we must look to the oceans as an even more effective "sink" for carbon dioxide than we have surmised.

The situation at the present time can be summarized briefly as follows. The atmosphere is becoming richer in carbon dioxide by a few tenths of one per cent each year. Altogether, the atmosphere is now holding an estimated 13 per cent more carbon dioxide than it held a century ago. The source of this added carbon dioxide has been reliably traced to the burning of fossil fuels. Were it not for the absorption of some of the added carbon dioxide by the oceans (plus an unknown, but probably smaller intake by terrestrial vegetation), the atmospheric increase would be roughly double what has been observed.

As long as we continue to rely on fossil fuels to meet the bulk of our energy requirements, the atmospheric buildup of carbon dioxide will continue. Here we arrive at the doorstep of the carbon dioxide "problem." In consideration of the vast and assessable fossil fuel reserves (mostly coal) known to still be in the ground, as contrasted with the increasing difficulties of developing new non-fossil fuel energy sources that meet acceptable standards of safety and economy, how reasonable is it to suppose that we will wean ourselves from reliance on fossil fuels before the reserves become very depleted—perhaps 100 or 200 years from now? My guess is that, not withstanding higher energy costs and the glamour of exotic energy technology such as the harnessing of solar radiation, we will continue to find fossil fuels an attractive source of energy for a very long time to come.

Suppose that no new inhibiting factor comes into the picture to discourage us from proceeding to consume the bulk of the known fossil fuel resources in the next few centuries. In that event, the combustion of all known fossil fuel reserves in the world would pour into the atmosphere a total amount of "new" carbon dioxide equal to somewhere between 5 and 14 times the total amount of carbon dioxide now present. Of that enormous quantity entering the atmosphere, the oceans would be unlikely to withdraw as much as the fraction (perhaps 40 per cent) they are believed to have withdrawn of the much smaller increase up to the present time. Terrestrial vegetation might be able to take up a substantial share of it, but only temporarily. This means that the increase of carbon dioxide in the atmosphere would aggregate to a major fraction of the total input—something in excess of 3 times the present atmospheric amount and conceivably as much as 10 times the present amount.

Once the atmospheric levels reached these high values, they would decline only very slowly. After a thousand years, more than half of the excess carbon dioxide would still remain in the atmosphere. Whatever the consequences of the carbon-dioxide buildup, including the consequences to our climate, they would endure for thousands of years after fossil fuels had been consumed.

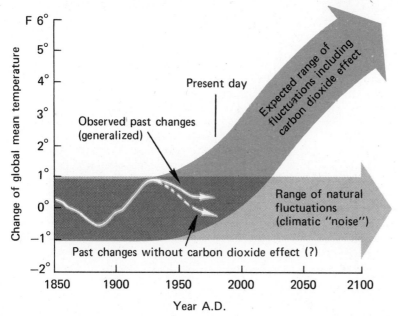

Graph showing how the accumulation of carbon dioxide in the atmosphere may affect mean earth temperatures. Increasing carbon dioxide levels may not have an easily detectable effect until near the end of the twentieth century, but thereafter may have dramatic and long continuing effects.

Water samples are frequently analyzed to determine the levels of carbon dioxide and other chemicals that might affect earth climate.

EPA Documerica

## WHAT OF IT?

If the levels of carbon dioxide in the atmosphere did increase by a factor of 3 to 10 in the next few centuries, what of it? This would cause no physiological discomfort to humans. It might even stimulate faster growth of forest and food crops, as suggested by experiments with carbon dioxide-enriched air in greenhouses.

The problem becomes clear when we consider the likely effect of so large a carbon dioxide increase on global climate. Carbon dioxide, in present-day atmospheric concentrations, is capable of absorbing and re-emitting a significant part of the heat radiation passing upward through the atmosphere from the earth. This outgoing terrestrial radiation balances the incoming solar radiation, to maintain the temperature of our planet near its accustomed "equilibrium" level.

## EFFECTS ON CLIMATE

Numerical models have been constructed in recent years in which the effects of carbon dioxide on atmospheric radiation fluxes and thus on climate have been simulated. All the models tell us to expect average earth temperature changes if the amount of carbon dioxide in the atmosphere changes.

The implications of these climate modeling experiments can be summarized as follows:
• The amount of carbon dioxide now in the atmosphere maintains the average temperature of the earth and the lower atmosphere at levels about 10° Celsius (18° Fahrenheit) higher than those we would experience if the atmosphere contained no carbon dioxide.
• A doubling of the amount of carbon dioxide in the atmosphere would increase the average annual temperature of the earth by about 2.4° to 2.9° Celsius (4.3° to 5.2° Fahrenheit).
• The dependence of temperature on the change of carbon dioxide follows an approximate mathematical relationship, such that a fourfold increase of carbon dioxide would result in a doubling of temperature increase.
• Based on one climate model in which the water cycle is included in detail along with other aspects of climate behavior, a doubling of carbon dioxide has been calculated to result in about a 7-per cent increase in global average precipitation. Most of this increase would be concentrated in the higher latitudes near the poles.
• A general retreat of snow and sea-ice cover, by perhaps as much as 10 degrees of latitude, would result in the Arctic regions.

The extent of such changes in the Antarctic has not yet been determined.

• Generally speaking, the effect of a doubling of carbon dioxide on surface temperatures would be two or three times greater in the polar regions than the average temperature change for the world as a whole.

## HOW ACCURATE ARE MODELS?

It cannot be asserted that a real doubling of carbon dioxide in the real world would have the same effects on real climate as a simulated doubling of carbon dioxide in climate models have on "model climate." No climate model is altogether realistic in its description of the real climatic system. For example, no climate model on which the above conclusions are based is capable of developing its own cloud systems in a realistic way. Most models must be instructed before hand where the clouds are assumed to exist, and the clouds remain there unchanged throughout the computer experiment using the model. We should be wary of this, because if the cloudiness were to change in the real world along with a carbon dioxide change, then the role of clouds in affecting the temperature of the earth might significantly alter the net temperature effect of the carbon-dioxide change as inferred from models that assume fixed cloudiness.

Very recently, some preliminary model experiments have been attempted in which the model is allowed to adjust cloudiness along with other weather variables as the calculation proceeds. Early indications are that allowance for cloudiness changes does not greatly alter the results of experiments using models with fixed cloudiness.

Altogether, our experience with climate models suggests that their use in evaluating the magnitude of temperature changes associated with changes of atmospheric carbon dioxide leads to results that are likely to approximate reality fairly closely. Models may be overestimating or underestimating the temperature and other climatic effects of carbon dioxide changes by as much as a factor of two. But, in balance, I share the view of most of my colleagues that the model results to date deserve to be taken as an unprejudiced, and a credibly realistic approximation to reality.

## WHAT PICTURE EMERGES?

Putting together the different parts of the story of climate and carbon dioxide, what picture emerges as to our future climate? If mankind does indeed rely for very long on fossil fuels to meet its energy needs, the consequences to climate are likely to become noticeable by the end of the twentieth century, but not become a serious problem until well into the twenty-first century.

On the longer, geological time scale, the picture that emerges is rather startling. In the words of Dr. Wallace Broecker of the Lamont-Doherty Geological Observatory, one

Considering the glacial and interglacial cycles of the last 150,000 years, we might expect a cooling trend toward a new ice age in the next several thousand years. The effect of man's activities—particularly the increased levels of carbon dioxide in the atmosphere—may, however, postpone this cooling trend for several centuries.

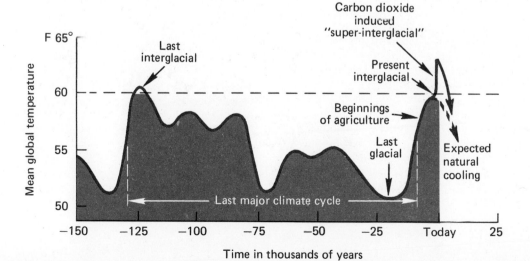

The amount of carbon dioxide in the atmosphere is monitored at several stations throughout the world. Here snow is being cut off a building at the South Pole Station in Antarctica for measurement of carbon dioxide levels.

NOAA

of the world's foremost authorities on the carbon-dioxide issue, consumption of the bulk of the world's known fossil fuel reserves would plunge our planet into what he describes as a "super-interglacial," the likes of which the world has not experienced in the last million years.

Admittedly, we are talking here of possibilities, not certainties. The climatic consequences of massive fossil fuel consumption may be different from what we think. Mankind eventually may discover a new energy source, or develop a way to offset the warming effect of added carbon dioxide in the atmosphere.

## CAN'T IGNORE THE POSSIBILITIES

All of this may strike you as a problem too far removed from the present to merit our concern. I would, however, like to end with a few additional thoughts. Suppose we elect to ignore the problem of carbon dioxide until it is staring us in the face—perhaps in another 20 years—in the form of a clear signal that a global warming trend has begun that is unmistakeably attributable to the further accumulation of carbon dioxide in the atmosphere. If we delay until then to take action to phase over to fuels other than fossil fuels, the transition will be likely to take another 40 or 50 years to complete. That puts us at least a half-century into the future before we will have managed to shut off the problem at its source. By then, much of the damage will already have been done.

To make matters worse, the effects of carbon dioxide would endure for thousands of years after we have abandoned our fossil-fuel economy, because it would take thousands of years for the atmosphere to rid itself of any excess carbon dioxide. A thousand years of unusually warm climate would be likely to result in substantial melting of the Greenland and Antarctic ice caps. This would raise sea levels around the world enough to submerge many of our coastal population centers and much productive farm land.

The alternative is clear. Ours is the generation that must come to grips with the carbon-dioxide problem and mount a vigorous research effort to allow us to understand all of its ramifications for the future. If we harbor any sense of responsibility toward preserving spaceship earth, and toward the welfare of our progeny, we can scarcely afford to leave the carbon-dioxide problem to the next generation□

□ SELECTED READINGS

*Climate Changes* by M. I. Budyko. Ameri Geophysical 1977.

*The Weather Machine* by Nigel Calder. Penguin 1977.

"Why Does Earth's Climate Change?" *Astronomy,* February 1978.

"Carbon dioxide and climate: carbon budget still unbalanced." *Science,* Aug. 26, 1978.

James Andanson, Sygma

Iceland is one of the earth's major hot spots. Here we see a brilliant eruption near Reykjavik.

# HOT SPOTS

## by Peter Vogt

GENERAL acceptance of the idea of continental drift by geologists in the United States dates only from the late 1960s. The continents are now known to lie embedded like rafts in rigid, thicker plates. These plates are fragments of the earth's outer shell, or lithosphere. The lithosphere is composed of the earth's crust and the uppermost part of the mantle. The lithospheric plates move slowly relative to each other—about 2 to 5 centimeters (1 to 2 inches) per year. The motion of these 80-to-160-kilometer- (50-to-100-mile-) thick plates causes earthquakes, volcanic action, and mountain building at the plates' edges. Plate motion and its consequences, including continental drift, are grouped together under a unifying concept known as plate tectonics.

Although now taken as virtual fact, plate tectonics is still begging for a driving force, a mechanism that moves the plates. Most investigators favor some sort of thermal convection in the earth's mantle, the plates being merely the frozen skin on top of this sluggishly convulsing system. Plate tectonics explains the regular creation of new oceanic crust along the axis of the mid-oceanic ridge, where molten material wells up from within the mantle. It also explains the existence of curved festoons of volcanic islands like the

Aleutians or the Marianas with their nearby deep-sea trenches and associated belts of intensive earthquake activity. These volcanic islands are surface expressions of oceanic plates descending into the mantle from which they were created tens or hundreds of millions of years before.

What plate tectonics by itself has not been able to explain is a collection of some dozens of relatively localized centers of intense volcanic activity, many of which are within the interiors of plates instead of at their margins. In this article, I refer to such localized volcanic areas as "hot spots." By that term I mean not only volcanoes of this type on the earth's surface but also the regions below them where the melting of volcanic material takes place.

### MANY HOT SPOTS ON EARTH

Although there appear to be more than 100 hot spots active at present on our planet, these spots do not expel equal amounts of material, and centuries or even millennia may pass without any volcanic eruption at all.

The most prominent hot spots currently active in the continental United States are in the area of Yellowstone National Park and in the northeastern corner of New Mexico.

Hawaii is the earth's other major hot spot. The photo at right shows Mauna Loa volcano erupting. Fiery lava flows outward as the crater itself smokes.

Dick Rowan, Photo Researchers

Both are dwarfed by the hot spot at Hawaii. A map of the globe shows that the worldwide distribution of hot spots is not random. There are large "spotless areas" such as the western Atlantic and eastern North America. The distribution of hot spots does not correlate strongly with the continents or ocean basins but many prominent hot spots tend to be close to the mid-oceanic ridge.

The two most familiar and most spectacular examples of hot spots are Hawaii and Iceland. A detailed look at them may thus be the best way to approach the problem of what causes hot spots. It might at first seem outrageous to lump together two such seemingly diverse places, but for all their differences, Hawaii and Iceland have several properties in common. Both represent unusual and long-lived volcanic activity that dates back tens of millions of years and seems to migrate over the lithospheric plates with time. The volcanic activity of Iceland is unusual because it is several times greater than that occurring elsewhere along the Mid-Atlantic Ridge. And the copious volcanism of Hawaii is unusual because it occurs in the midst of more than 250,000,000 hectares (about 1,000,000 square miles) of volcanic quiescence, far from the nearest mid-oceanic ridge.

Iceland contains numerous volcanoes of various kinds and is one of the most active volcanic regions on earth. Most of its recent volcanic activity is restricted to a few belts that extend northwest through the middle of the island. Rocks at the center of the island are new and young, but as one moves either westward or eastward away from the center, the rocks get progressively older, dating back 15,000,000 or more years at the eastern and western coasts. Massive submarine extensions of the island connect it to Greenland on the west and the Faeroe Islands in the North Atlantic on the east. These underwater extensions form a transverse ridge, perpendicular to the axis of the Mid-Atlantic Ridge. Where the transverse ridge emerges above sea level in Greenland and the Faeroes, volcanic rocks that erupted about 60,000,000 years ago cap the ridge edges. Thus, whatever is causing the profuse volcanic activity on Iceland today has existed more or less continuously for 60,000,000 years.

In the case of Hawaii, the islands west of the volcanically active Big Island—Hawaii—get progressively older and volcanically deader. Whatever produced the Hawaiian chain and its continuation as the Emperor seamounts must have existed for at least the last 70,000,000 years, since that is

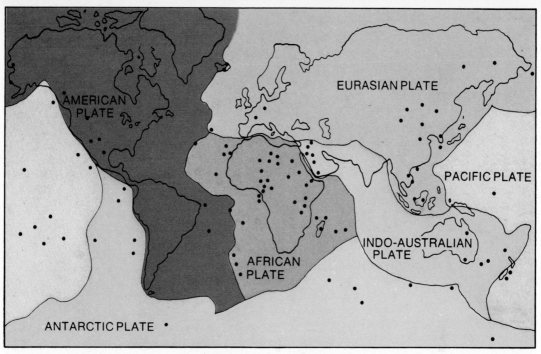

The 100 or so active hot spots on earth today are not randomly distributed. There are large spotless areas, such as the western Atlantic, and other areas, generally along the mid-oceanic ridge, where many hot spots are concentrated.

the age of the oldest surviving seamounts at the northern end of the chain.

The progressive aging of volcanic rocks the farther away they lie from the area of recent activity is not a new discovery. But the systematic aging in a certain direction could not itself be understood until plate tectonics came along in the mid-1960s. It was then that the Canadian geophysicist J. Tuzo Wilson conceived the basic explanation of the hot spot.

## WHAT EXACTLY IS A HOT SPOT?

There must be a relatively fixed region of persistent mantle melting below the lithospheric plates, Wilson reasoned. This region, the hot spot, produces batches of magma, or molten rock. Being lighter than the surrounding rock, the magma makes its way upward through the plate and flows out on the earth's surface in the form of volcanoes. Plate motion slowly moves the volcanoes away from the fixed hot spot that formed them. Through this process, the Hawaii-Emperor chain has become a 70,000,-000-year-long "track" of the motion of the Pacific plate over one hot spot. If the Pacific plate had been stationary the entire time, all the volcanic material created during 70,000,-000 years would have piled up in one place.

Iceland straddles the Mid-Atlantic Ridge. Its volcanoes thus deposit basalt on the two diverging Eurasian and American plates. These plates are moving apart at the slow rate of two centimeters (about 0.75 inch) per year. The Pacific plate, by contrast, is moving at the relatively rapid speed of 5 to 15 centimeters (about 2 to 6 inches) per year. This difference in rate of plate motion probably explains the squat shape of Iceland and its submarine extensions as compared to the long chainlike configuration of the Hawaii–Emperor islands, formed over approximately the same geologic period of time.

## DO HOT SPOTS MOVE?

If plates move over hot spots, do the hot spots themselves move with respect to the deeper mantle? Opinion on this question is divided. Data referring to the last 5,000,000 to 10,000,000 years indicate that hot spots have not moved. In my view, hot spots apparently do not move—or if they do, they generally move more slowly than lithospheric plates. This relative "fixity" of hot spots was shown in 1971 by geophysicist W. Jason Morgan at Princeton University using paleomagnetic data.

The magnetism in certain rocks registers the direction toward the north magnetic pole

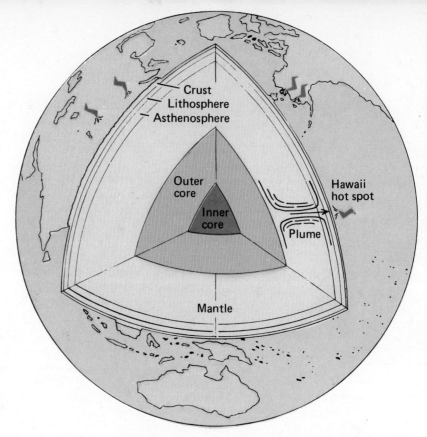

According to one theory, hot spots develop as relatively hot material from the earth's mantle rises in a convection plume, and expresses itself on the earth's crust as an area of active volcanism.

adapted with permission from *Natural History.* © The American Museum of Natural History, 1977.

as well as the latitude at which the rocks were originally formed. If the area in which the rocks are currently found is part of a moving lithospheric plate, the magnetism in the rocks can provide information about the motion of the plate.

Morgan showed that hot-spot traces and data on rock magnetism yield a consistent picture of plate motion if the cause of the hot spots is geographically fixed. Hot-spot traces have thus proved very useful in reconstructing the actual motion of the plates over the earth with respect to the deep mantle.

The relative fixity of hot spots had another and perhaps deeper significance. It was one of the observations that led Morgan to the idea of thin columns of relatively hot material rising in the earth's mantle. Each such column, or "convection plume," expresses itself as a hot spot. Plumes possibly extending down as far as 2,900 kilometers (1,800 miles) to the bottom of the earth's mantle would not be expected to shift rapidly about.

RISING CONVECTION PLUMES

Morgan's hypothesis likened the plumes to "thunderheads" in the mantle. They were postulated as areas of rapid (2 meters, or 6.5 feet, per year), narrow upward convection of hot mantle material that spreads out in the upper mantle and then sinks slowly in regions distant from the place of origin to complete the convection circuit. This was a novel approach to the old idea of mantle convection, according to which convection is not restricted to narrow zones but consists of wide cylindrical cells.

Is there any way to prove that hot spots are really evidence of rising convection plumes? In Morgan's model, the top of the plume is in the soft, semi-molten earth layer just below the lithospheric plates. This mushy zone is commonly referred to as the asthenosphere. Plumes bring material up vertically out of the deeper mantle; at depths of about 160 kilometers (100 miles), the first tiny melt pockets develop in the rock.

This partially molten "crystal slush" then moves radially outward into the asthenosphere, much as a glacier moves away from a mountain. The greatest amount of melting would occur directly above the rising plume, thus causing the observed volcanic activity at the hot spot. This theory would receive support if the flow of molten material below the plates could be measured.

Vance Henry, Taurus Photos

Helgafell volcano spews forth smoke and pours ash on Vestmannaeyjar village on Iceland's Heimay island. Measuring the amount of volcanic discharge is one way some scientists hope to determine the rate of mantle flow.

In 1971, the same year Morgan introduced his mantle plume ideas, a research team from Columbia University published measurements taken off the coast of Iceland that suggested that flow below the plates could be measured.

## MEASURING MOLTEN MATTER

Projecting southwest from Iceland, the Reykjanes Ridge forms a northern extension of the Mid-Atlantic Ridge. The Reykjanes Ridge has a crestal zone of elevated volcanic topography close to the line where new magma is coming up. This "line" is a narrow zone, no more than a few kilometers wide, where new crust is being added to the steadily diverging American and Eurasian plates, to the accompaniment of frequent earthquakes and submarine volcanism.

The crestal zone of the Reykjanes Ridge shoals gradually northeastward and then emerges in Iceland as Reykjanes, a peninsula. The capital city of Reykjavik, on the peninsula, is on the very edge of the American plate, on ocean crust so young and hot that geothermal waters can be tapped not very far below the surface. A short distance to the southeast one can walk along the lava flows of the newly born "ocean crust" of Reykjanes and across to the Eurasian plate, of which eastern Iceland is a part.

In addition to the Reykjanes Ridge crest, there is a second young volcanic belt—one that includes such famous volcanoes as Hekla, Katla, Surtsey, and Heimaey—still farther east. It appears that the line demarking sea-floor separation is in the process of shifting to the eastern zone of volcanoes. If so, the volcanic fires of Reykjanes may someday—perhaps in 1,000,000 years—be stilled. Shifts such as the above are not too common in the world ocean.

The fact that many of the known shifts have occurred near hot spots tends to lend credence to the plume theory. Outward flow from plumes could weaken plates so much that other forces could separate them.

## FLOW CHANNELED INTO "PIPE"

If there is a flow below the plates, does it spread out evenly in all directions? Probably not. Since plates get thicker with age, a natural conduit is formed below the mid-oceanic ridge. Much of the plume flow would be channeled into this "pipe"; irregularities in the flux leave a record of flow speed imprinted like frozen wakes on the ocean crust. The mid-oceanic ridge and the pipe below it are displaced at major fractures zones. Such displacements would block or interrupt the flow in the pipe to various degrees. The result of these new discoveries is a complex plumbing system wherever plumes exist below the mid-oceanic ridge—for example, near Iceland, the Azores, or the Galapagos Islands.

Independent verification of flow below the crest of the Mid-Atlantic Ridge and even of damming at fractures in the earth's crust that tend to run at right angles to the ocean ridges has emerged from studies which found that Icelandic volcanic rocks derive from a distinct plume-type mantle. As the mantle flows under the Reykjanes Ridge, it becomes mixed with mantle distant from plumes, with the result that rocks dredged along the Reykjanes Ridge become progressively less "Icelandic" in their chemistry as distance from the hot spot increases.

To have a better understanding of what is going on in the deep mantle we should

John Running

Study of volcanic activity, rock ages, and sea-mount movement in the Hawaiian Island chain has greatly contributed to theories of mantle flow.

really have a historical index of activity that shows how much mantle the plume brings upward per year over periods of geologic time. Needless to say, there is no direct way to measure the upward flow in a mantle plume. However, the average annual rate of lava and ash poured out by a hot spot's volcanoes can be measured. To compute from this measurement the volume of mantle brought up, we would have to know what fraction of mantle actually melts and escapes to the earth's surface. The chemistry of the basalt rocks involved indicates that the rate of volcanic discharge needs to be multiplied by anywhere from 10 to 100 to give the volume of mantle that produced the lava.

There are two possibilities for estimating volcanic discharge rate. First, the volcanoes can be monitored and the volume of erupted rocks measured directly after each eruption. Since volcanoes are notoriously erratic—many years may elapse between eruptions—a long historical observation record may be necessary to establish a geologically meaningful, long-term average eruption rate.

The second way to estimate volcanic discharge rate—one I have made use of—begins with dividing the Hawaiian chain into 23-kilometer- (15-mile-) wide strips running across the chain from the southwest to the northeast. The volume of volcanic topography—that is, islands, submerged island

bases, and seamounts—above the abyssal sea floor was calculated for each strip. The volume was then divided by the time it took the plate to move across the 23 kilometers (15 miles) of the strip. The time was derived from the ages of various volcanic islands and seamounts along the Hawaii–Emperor chain.

The measured discharge rate for Hawaii, as ascertained by the first method, is astonishingly close to the figures I arrived at using the second. This correlation suggests that if the 1952 to 1971 discharge rate had applied from one million B.C. onward, the observed volume and oldest ages of the Big Island of Hawaii can be accounted for. We do not know whether or not there are large fluctuations in basalt discharge over time periods measured in centuries or in thousands of years. If there are, the recent historical rate happens, fortuitously, to equal the long-term, or million-year average. On the other hand, it is possible that a hot spot's volcanic output over centuries and millennia is relatively constant, in which case a few decades or a century of observation will provide a good approximation of the million-year average.

But when we examine the output of the Hawaii hot spot over still longer time periods—say, 10,000,000 years—it is no longer true that productivity can have remained constant. Since there are now numerous rock age dates along the Hawaii–Emperor chain, the massive portions of the chain around Gardner Pinnacles, west of Niihau, and, likewise, between Oahu and Hawaii seem to represent a higher than average lava discharge rather than slowdowns of the Pacific plate. The topography of the Hawaiian Islands clearly shows a progressively increasing discharge that began about 6,000,000 years ago—the time when Kauai and Niihau islands were formed at the geographic site currently occupied by the Big Island—namely, over the Hawaii hot spot. The Big Island is aptly named—I cannot think of a larger, purely volcanic island, either visible or sunk below the sea, with the single exception of Iceland. And Iceland is largely a bulge in the ocean floor itself, not a volcanic edifice constructed, lava flow by lava flow, from the abyssal depths. In terms of the surviving 70,-

000,000-year volcanic trail left on the Pacific plate by the Hawaii hot spot, the "geologic present"—that is, the last one or two million years—has been truly exceptional.

## SYNCHRONIZED WAXING AND WANING

What about the discharge rates of other hot spots around the world? Most are less well known than Hawaii and less plentiful in their volcanic output. I have compiled discharge histories of a number of hot spots, with the following surprising result: there seems to be a globally synchronized waxing and waning of volcanic discharge rates at widely spaced hot spots. For example, the twelve- to eighteen-million-year-old peak in discharge rate that produced the massive part of the Hawaiian Ridge near Gardner Pinnacles and French Frigate Shoal corresponds in time to the extrusion of the vast Columbia basalts in Oregon by a hot spot at present under Yellowstone National Park. That peak discharge rate marked the beginning of strong volcanic activity in the Canary and Cape Verde islands and other hot spots. The increasingly abundant volcanism of the last 6,000,000 years also affected various other hot spots in addition to Hawaii.

## VOLCANOES BELCH SIMULTANEOUSLY

If a seeming correlation between the ups and downs of volcanic activity at different hot spots was unexpected, so was the finding that ash layers in oceanic drill cores revealed discharge highs for the same periods—from 12,000,000 to 18,000,000 years ago and from 6,000,000 years to the present. Most of this ash does not come from hot spot volcanoes. It comes instead primarily from the notoriously explosive volcanoes situated along such island arcs as the Aleutians, Kuriles, Japan, and the West Indies, where oceanic plates descend into the mantle.

The available evidence suggests to me that the world's volcanoes belch simultaneously in a global chorus, a result as surprising as it is unexplained. By "simultaneously" I am, of course, referring to million-year averages, not annual averages. Why should hot spot volcanoes and island arc volcanoes vary their output concurrently? One possibility might be that plume convection, responding

John Running

Geyser erupting during winter in Yellowstone National Park, the most prominent hot spot in the continental United States.

to episodic instabilities deep in the mantle, accelerates the plates, which in turn cause more island arc volcanism as they are forced into the mantle at a higher rate.

Whatever the cause of hot spots may be, there is still much that we have yet to learn about them. For example, do they contribute in a manner not now understood to the process of continental drift?

W. Jason Morgan, who originated the mantle plume idea, has suggested a rise speed of about 2 meters (6½ feet) a year for mantle material in the ascending plume. At that rate it would take one or two million years for an increase or decrease in plume activity to take effect on the earth's surface after originating at depths as great as the core–mantle boundary. Our volcanic future a few million years hence—with all its possible consequences—may therefore already be preordained deep in the mantle □

 SELECTED READINGS

"Hot spots on the earth's surface" by K. C. Burke and J. T. Wilson. *Scientific American,* August 1976.

*The Making of the Earth: Volcanism and Continental Drift* by Haroun Tazieff. Saxon Publications, 1974.

"Volcanic activity and great earthquakes at convergent plate margins" by M. J. Carr. *Science,* August 12, 1977.

The submersible *Alvin,* shown here alongside its mother ship, was used to collect samples of the water from the Galápagos Rift area and to take numerous measurements and photographs.

Woods Hole Oceanographic

# THE GALÁPAGOS RIFT

## by Robert D. Ballard

THE research vessel *Knorr* of the Woods Hole Oceanographic Institution in Massachusetts steamed out of the Panama Canal February 8, 1977, headed for the Galápagos Rift in the Pacific Ocean some 330 kilometers (200 miles) northeast of the Galápagos Islands and 640 kilometers (400 miles) west of Ecuador. The vessel was on a mission to make a detailed study of several warm-water vents on the ocean floor in depths of between 2,500 and 2,700 meters (about 8,200 to 8,900 feet). The voyage marked the third major expedition since 1973 to centers where lava from the earth's mantle erupts and pushes adjacent parts of the earth's crust aside.

### GETTING INTO POSITION

On February 12, after four days at sea, a series of fixes taken on orbiting satellites indicated that the *Knorr* was in the general area of the Rift. With speed reduced and the ship secured for quieter running, the bottom echo sounder was turned on and the ship began making a series of north-south runs across the rift-valley floor. The *Knorr* had aboard fine-scale topographic maps of the valley that had been prepared by the U.S. Navy. As the ship crossed back and forth across the rift valley floor, the echo-sounding profiles were compared to the maps. Slowly, features on the ocean floor became recognizable. The north and south walls that flank the inner rift valley were located, as well as the central axis running down the middle of the valley. Later, individual volcanoes were identified. Assured by these profiles that the ship was in the proper area, preparations were made to install a network of bottom acoustic devices that would serve as reference beacons once work began. Both the manual submersible craft *Alvin* and an unmanned sled named *Angus* (acoustically navigated geophysical underwater system) would be tracked by this network.

### BACKGROUND OF THE PROGRAM

From the results of earlier studies in the Galápagos Rift area we can reconstruct an

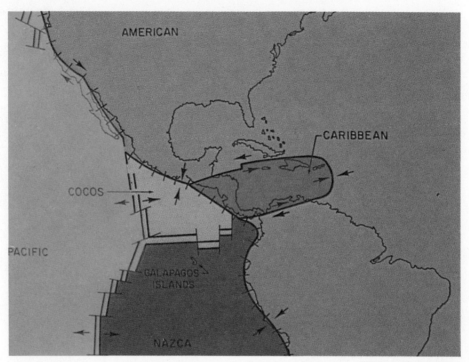

Map showing the Galápagos Rift area. The dives were made along the boundary between the Cocos and Nazca plates, which are slowly moving apart.

interesting story. The Rift, for example, is part of a global mid-oceanic ridge system. In this system, the crust of the earth is separating under the influence of what are thought to be convective processes within the earth's interior. Previous studies indicated that the Galápagos Rift is similar to other regions of crustal separation, such as the Mid-Atlantic Ridge and the East Pacific Rise, but that the temperature of the crust in the Galápagos region showed unusual patterns when measured by heat flow probes. It became clear that circulation of heated water within the upper segment of the newly formed oceanic crust might be responsible for the pattern of heat-flow values. If this proved to be true, the possibility would exist that warm water could be flowing out of the ocean floor into the sea. This condition was discovered in 1972 by the Woods Hole Oceanographic Institution and confirmed in 1976 when scientists of the Scripps Institution of Oceanography detected warm-water irregularities within the Rift valley. The Scripps investigators left two of their acoustic devices on the bottom to mark the area where these anomalies were recorded. These devices were used by the *Knorr* as it positioned itself for its work.

## LOWERING *ANGUS*

After the acoustic net was installed and surveyed, the search began for the water vents. The two-ton *Angus* sled was readied. Its photographic equipment was checked, as well as its bottom pinger and water-temperature measuring unit.

The *Knorr* was brought into a stationary position and the heavy *Angus* sled was lowered over the side. At the same time, acoustic tracking began. As data were sent back to the mother ship, computers were used to calculate the location of the sled within a three-dimensional frame of reference.

The first lowering lasted 12 hours and was conducted in a weaving pattern back and forth across the central axis of the valley floor. This was the region where the most recent volcanic eruptions were thought to have occurred.

As the sled was lowered, its altimeter telemetered back the distance to the bottom. At 90 meters (about 300 feet) off the bottom, the winch operator was told to slow the descent. From this point on, we began carefully to lower the sled the remaining distance.

Startled crabs scurry away from *Alvin's* sampling basket in the bacteria-laden warm waters of Clambake I area.

Woods Hole Oceanographic

With the bottom near, we started moving the ship forward, increasing the speed over the bottom until the computer indicated both ship and sled were moving at about 1.3 kilometers (9/10 mile) per hour across the floor.

Forty-five minutes into the lowering, the camera automatically turned on and began taking pictures by strobe light every 10 seconds. At the selected speed, this gave us a continuous photographic strip beneath the camera some 6 meters (19 feet) in width as we raised and lowered the sled, trying to keep it no more than 4.5 meters (15 feet) above the bottom. Periodically, the bottom would suddenly rise, and, if the winch operator did not raise the sled fast enough, it would crash into the bottom. On numerous occasions, the tension of the wire rose rapidly; if it had exceeded 9,000 kilograms (about 20,000 pounds), the cable would have snapped with the loss of approximately $100,000 in equipment.

## VIGIL BEGINS

Fortunately, it never did. Within a few minutes the towing operation had stabilized, and we settled into an all-night vigil—one person monitoring the sled altitude; another watching the computer plots, asking the bridge to change course or speed; and a third watching the temperature of the water that the sled was passing through.

Six hours into the watch—after a lot of coffee, popcorn, and listening to record albums—the telemetered water data indicated a major temperature anomaly that lasted less than three minutes. The precise time was noted, the computer print-out of the navigation data was reviewed, and the X and Y coordinates of the time of the temperature anomaly were circled. When the temperature returned to normal—approximately 2.01° Celsius (35.6° Fahrenheit)—the vigil began again.

After 12 hours, the *Angus* sled camera was out of film, having taken 3,000 color photographs. Sixteen kilometers (ten miles) of bottom terrain had been traversed, with only one temperature anomaly recorded. The order was given to raise the sled; an hour later it was aboard. The sled had been in near-freezing water, so, to prevent condensation from damaging the film, we waited two hours for the camera housing to warm up before unloading the film. The roll was then taken to the film lab for processing, while the *Angus* crew caught some sleep.

## LAVA FORMS VIEWED

The first few frames were blue because the camera had turned on just before reaching the bottom. The first picture of the sea floor showed that it was covered by a massive and complicated pile of fresh "pillow" lava.

As the crust of the earth is pulled apart under the forces of sea-floor spreading, cracks develop in the floor of the rift valley. These cracks widen and deepen with time. This eventually releases pressure at depth, which leads to a partial melting of the hot interior. The newly formed magma rises up through the fractured crust to the valley floor, where it flows out as lava at a temperature of 1,250° Celsius (almost 2,300° Fahrenheit). The lava comes into contact with cold seawater that has a temperature of 2° Celsius (35° Fahrenheit). It quickly cools, forming pillows that resemble mounds of toothpaste.

We viewed this barren lava terrain frame after frame, witnessing an endless variety of sculptured pillow forms. After about an hour, we noted that the sled had moved out across a massive flat-lying surface to the south of the pillowed central axis. Here, the lava forms were quite different. Instead of pillows, the lava resembled forms previously observed near Hawaii called "pahoe-hoe" flows. Having a fresher and glassier outer surface, these flows were clearly younger in age. Their smooth surface and ropey, often whirly features suggested a much faster flow of magma.

## SUDDEN APPEARANCE OF LIFE FORMS

The sled soon crossed back into pillow lava terrain, which made up the low relief volcanoes running down the central axis. As we watched the film, we also kept an eye on the time. In the lower left hand corner of each frame there was a notation of the precise time the photo was taken. We waited to see the point where the temperature anomaly had taken place. The photograph taken just seconds before the temperature anomaly showed only barren, fresh-looking lava terrain. But for thirteen frames—the length of time the temperature irregularity had been measured—the lava flow was covered with hundreds of white clams and brown mussel shells. This dense accumulation, never seen before in the deep sea, quickly appeared through a cloud of misty blue water and then disappeared from view. For the remaining 1,500 pictures, the bottom was once again barren of life.

## MANNED DESCENT

By the time the review of the film was completed, the ship *Lulu* had arrived on station and *Alvin* was ready to dive. The center of activity shifted to *Lulu* as the *Knorr* headed south to begin work in another region, 16 kilometers (10 miles) away, suspected to be hydrothermally active.

While the final checks were being made on *Alvin,* the navigator moved *Lulu* to the launch site over the location of the clam and mussel pictures. *Alvin* was then lowered on

Alvin's mechanical arm picks up a large clam, some 30 centimeters (12 inches) long, in the Clambake I area.

In the Clambake II area no warm water was found and the animals were dead. Here we see bivalve shells scattered over pillow lava.

Woods Hole Oceanographic

its cradle. After an hour and a half, *Alvin* reached the bottom—approximately 2,700 meters (8,000 feet)—about 270 meters (800 feet) south of the target.

Driving first across the fresh, glassy pahoe-hoe flows and then up onto the pillow lavas of the central axis, the scientists inside the submersible observed the same features that had been captured through the lens of the *Angus* camera. But when they reached their target coordinates, *Alvin* and its three-man crew entered another world.

Coming out of small cracks cutting across the lava terrain was warm, shimmering water that quickly turned a cloudy blue as manganese and other chemicals in solution began to precipitate out of the warm water and were deposited on the lava surface, where they formed a brown stain. But even more interesting was the presence of a dense biological community living in and around the active vents. The animals were large, particularly the white clams, which were up to 30 centimeters (12 inches) long. This basis of life was only 50 meters (150 feet) across and totally different from that of the surrounding area. What were the organisms eating? They were living on solid rock in total darkness.

## HOW COULD LIFE EXIST THERE?

An answer to the question of what the organisms were eating and how they could live began to emerge later when the water samples obtained from inside the vents by *Alvin* were opened for analysis aboard the *Knorr*. As the chemists drew the first water sample, the smell of rotten eggs filled the lab. Portholes were quickly opened. The presence of hydrogen sulfide was the key.

The cracks in the floor of the rift valley provided avenues for cold seawater to enter and circulate within the hot, newly formed crust. As the seawater traveled deeper into the hot crust, the water temperature rose and its chemical composition began to change. Losing some chemicals to the rock, the seawater picked up others. The sulfate in the seawater was converted to hydrogen sulfide. Now heated, this altered water began to rise back to the surface, mixing with fresher seawater from above. Traveling up the small cracks, some of the warm water flowed out of the rock at 8-16° Celsius (45-60° Fahrenheit) to form a series of vent areas. The hydrogen sulfide in this warm water was quickly taken up by bacteria that rapidly multiplied. A food chain was thus initiated in total darkness independent of the sunlight at the surface.

## FIVE VENT AREAS PROBED

By early into the second leg of the expedition, *Alvin* and *Angus* had located and investigated four more vent areas along an 8-kilometer (5-mile) stretch of the central axis. Four of the vents were active, while one vent was inactive with only dead clam and mussel shells found scattered over the lava flows. A massive kill apparently had taken place when the vent was closed off, and the bottom organisms were unable to move to an

Unidentified, spaghetti-like tube worms were found draped over a fissure near one of the vents.

Woods Hole Oceanographic

active vent, some 225 meters (675 feet) to the east.

## NO TWO ALIKE

Another interesting aspect of these isolated worlds was that no two were alike. The first vent area was dubbed "Clambake I." It was characterized by large white clams, brown mussels, and numerous, white crabs. In addition, a purple octopus, one of the few predators in the area, was observed.

The second vent region was called "Clambake II," but no warm water was found, and all the animals were dead. Hundreds of clam and mussel shells were observed slowly dissolving in the cold water, which was unsaturated in calcium carbonate.

The third site was termed the "Dandelion Patch" for its abundance of a small animal (still unidentified at this writing), about 2.5 centimeters (1 inch) in diameter. It resembled a dandelion gone to seed, but instead of being on a stalk, this organism held itself in place several centimeters above the bottom, using an intricate pattern of radiating fiber elements up to 16 centimeters (6 or 7 inches) long. This vent area, having a fairly simple population, appeared to have become active relatively recently.

The fourth site was called the "Oyster Bed," although it did not have any oysters. (There wasn't a single biologist on the entire cruise—only geologists, geophysicists, chemists, geochemists, physicists, and a science writer).

The fifth vent area was the most interesting. It was one of the larger areas and had several active vents. It was termed "the Garden of Eden" for its numerous and interesting life forms. Saturation photographic runs by *Angus* showed this vent area to have distinct rings about the active vents in which certain organisms dominated. The outer ring consisted of dandelions and white crabs. The next ring contained a small worm attached to the rock surface. The dandelions then disappeared close to the vent. Limpets, pink fish, and tall, white-stalked worm tubes with bright red tops were observed at the entrance to the vents themselves.

## FAR-REACHING DISCOVERIES

In all, two months were spent investigating the Galápagos Rift and the hydrothermal deposits to the south. Twenty-four dives were made, numerous samples were collected, and more than 100,000 color pictures were taken. The discoveries made on this expedition, particularly the very surprising finding of life forms in warm-water vent areas, will likely have a major effect on all disciplines of oceanography □

 SELECTED READINGS

"Alvin: work in the deep" by K. J. Sulak. *Sea Frontiers,* March 1977.

"Life in the ocean's depths" by Joan Arehart-Treichel. *Science News,* June 19, 1976.

"Oases of life in the cold abyss—deep-sea exploration of the Galápagos Rift" by J. B. Corliss and R. D. Ballard. *National Geographic,* October 1977.

George Holton, Photo Researchers

# DESERTIFICATION

## by Romaine Bamford

More than 20 per cent of the earth's land surface is true desert, incapable of supporting life. And more land becomes desert each day. Can the seemingly relentless march of the desert be stopped before it is too late?

ABOUT 43 per cent of the earth's land surface is desert or semidesert. More than you thought, right? And the amount is increasing steadily. It is estimated that over the next 25 years one third of today's remaining arable land could be lost to deserts—land that we can ill afford to lose if civilization as we know it today is to continue.

The typical desert landscape is dry and barren. The ground consists largely of stony rubble and rocky outcrops, although in parts there are vast tracts covered by sand. The true desert supports no life.

The creation of deserts or desertlike conditions is called desertification. Each year about 5,600,000 hectares (14,000,000 acres) of productive land are turned into total desert. Since 1925 some 650,000 square kilometers (250,000 square miles) of farm and grazing land along the southern edge of the Sahara alone have been swallowed up. The soil has become useless, incapable of supporting any life at all.

In the semidesert regions, which make up about one half of the world's total desert area, the story is somewhat different. Semideserts are habitable. The soil is poor and the land barely productive, yet these marginal drylands are vital in supporting life on earth. About 630,000,000 people, or about 14 per cent of the world's population, live in such areas. Many of these people are subsistence farmers and livestock herders, totally dependent on their harsh surroundings for their livelihood. If the process of desertification continues, these people face a serious problem. Even now, threatened by the prospect of losing their means of livelihood, many are flocking to already overcrowded cities to try to seek jobs for which they have no skills. Poverty, malnutrition, and social unrest invariably follow.

### OLD PROBLEM WITH NEW TWIST

The problem of desertification is not new. The land between the Tigris and

Euphrates rivers in Iraq where one of the earliest forms of western civilization is thought to have begun was once known as the "fertile crescent." Today it is barren wasteland. The fall of the great ancient cities of Babylon and Ur was also probably due at least in part to the spread of the desert.

Until the early 1970s, however, the world paid little attention to the problems posed by the spreading deserts. Then a prolonged and severe drought in the Sahel—a band of land along the southern edge of the Sahara that includes the countries of Senegal, Mauritania, Mali, Upper Volta, Niger, Chad, and Gambia—and a subsequent famine were so well reported that desertification began to attract worldwide attention.

Drought and crop failures have been facts of life in desert areas ever since antiquity, but the drought in the Sahel was made worse by a number of distinctly twentieth-century factors. Improved health facilities allowed populations to expand to all-time highs. Larger crops than usual, watered by newly dug wells, were planted, and larger herds, made possible by improved veterinary medicine, grazed the land. In normal seasons the land could withstand these extra strains imposed on it—just barely. When the rains

didn't come, the crops failed and the cattle quickly devoured any remaining vegetation. With no plant cover the thin topsoil soon eroded, leaving only rock and sand behind. People fled to neighboring areas, spreading the disaster. When the rains finally came in 1974, damage to the soil over a wide area was irreversible. The desert had made another advance.

The impact of the disaster in the Sahel and fears that the Sahara would continue relentlessly to move south prompted the United Nations to call for a conference on desertification. The conference, held in Nairobi in August and September 1977, spurred research on the climatic, ecological, social, and technological aspects of desertification and led to some surprising findings.

## THE WORK OF NATURE

The world's major deserts—the Sahara, Gobi, Kalahari, and so on—lie mainly between the latitudes of 15° to 30° north and south of the equator. Global air circulation patterns are such that areas between these latitudes receive downward flowing air currents that warm up as they approach the land surface. Heated air can hold more moisture than cold air. As the downward-moving air

Sheep are often the only wealth semidesert dwellers know. Yet overgrazing by large herds of sheep and the taking of sheep herds to border lands for grazing are some of the major causes of the increased rate of desertification in the world today.

Victor Englebert, Photo Researchers

Hungry children and dying livestock are all too familiar sights as land once barely able to support life becomes totally useless.

in these regions is heated, it absorbs any moisture present in the air. As a result very little or no rain falls.

Currents then shift the moisture-laden air toward the equator, where it rises, cools, and releases its moisture as rain. At one time it was thought that changes in global climatic conditions were responsible for the spread of deserts, but recent studies show no evidence that the air circulation pattern has changed or is changing in any way that would cause the appearance of new desert regions.

There is, however, some evidence that once an area that has supported plant life becomes a desert the changed land surface may prevent rain from falling there in the future. This sets up a vicious cycle in which a newly formed desert area becomes less likely than ever to receive the rain it needs and thus has little chance of ever recovering its fertility.

### THE WORK OF PEOPLE

If climatic changes are not responsible for the spread of deserts, what is? The view that emerged at the UN conference is that desertification is being caused by the activities of people rather than by the activities of nature. The Sudan region provides an example of how people's activities have had a devastating effect on the land.

The Sudan could become a "breadbox." The soil in certain areas is among the richest and most fertile in the world. But the Sahara is swallowing parts of the Sudan at an alarming rate. Between 1958 and 1975 the Sahara moved between 90 and 100 kilometers (55 and 65 miles) southward into the Sudan's marginal farmlands.

The abandonment of traditional crop-rotation methods in the Sudan has greatly contributed to this march of the desert. Traditionally the acacia trees that covered a Sudanese farmer's land were burned and the land planted with millet, sorghum, maize, sesame, and other crops for a period of four to ten years. After this period, the soil, then impoverished and depleted of its minerals, was left to lie fallow, with some limited grazing allowed. The acacia trees began to grow again, and after eight years or so could be tapped for gum arabic—a substance used in many foods and candies. Gum arabic provided a useful and valuable cash crop for the farmer who typically tapped the trees for about six to ten years. By that time the trees had died and the farmer typically restarted the cycle, burning the trees and planting. Repeated every 18 to 28 years, this agricultural cycle ensured that the soil never became so impoverished that it could not recover.

Today, however, to feed an increased population, the Sudanese farmer must often extend the period of crop cultivation for a few years. This leaves the soil so depleted that it cannot fully recover as it lies fallow—and is grazed by larger herds. Acacia trees have little chance to reestablish themselves and those that do are frequently chopped down for firewood and not tapped for gum arabic. Then the farmer, with an important source of income lost, has little alternative but to replant his crops on still impoverished soil. The soil becomes increasingly overworked and poor and finally degenerates into useless sand.

## BEWARE TECHNOLOGY

Land to the north of the Sahara is also suffering from desertification. About 100,000 hectares (250,000 acres) are lost each year as a result of overgrazing and overcultivation of land that cannot support the strain. This strain is a direct result of a sixfold increase in the population of northern Africa since 1900.

Technological innovations introduced to increase food production have not helped.

In Tunisia, for example, mechanized plowing turned out to be disastrous: the plows cut so deeply into the thin topsoil that much of it was loosened and blew away. The digging of wells also had unforeseen effects. Apart from encouraging farmers to plant larger crops, thereby straining the soil, the green areas around the wells became so heavily trampled by people and animals that the vegetation disappeared, leaving the land ready for erosion. These barren areas gradually spread as more and more people overused the wells and brought more animals to graze there.

Badly managed irrigation projects have also added to the problem both in northern Africa and in northeastern India. Water that does not drain properly leaves salt deposits that over the years build up to levels that render the soil infertile.

## OVERGRAZING

Overgrazing has led to the disappearance of vast areas of semiarid grasslands once used as rangeland in many parts of the world—in Kenya, Tanzania, and Ethiopia; in Iraq, where experts say that land capable of supporting about 250,000 sheep is now being grazed by four times that number; and in Syria—to name just a few regions.

Good rangeland becomes degraded in several stages. First, overgrazing by sheep leads to the disappearance of the very plant

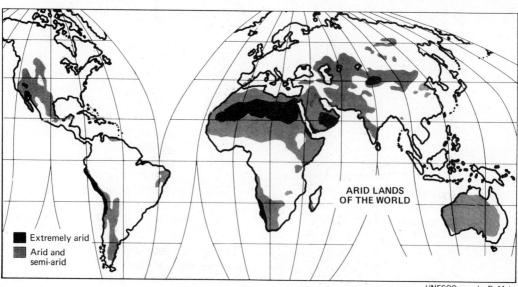

ARID LANDS OF THE WORLD

■ Extremely arid

▨ Arid and semi-arid

UNESCO map by P. Meigs

Georg Gerster, Rapho, Photo Researchers

Oases and well areas in desert regions must be very carefully used. If abused by too much planting, too much grazing, and too many people, the vegetation will gradually disappear, leaving the fragile soil ready for erosion.

species that the sheep require. Other plants suitable only for hardier goats and camels take over. But then the goats—voracious grazers—strip the land of everything that is edible. With no plant cover left, the topsoil then blows away, leaving a layer of gravel or sand.

Some ecologists have suggested only half-jokingly that desertification could be slowed in some areas if the goat could be re-moved from the area. This is, however, impossible: the goat is invaluable to desert peoples, supplying them with milk, meat, and hide.

The Rajasthan desert in northern India is the world's most densely populated arid zone. Population pressures have caused overgrazing and overcultivation and a vicious cycle that seems to lead to only one thing: increased desertification. The livestock population has increased even as available grazing land has decreased, as more and more is taken for crop cultivation. In spite of the availability of this extra land, crop yields have decreased—the land is just too poor to support the crops. Meanwhile larger and larger herds continue to impoverish the remaining soil. Erosion is so bad that the area is one of the world's driest and dustiest places. The dust forms such a thick layer that warm air is prevented from rising even a little; and therefore no cooling occurs and little or no rain falls.

## EROSION

In the foothills of the Himalayas the need for farmland and firewood has caused extensive deforestation on the hillsides. With no vegetation cover, the soil turns to mud during the rainy season and slides down the hills, leaving them useless for agriculture.

In semiarid northeastern Brazil vast tracts of Amazonian forest have been cut down, leaving only sun-baked earth. Desert-like zones are spreading into the moister, more humid interior as farmers and ranching corporations continue their tree-cutting exploitation farther and farther into the interior.

Whether overcultivation, overgrazing, deforestation, or unwise irrigation is the first culprit, the result is the same: soil erosion. Erosive factors have been in operation for hundreds of years but it is only recently that increases in human and livestock populations have placed such a burden on the land

In an effort to halt the spread of the Sahara northward, several north African nations have agreed to plant a "green belt." Algeria has already begun planting groves of trees and palisades of shrubs and fronds.

Georg Gerster, Rapho, Photo Researchers

that it cannot recover, given enough time. The problem is aggravated as traditional methods of coping with the poverty of the soil in drylands—nomadism and crop rotation, for example—are abandoned or become inadequate. And so the desert wins.

## WHAT CAN BE DONE

The result of the UN conference on desertification was an ambitious plan designed to halt the spread of deserts by the year 2000. One of the most successful anti-desertification projects has been carried out by the Israelis in the Negev desert. Much of this land has been reclaimed using an ancient technique that involves collecting runoff water from rainfall and using it for irrigation. Water collected in catchment areas is fed to fields in channels small enough to prevent large-scale flooding. Surplus water is fed to lower fields through stone spillways. Experimental farms constructed on these principles have been able to produce olives, pomegranates, figs, almonds, grapes, onions, peas, artichokes, and asparagus even in years of very low rainfall.

Another plan involves the planting of groves of trees and shrubs along the northern perimeter of the Sahara to try to cut down erosion. Algeria has already planted this barrier, and Egypt, Tunisia, and Libya have agreed to help build a "green belt."

The nations of the Sahel are working together on a plan that would allow nomadic cattle herders to raise their animals on the marginal rangelands without further endangering their productivity. When it is time for the cattle to be fattened prior to marketing, the herders would be allowed to bring their animals south to wetter, hardier pastures. Another approach calls for the setting up of cooperatives for nomadic herders. The cooperatives would regulate grazing, provide security against loss of animals, and establish channels of communication with local governments.

Regulation of livestock numbers is another possibility. Experts have estimated that the number of livestock in the Sahel in the early 1970s was at least double what the land could safely support. If that number could be halved and modern management methods introduced, the yields of meat and milk could be double their previous level.

Other countries seriously affected by desertification have also agreed to work

Tom McHugh, Photo Researchers

Desertification is not just a problem in the world's less developed nations; it is also a growing problem in some industrialized countries—the United States and Australia, to name just two. Above is a photo of a dried-up reservoir in California, the result of a long period of low rainfall.

together. Pakistan, India, Iran, and Afghanistan will use data from U.S. Landsat spacecraft to measure the rate of desertification in their areas. In the Middle East, Egypt, Libya, Chad, Sudan, and eight other countries have agreed to forget their political differences and to work together in the management of shared underground aquifers.

At first sight it might seem a relatively straightforward matter to halt desertification simply by not permitting overgrazing or extensive deforestation or by insisting that livestock numbers be kept within limits. But it is extremely difficult to implement these ideas. How, for instance, can an illiterate herder be persuaded to reduce his herds when they represent his livelihood, his insurance against drought, and in some cases his only idea of wealth? How can villagers be persuaded not to cut down trees for firewood when they lack the money to buy alternative fuel?

## A WORD OF WARNING

So far we have talked of desertification as if the problem existed only in the world's less developed countries. But it does exist to some extent in the highly industrialized nations also. In Australia, poor land management has already caused some deterioration of rangeland. In the United States the Bureau of Land Management recently found one half of the land it controls to be in a "fair" state only and another 33 per cent to vary from "poor" to "bad," meaning that vegetation cover had deteriorated to such an extent that, in some cases, topsoil had almost vanished. The damage is due primarily to overgrazing.

All the nations of the world must take the warning. A conflict between social systems and ecosystems exists. Unless changes —not necessarily technological changes but rather social changes—are put into action, there may well be a series of "natural" disasters, which will in reality have been shaped to a great extent by the hands of people □

 SELECTED READINGS

"Desertification" by C. L. Rogers. *Science News,* October 29, 1977.

"Deserts made by man" by S. Galal. *National Parks and Conservation Magazine,* November 1977.

"Sifting sands" by F. Golden. *International Wildlife.* January 1977.

"Spreading deserts—hand of man" by E. Eckholm and L. R. Bruce. *Focus,* September 1977.

*UNESCO Courier,* July 1977.

# EARTHQUAKE LIGHTS

## by John S. Derr

*The earth speaks softly to the mountain*
*Which trembles*
*And lights the sky*

This ancient Japanese hokku, or saying, refers to the appearance of lights at the time of an earthquake. Although earthquake lights have long been observed, they have been the subject of few investigations by scientists. The reason is simply that most reports of these lights are the personal observations of untrained observers. And as such, they are often difficult to analyze and study.

### FIRST KNOWN INVESTIGATION

The first known investigations of earthquake lights were done in the early 1930s by two Japanese seismologists, Torahiko Terada and Kinkiti Musya, whose studies were described by Charles Davison in 1937. Musya collected some 1,500 reports of lights from the Idu Peninsula earthquake which occurred at 4:30 AM on November 26, 1930.

Davison reported:

"In most of them [observations of earthquake lights] the sky was lit up as if by sheet lightning, and nearly all the observers agree in estimating the duration of a single flash as decidedly longer than that of lightning. At one place on the east side of Tokyo Bay, the light resembled auroral streamers diverging from a point on the horizon. Beams and columns of light were seen at different places, several observers comparing the beams to those of a searchlight. Others describe the lights as like that of fireballs. Some state that detached clouds were illuminated or that a ruddy glow was seen in the sky.

"The lights were seen to a distance of [80 kilometers] 50 miles to the east of the epicenter, nearly [112 kilometers] 70 miles to the northeast, and more than [64 kilometers] 40 miles to the west. They were seen both before and for some time after the earthquake, but were most conspicuous during the middle of the shock.

"During the year following the Idu earthquake, Mr. Musya studied the luminous phenomena attending four other Japanese earthquakes. They were seen before the earthquake by 26 observers, during it by 99, and after it by 22."

### PROBLEMS IN INTERPRETING OBSERVATIONS

In trying to explain these luminous phenomena, we should remember two things. First, people under the stress of an earthquake may give very distorted testimony of what they think they have seen. Second, they are naturally aware of anything that may happen during an earthquake, even though the same things happen on other occasions totally unconnected with earthquakes.

In his 1942 textbook, earth scientist Perry Byerly described reports of earthquake lights at sea. These observations are particularly important because if they have the same cause as those on land, it places severe restrictions on how such lights are generated.

Byerly wrote:

"At the time of the earthquake off the coast of northern California in January, 1922, one observer reported a glow at sea which he at first took to be a ship on fire. At the time of the earthquake of October, 1926, centering in Monterey Bay, an observer reported a flash at sea which resembled 'a transformer exploding.'"

### PHOTOGRAPHS OF THE LIGHTS

More recently Yutaka Yasui collected photographs of lights seen during the Matsushiro earthquake swarm in Japan from 1965 to 1967. At least 18 of the 35 sightings are not explained by meteors, twilight, zodiacal light, arcing power lines, or distant lightning.

The only known photographs of earthquake lights are from the Matsushiro area and were taken by Mr. T. Kuribayashi, a dentist. One of the photographs is reproduced with this article.

Yasui lists six common properties of the Matsushiro earthquake lights:

The earthquake light phenomenon as photographed by a dentist in Matsushiro, Japan. The photo was taken at night, and the sighting could not be explained by meteors, zodiacal luminescence, or man-made lighting.

1. The central luminous body is a hemisphere with a diameter about 20 to 200 meters (65 to 650 feet), contacting the surface. The body is white, but reflections from clouds may be colored.

2. The luminescence generally follows the earthquake with a duration of from ten seconds to two minutes.

3. The luminescence is restricted to several areas, none of which are the epicenter of the earthquake. Rather, the lights typically occur on mountain summits.

4. Radio interference generally follows the luminescence and is strongest in the 10- to 20-kilohertz range. (One kilohertz equals 1,000 cycles per second.)

5. The luminescence occurs frequently at the time when a cold frontal air mass is passing.

6. There is no effect on magnetometers at the local observatory. That is, there are no apparent magnetic effects associated with the lights.

Yasui believes that ionization in the lowest atmosphere becomes unusually large at the time of an earthquake and causes the luminous phenomena at the place where the electrical potential gradient is highest. The electric field is not expected to be large, as it is under a thunderstorm, nor is the atmospheric conductivity expected to be high. Therefore, some action of the earthquake must contribute to triggering luminescence—for example, violent perturbations in the atmosphere.

## MANY RANDOM POINT DISCHARGES

An unusual report of earthquake lights near Hollister, California, was given to my colleague R. D. Nason. In this case, the lights were seen as discrete sources against a hill rather than as the more commonly observed sky luminosity.

Reese Dooley, a poultry rancher living south of Hollister, observed lights in 1961. There were two earthquakes about 2½ minutes apart. It was dark when he felt the first one, which was strong enough to make him want to go home to check on his family. Just as he reached his car, the second one started. As he looked west toward a hill, he saw a number of small, sequential flashes from different places on the hillside. Nason inspected the hillside and found no electric wiring or any other conventional explanation for the lights. Clearly, Mr. Dooley had been very close to the source of the lights. This observation suggests that the lights observed in

Japan which lit up most of the sky could be caused by a great number of small, random point discharges over part of the epicentral area.

## MANY POSSIBLE THEORIES

In 1968, J. E. McDonald investigated several mechanisms for producing electric potential gradients in the earth. One area of his study involved streaming potentials, which are the electric potentials caused by movement of fluids through porous rock. In this case, water flow through porous rocks and soils was caused by differences in pressure developed after underground nuclear explosions. The maximum potential difference found was a few hundred millivolts over distances of about 300 meters (1,000 feet) from ground zero. This is far too small to have any effect on corona discharge in the atmosphere or to produce any air luminosity.

McDonald also investigated several examples of earthquakes at sea where luminosity was reported. He decided that none of the mechanisms proposed for generating potentials on land could produce luminosity at sea.

It is possible that some observations of earthquake lights might be traced to ball lightning. If an earthquake should occur in thunderstorm weather, one might expect some reports of luminous phenomena originating as fireballs descending from clouds. The light might be associated with a hissing sound, might last for several seconds ending with an explosion, and might produce an odor and/or smoke. However, there would also be abundant stroke lightning in the vicinity, so that an investigator would naturally tend to discount any reported lights as being due to atmospheric electricity. If higher electric potentials are generated in the ground during some earthquakes, then it might be possible for earthquake lights to be caused by both stroke and ball lightning. At the present time, we have yet to prove even the existence of the electric potential in the ground.

## ELECTRIC FIELD IN ROCKS

The most recent work on earthquake lights was reported by David Finkelstein and J. R. Powell in 1971 at the International Union of Geodesy and Geophysics in Moscow. Their work concerns the feasibility of generating the required electric field in rocks, both before and during earthquakes, and is a continuation of their studies of ball lightning.

Ball lightning is caused by ground-to-ground electric discharges called arch lightning. Some evidence exists that the stress accumulated in rocks over a period of years may begin to be released very slowly several days before a large earthquake. Some minerals, called piezoelectric minerals, are known to produce electricity when subjected to pressure. The straining of rocks against one another could lead to generation of a high-seismoelectric potential, generated by stress on piezoelectric quartz in the rocks. The resultant discharges might be seen several hours before the actual fault break of the major earthquake. (It should be noted here that Yasui, Byerly, and others have reported luminescences before, during, and after earthquakes.)

Most seismologists hearing the paper were of the opinion that enough evidence exists to warrant investigations and that the subject should no longer be ignored.

## CONCLUSIONS

The existence of earthquake lights is well established. The luminosity occurs in the air close to the ground, generally over certain areas in the epicentral region principally during, but also before and after, the earthquakes. Sightings occur both on land and at sea and have been reported from as far as 3° to 4° from the epicenter of a moderate shock.

Two theories have been advanced which are worthy of further investigation: (1) violent low-level air oscillation and (2) piezoelectric effect in quartz-bearing rock. If the latter theory is correct, it may be possible to develop electrical monitoring methods for earthquake prediction. Observations of lights at sea might be explained by air oscillation but probably not by the piezoelectric effect. On the other hand, observations 3° or 4° distant from the epicenter are probably more easily explained by the piezoelectric effect than by air oscillation□

The American Museum of Natural History

*Tyrannosaurus* (background) was probably the largest meat-eating animal that ever lived, *Stegosaurus* (foreground) was an armored vegetarian. An analysis of the feeding habits and gait of dinosaurs is leading to some new theories about their relationship to other animals.

# WERE DINOSAURS WARM-BLOODED?

## by John H. Ostrom

THE dinosaurs were very successful creatures. Thousands of fossil specimens from all the continents except Antarctica testify to their 140,000,000-year success story. Part of their success lay in their diversity. There were dinosaurs of all different sizes and shapes, reflecting wide differences in life style and habitat. Close to 1,000 species have been named, although many of these are based on fragmentary and inadequate remains.

The dinosaurs have always been classified as reptiles because they possessed certain anatomical features that are today found in reptiles—in lizards, snakes, crocodiles, and turtles—and lacked other anatomical features characteristic of birds or mammals. That is the reason that dinosaurs have usually been interpreted like modern reptiles as regards their physiology, or body functioning, their metabolic rates, and their temperature regulation. In recent years, however, some scientists have found evidence

that this traditional way of thinking about dinosaurs might not be correct. They now ask "Should dinosaurs be classified as reptiles or placed in their own class? Were some of them not more closely related to birds?"

One of the basic factors involved in discussing whether dinosaurs should be classified as reptiles or not involves temperature regulation.

### TEMPERATURE REGULATION

Most living reptiles are poikilotherms, or cold-blooded creatures, whose temperatures fluctuate with that of the environment. They are ectotherms, dependent on external sources of heat—sun, atmosphere, or substrate—and lack internal temperature-regulating mechanisms. In general, they are incapable of raising or lowering body temperature above or below that of their environment by internal processes. They must instead control their temperature behaviorally—seeking shade or basking in the sun.

Mammals and birds, on the other hand, are capable of internal temperature regulation, or endothermy. They can raise or lower their body temperatures relative to their environment by internal metabolic processes. Consequently, they are able to maintain fairly constant (homeothermy) and relatively high (warm-blooded) body temperatures.

Each reptile, bird, and mammal species has its own optimum temperature for normal to maximal activity. In general, reptiles operate at cooler and more varied temperature levels than do birds and mammals. Reptiles are also generally characterized by lower metabolic rates than are similar-sized birds and mammals and also are less capable of long intervals of high exercise. Until ectotherms have warmed up to their optimum level, they are relatively inactive, or torpid, in contrast to nonhibernating endotherms that are always at optimum temperature for maximum activity.

A number of seemingly unrelated lines of evidence strongly suggest that some and perhaps most of the dinosaurs were warm-blooded and homeothermic and perhaps even endothermic. In other words, they had fairly constant, relatively high body tem-peratures, which they may have been able to maintain by internal body processes.

## UPRIGHT GAIT

The majority of the dinosaurs had an upright or erect posture and gait. This is known from the shape of fossil limb bones and hip and shoulder sockets and from the very narrow width of all known dinosaur tracks. Among modern vertebrate animals, erect posture and gait are true only of endotherms—mammals and birds. Contrarily, all ectotherms are sprawlers and incapable of true upright carriage.

There is no known cause-and-effect relationship between posture and temperature control, but researchers wonder whether ectothermy may well make erect posture and locomotion impossible. They theorize that the externally affected body functioning of an ectotherm is so unstable, erratic, and incapable of sustained activity that transition from a primitive sprawling condition to an erect carriage is impossible. The fact that several dinosaur groups were two-footed—suggesting that they had an activity level comparable to that of modern flightless birds—seems to strengthen the idea that a basic body functioning factor like tempera-

A reconstructed skeleton of *Triceratops,* an herbivorous dinosaur. Its horns and bony skull plate protected it from larger, predatory meat-eaters.

The American Museum of Natural History

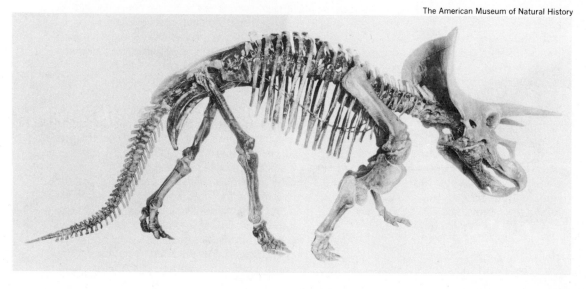

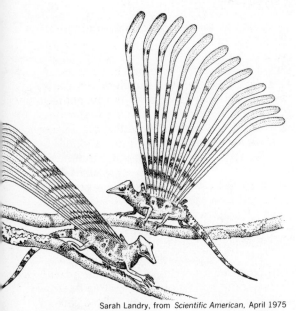
Sarah Landry, from *Scientific American,* April 1975

The *Longisquama,* a small fossil animal was a thecodont, a form believed to be the ancestor of both dinosaurs and birds. Its body structure suggests a stage in the evolution of feathers.

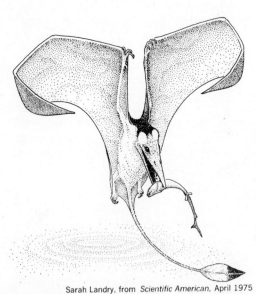
Sarah Landry, from *Scientific American,* April 1975

*Sordus pilosus* was a pterosaur, or flying reptile. Fossils show that the animal was insulated with a dense growth of hair or hairlike feathers, a strong indication of endothermy.

ture regulation is involved in the upright posture of dinosaurs.

FEEDING

The feeding apparatus of some dinosaurs seem to suggest that they were capable of high metabolic activity levels. This suggests they may have taken in a larger volume of food per unit of body weight than a comparable sized ectotherm would need.

Several kinds of dinosaurs were equipped with large specialized grinding or slicing teeth, well adapted for processing large quantities of plant food. These were the bipedal, or two-footed, herbivores, especially the duckbills, and the horned dinosaurs. Many dinosaurs also had the passages for air and for food well separated, thus freeing the mouth from much respiratory activity and allowing it to process large volumes of food. We cannot, however, know if the large food intake of dinosaurs was simply a result of their very large size or was a result of high metabolic rate and endothermy.

PREDATOR-PREY RELATIONSHIP

A related line of evidence involves the predator-prey relationship. Endothermy is more expensive than ectothermy. Modern ectotherms consume something on the order of their own body weight in food every two to four months, but similar-sized endotherms ingest that amount every one to four weeks and very small endotherms consume two or three times their weight every 24 hours. A given number of prey animals can support a much smaller number of endotherm predators than it can ectotherm predators.

A census of carnivore versus herbivore dinosaur specimens in the Alberta, Canada, region revealed a predator-prey ratio that is interpreted by some researchers as very strong evidence that dinosaurs were endotherms, expensive food takers.

The evidence suffers from several weaknesses, however. First, the sample was too small to be reliable and did not take into adequate consideration habitat preferences among dinosaurs. Second, the whole line of reasoning considers only predators and can not be extended to infer anything about temperature regulation in herbivores.

Skeleton of *Tyrannosaurus rex*. From reconstructions of skeletal parts of dinosaurs, scientists hope to be able to piece together facts about the life of dinosaurs and about why they disappeared from earth.

The American Museum of Natural History

## GEOGRAPHIC DISTRIBUTION

The geographic distribution of dinosaur specimens has occasionally been given as evidence that they were not ectotherms. Emphasis is placed on dinosaur discoveries at high latitudes, such as the dinosaur footprints found in Spitzbergen, Norway, not too far from the North Pole and in environs totally hostile to terrestrial ectotherms. There is, however, a serious flaw in this argument.

Geologic evidence has now firmly established that landmasses are not fixed but rather move and drift about during geologic time. The latest data indicate that Spitzbergen was much closer to the equator than to the North Pole in Cretaceous times, some 65,000,000 to 135,000,000 years ago. Thus the present day latitudinal distribution of dinosaur remains does not record the actual distribution of dinosaurs during the Mesozoic era, from about 235,000,000 to 65,000,000 years ago.

If the movement of land masses is considered, then it seems that most dinosaur finds come from areas between 40° and 50° latitude, or today's tropical and subtropical areas. The geographic distribution of dinosaur remains would then not favor endothermy, but rather ectothermy, since the tropical to low-temperature-zones are today home to the vast majority of terrestrial ectotherms.

## RELATIONSHIP TO BIRDS

A final line of evidence about temperature regulation in dinosaurs concerns only one of the many groups of dinosaurs—the theropods, or carnivorous dinosaurs. Recent studies have shown that the earliest known bird—*Archaeopteryx* from the middle of the dinosaur era—probably was a direct descendant of some small carnivorous dinosaur. In nearly every feature of the skeleton (except the wishbone), *Archaeopteryx* is virtually in-

## BLOOD PRESSURE

Perhaps the most interesting theory in support of internal temperature control in dinosaurs involves blood pressure. As a consequence of erect posture, virtually every dinosaur had its head elevated well above the level of the heart. This implies that dinosaurs had comparatively high blood-pressure levels. Otherwise, adequate blood circulation and oxygenation of tissues across the vertical distance between the heart and the head could not be achieved. It is interesting to note that high blood-pressure levels do not occur in living ectotherms.

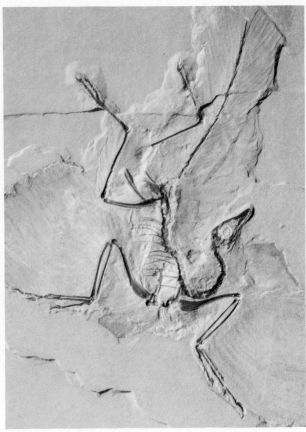

The American Museum of Natural History

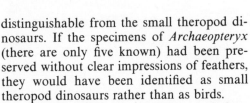

Restoration of the skeleton of *Archaeopteryx,* the earliest known bird. Studies now indicate that Archaeopteryx was probably descended from a small carnivorous dinosaur.

distinguishable from the small theropod dinosaurs. If the specimens of *Archaeopteryx* (there are only five known) had been preserved without clear impressions of feathers, they would have been identified as small theropod dinosaurs rather than as birds.

Today's birds are, of course, endothermic and of high temperature and metabolic levels. *Archaeopteryx,* with its feather covering, also appears to have been an endotherm and independent of external heat sources. That raises the obvious question: were the very similar and presumably closely related theropod dinosaurs also endothermic? Is it possible that the small theropods like *Compsognathus* might have had plumage also? So far none with feathers have been recognized, but should one come to light, how could we determine whether it was a bird or a small feathered theropod?

## SUMMARY

In my opinion, the fact that nearly all dinosaurs were large (over 450 kilograms, or 1,000 pounds) and the fact that worldwide climates during the Mesozoic were equable and subtropical-to-tropical, make it very likely that most dinosaurs were warm-blooded and homeothermic. Their large body size alone would insure more or less uniform temperature as the affects of daily fluctuations would be damped out. That dinosaurs were endothermic as well, regulating their body temperature through internal body processes, has not been established. The evidence for endothermy is highly suggestive, however, especially for the theropods. But none of the evidence is conclusive, and so we are still left wondering □

SELECTED READINGS

"Dinosaur Renaissance" by Robert T. Bakker. *Scientific American,* April 1975.

*The Hot-Blooded Dinosaurs* by Adrian Desmond. Warner Books, 1977.

*The Dinosaur World* by Edwin H. Colbert. Stravon Books, 1977.

National Coal Association

After many years during which oil and natural gas were thought of as the major fossil fuel energy sources, coal is now receiving increased attention. The United States and many other nations still have very large untapped coal reserves. Here a loading machine with crablike arms moves through a mine, sweeping lumps of coal onto a conveyor that will carry it out of the mine.

# ENERGY
## contents

**155**

# ENERGY

## review
## of the year

This colossal offshore drilling and production rig will be used to tap the oil deposits of the North Sea.

Oil spills, both those far out at sea and those along coastlines, continued to be a problem during the year, but progress is being made in cleanup techniques.

Although experts predicted energy shortages in the decades ahead, the end of 1977 found the world awash in oil. The reason: the industrialized nations of Europe tightened their collective "energy belts" since the Organization of Petroleum Exporting Countries (OPEC) quintupled the price of oil since 1973. ■ Because of the world surplus OPEC decided at a year's-end meeting in Caracas, Venezuela, not to raise prices again. They did, however, agree to hold an "extraordinary meeting" in 1978 to consider increasing prices and to use the extra funds to help the poor Third World nations, who have been driven into near bankruptcy by skyrocketing oil prices; the proposal had little chance, however.

**U.S. Energy Policy.** While the rest of the world economized, the United States continued to burn energy almost without limit. The year 1977 began with the worst winter in 100 years with schools and factories closed and one million workers idled because of fuel shortages. Even so, the year ended without a national energy policy. President Carter proposed an energy program, but it appeared it would be defeated piece by xiece. Essentially the program would have held down the prices of U.S.-produced oil and gas to a little more than one half of the cost of foreign imports. To persuade U.S. residents to use less energy, it proposed a tax on domestic production that would bring the price up to world levels, a tax that critics quickly pointed out would be the largest tax in the nation's history. At year's end, a Harris poll showed 56 per cent of the public opposed to the plan, with the majority opinion seeming to be "The trouble with the Carter energy program is that it puts all the emphasis on conservation and very little on how to get new sources of energy." Oil-industry spokesmen agreed and pointed out that at world prices, or less, huge reserves of oil and gas could be developed in the United States.

**Oil and Gas.** Oil and gas provided 75 per cent of world energy needs in 1977. Outside of the Arabian countries, much of the world's future reserves will be found off the coastlines of continents and in the oceans. There were several developments concerning offshore oil in 1977 and early 1978. The largest structure ever built and floated—a 180-meter (590-foot) tall, 340,000-metric ton offshore drilling and production platform was built and will be towed to the Ninian field near the Shetland Islands in the North Sea. It will be used to drill 40 wells in an important step in Great Britain's hope to become nearly energy self-sufficient. ■ Meanwhile, plans to drill offshore deeper than ever—in 1,300 meters (4,300 feet) of water off the coast of Newfoundland—were announced by two oil companies. ■ In early 1978 the U.S. government granted permission for oil companies to begin drilling off the eastern coast of the United States despite strong environmental opposition.

Oil spills continued to be a problem with worldwide tanker-related spills increasing during the first nine months of 1977. Progress was made, however, in lessening damage from tanker disasters, notably by a French team that quickly sprang into action after an East German tanker sank and successfully transferred the oil from the tanker to a salvage ship. They claim that their technique can be improved in future similar wrecks.

**Coal.** Today coal provides 19 per cent of U.S. energy needs and the United States has enough coal to last for hundreds of years. The problem is converting power houses and factories from oil and gas to coal and mining enough coal to meet increased demands. At the end of 1977 a National Coal Association official said that the coal industry would meet President Carter's goal of doubling U.S. coal production by 1985 "if the government does not impose unreasonable restraints." This might be a rather large "if." There is considerable difference of opinion between the Environmental Protection Agency and the coal industry about acceptable clean air standards for coal burning as well as about how mined-out land should be reclaimed. Despite the problems more than 100 coal producers plan 190 new mines to produce 424,000,000 tons annually as well as expansion of existing mines to add another 170,000,000 tons by 1985. ■ Some industries are reluctant to convert to coal-burning furnaces, arguing that given the clear air standards it might be cheaper to keep their present gas-fired boilers and burn synthetic gas made from coal. And they point to studies that show enormous reserves of natural gas in the United States that could be developed for less than the cost of making gas from coal, if the government would deregulate natural gas prices.

One solution for power plants and factories located near coal deposits might be "underground coal gasification," a method long used by the Soviets. The method is relatively simple. Two wells, from 20 to 50 meters (60 to 150 feet) apart, are drilled to the base of a coal seam. Lighted charcoal is dropped into one well to ignite the coal, and air is injected into the second well. Air from the second well seeps into the first, drawing the flame toward it and by this process linking the two wells. By controlling the rate of flow of injected air, it is possible to obtain partial coal combustion so that low-energy gas is emitted from the first well.

**Nuclear Energy.** Industry experts predict that by 1990 nuclear energy will provide 14 per cent of U.S. energy needs, up from today's three per cent. This growth is opposed by a growing number who point to the problem of storing and disposing of nuclear waste.

**Renewable Energy Resources.** Although industry and government studies estimate that in 1990 water power, wind, sun, and other renewable resources will supply only three per cent of U.S. energy needs, down from today's four per cent, the dream of clean, inexhaustible energy is spreading. There was a marked increase in the sale of solar collectors in 1977. ■ In Canada, work on the world's largest hydroelectric complex continues, and the use of small dams to generate electricity for nearby farmers, businesses, and villages increased worldwide. ■ "Garbage power" also came into its own in 1977. Following the example of Japan and Europe, the United States increased its building of resource-recovery plants to burn trash to supply heat and generate electricity. By the end of 1977 there were 16 full-fledged plants in operation, 12 under construction, and many more planned. New York City announced plans to process 2,400 tons of garbage a day to supply nearby industrial users with heat and electricity. ■ Enthusiasts claim that with government help clean energy sources could provide 40 per cent of the world's energy needs by the year 2000 and 75 per cent by 2035.

David M. Evans

U.S. Dept. of Energy

Low-level radioactive wastes are transported in special, double-walled steel railcars to storage and disposal sites.

Storms and rough seas pose special problems for offshore oil drilling.

Texaco

# AN ADVANCED SOLAR HOUSE

## by Peter Britton

PASSERSBY on Dune Road in Quogue, on New York's Long Island, are startled and intrigued when they spot an unusual structure. Many guess that some sort of advanced solar device covers half the roof. They are right.

Outfitted with the latest solar collectors, the ultramodern home—dubbed Sunship—is a prototype "high-technology" solar space-conditioning system. The house has been occupied for almost two years now, signaling practical, everyday use of one of the newest and most promising tools in the growing solar-energy store.

### NEW TYPE COLLECTOR

This is the so-called evacuated-tube collector, an apparent whiz at putting free and plentiful solar energy to work heating buildings and supplying hot water and air conditioning.

The collector being used in the Quogue house is called Sunpak, manufactured by Owens-Illinois. (There are several makes of evacuated-tube collectors. Other variations are under development by several other companies.) The Sunpak collector is still in a developmental stage. Nevertheless, working in conjunction with computerized heat-distribution controls made by Sunkeeper Corp., this method of exploiting solar energy could, if all goes well, make a significant contribution to space-heating technology.

A laboratory-constructed array of collectors had been on the roof of the home for about a year when I drove by and thought, "By golly! That looks like a solar home." Subsequent talks with owner Philip Barbash and officials from Owens-Illinois and Sunkeeper indicated that during the initial year of operation, the collectors, heat-circulating equipment, and computerized control mechanisms had been working nearly perfectly, supplying over one-half of the house's total energy demand for heat and hot water while using only 60 per cent of the system's annual output.

Of course, a few problems did exist: noisy pumps, several leaking plumbing connections on the roof, and some minor computer snafus. The only orthodox heating assistance came from a propane heater, some sporadic contributions by water "grates" in two fireplaces, and abundant fiberglass insulation.

Because of the building's good insulation, design, and location, the Barbashes find no need for air conditioning. However, the manufacturer says that its collectors can easily obtain temperatures needed to run absorption-type air conditioners.

The Barbash home was the first residential installation of the evacuated-tube system. This prototype was made of hand-built collectors, but later the original array was replaced with pilot-line collectors, one step away from assembly-line mass production. The new 450-square-foot array cost about $8,800, figured at roughly $20 a square foot (not installed). Each collector equals about 1.1 square feet and is priced by modules of 24 collectors at $548. The manufacturer thinks that this figure will have to come down to about $10 a square foot (not installed) to make the Sunpak-Sunkeeper system commercially practical.

### RIGOROUS ENVIRONMENT

The 3,000-square-foot, three-story Barbash house sits about 300 yards from the Atlantic Ocean, behind a low rise of dunes. It is an area that has all the elements for rigorous testing: summer heat in the high 90s and winter cold in the low teens; sweeping wind; salt and sand spray; high humidity; occasional storms. As Hurricane Belle approached Long Island on August 9, 1976, officials of Owens-Illinois nervously monitored by telephone the whirling wind-measuring device on the roof in Quogue. Gusts of 120 kilometers (75 miles) an hour had been recorded when the power went off an hour before Belle struck. Result to Sunpak collectors: no damage.

Peter Britton

One of the world's most advanced solar homes: the house was constructed so as to provide sloping surfaces for mounting solar collectors on the roof.

Exposed to this meteorological mélange is what may become a familiar rooftop sight: in this case, 384 glass collectors angled at 57.5 degrees above horizontal to make the best use of the sun's rays for heating purposes at latitude 40 degrees.

Nearly 400 glass tubes may seem a lot for one's roof, but, for the Barbash home at least, the effect is not unpleasing. Actually, only about 20 per cent of the roof area is covered. Mrs. Barbash, who is deeply interested in energy conservation, sees the array from a delightfully original point of view: "When I first saw them," she says, "I thought, somehow, of music. And they remain that way to me: mathematical and musical and modern and comforting—as well as practical and energy-saving."

This reaction is quite likely a tribute to all of those involved with the Barbash house. Y. K. Pei, brother of famed architect I. M. Pei, is the inventor of the evacuated-tube collector. Noted sculptor Robert Berks was

employed to design attractive moldings to house the manifold and collector ends. New York architect John Whedbee designed the house for solar-energy use, which dictated its slanting and "sailing" effect. The inner workings are by engineer Joseph Frissora.

The black and silver-gleaming collector array commands attention both aesthetically and as high-technology solar-energy equipment. Each tube is about 44 inches long with a diameter of about two inches and is made of borosilicate glass with low-expansion, high-strength properties. Indeed, in addition to hurricane Belle's blows, they have withstood a deluge of large hailstones, intense internal and external heat, heavy, wet snows, and blown sand.

The Barbash house has 16 four-by-eight-foot collector modules arranged in four rows. The modules weigh about 185 pounds each when filled with water, and most roofs will need little or no extra support. Each row of modules works independently of the other

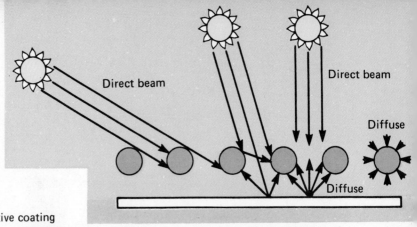

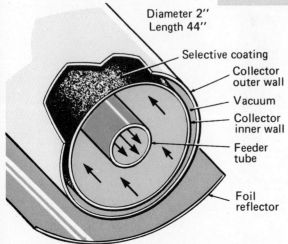

## SUNPAK SOLAR COLLECTOR
cross section (not to scale)

Diameter 2''
Length 44''

Selective coating

Collector outer wall

Vacuum

Collector inner wall

Feeder tube

Foil reflector

Direct beam

Direct beam

Diffuse

Diffuse

adapted from Owens-Illinois and *Popular Science,* July 1977

Left: cross section of the Sunpak solar collector tube. Each tube is about 44 inches long and about 2 inches in diameter. A medium for transfering heat—water in the case of the Barbash house—enters through feeder tubes, gathers heat as it flows, and flows back through the space between feeder tube and the inner wall of the collector. The tubes are very carefully positioned on the roof so that they receive the maximum possible amount of sunlight. The diagram above shows a possible arrangement where the collectors receive both direct and diffuse beams of sunlight.

rows. Collectors are held firmly in place by aluminum brackets at one end and a common manifold at the other. The manifold routes the fluid through the tubes. The collectors are arranged parallel to each other about two inches apart and six inches from the roof. This separation allows sunlight to strike the white roof (or curved aluminum reflectors sold by the manufacturer) and rebound to hit virtually the entire surface of each tube.

### SUNPAK'S SECRETS

How does the Sunpak obtain high enough temperatures for winter heating, summer cooling, and year-round hot water? The secrets are selective coating and the vacuum. The outward-facing surface of the inner wall of the collector tube has a blackened coating that absorbs both direct and reflected rays from the sun but radiates little so there is minimal heat loss. A vacuum is created in the 1-inch space between the outer and the inner walls of the collector via a hermetic seal at one end. The vacuum is kept at a constant pressure that inhibits heat loss from convection and conduction and also helps prevent tubes and liquid from freezing. It is roughly the reverse of the Thermos bottle, which employs a silver surface to reflect heat inwards.

The heat-transfer fluid may be water, a mixture of ethylene glycol and water, or air; it is water in the Barbash home. The fluid flows into a feeder tube from the manifold and back through the space between the feeder tube and the inner wall of the collector. The system is arranged so that the heat-transfer fluid will flow through every tube in a row of modules, gathering heat as it goes.

### HIGHLY EFFECTIVE

The manufacturers say that their Sunpak collectors work well on overcast and hazy days and are virtually unaffected by wind and fluctuations in air temperature. They add that the Sunpak can operate in areas of low sunlight, from two to five times more effectively than existing flatplate collectors under load conditions.

Inventor Pei reports how snow began to fall during a government testing session of solar collectors at the U.S. National Aeronautics and Space Administration's Lewis facility in Cleveland, Ohio, last winter. While flat-plate collectors registered a loss of heat, the Sunpak continued to register an energy gain. The collectors' efficiency can be increased even more with the aluminum reflector, which is said to increase collector output by 25 to 30 per cent. A more definitive picture can be presented in terms of Btu.

One Btu is the amount of heat needed to raise one pound of water one degree on the Fahrenheit scale.

The Barbash house has a peak heating demand of about 75,000 Btu per hour on a 10-degree day to keep the temperature at 72° Fahrenheit. Each square foot of Sunpak collectors can deliver up to 175 Btu per hour, and thus handle this demand during hours of bright sunshine. No heat is stored, however, and auxiliary energy sources take over as daylight fades. But this is something that solar systems must live with, say the engineers. Conventional heating plants can be designed for "worst" conditions more economically than can solar systems. Designing for "worst" with solar would create excessive energy waste in off-peak periods. For this reason, average load days are the aim of solar-heating systems such as Sunpak.

## DELIVERING THE ENERGY

But collecting solar energy is only part of the task. The energy still has to be efficiently delivered where needed. At the Barbash home this is where Sunkeeper takes over. The solar-heating controller system contains two basic sections: hydronics, or water-flow, control and electronics and instrumentation.

The nearly 400 glass-tube collectors on the Barbash home have been found to be highly effective and able to withstand severe conditions, including hailstones, blown sand, rain, snow, and hurricanes.

The water-flow-control section is made up of three parts. One part controls the flow of water to the collectors; another controls the flow to the zone heaters and excess-energy dump; and the third controls the water flow to the auxiliary energy sources. The electrical and instrumentation section includes a Modicon 184 minicomputer, power supplies, motor-starter relays, control switches, and status displays.

A school in Maryland has been specially designed to save energy. Named Terraset, the school is buried and provided with a hill with windows, a skylight, and a courtyard. The dirt provides good insulation and solar collectors on the hill roof collect the sun's rays, which are used to heat and cool the building.

This NASA-built experimental "house of the future" is also heated and cooled primarily by solar collectors mounted on the roof.

NASA

The headquarters of the system is in a basement room directly behind the bottom of the roof on which the collectors are mounted. Hot water from the collectors is circulated to an insulated 1,000-gallon fiberglass-reinforced-plastic storage tank at temperatures up to 210° Fahrenheit, depending on the operating mode of the collectors. (The Barbash array is set to produce a temperature lower than usual because there is no air conditioning.) Additional heat comes as needed from copper coils that circulate heated water from the propane heater and fireplace water grates.

Within the solar storage tank are other copper coils filled with water, which absorb the heat in the tank water (maintained between 120° and 180° Fahrenheit) and in turn carry it to radiatorlike units at the base of ducts. Here, fans force the air warmed by the coils into the ducts and hence throughout the house to where it is needed. Also, domestic hot water is preheated up to 140° via a heat exchanger in the storage tank.

## "BRAINS" OF THE SYSTEM

The prototype computerized control was developed for the Barbash home at a cost of $100,000. Sunkeeper officials expect that as a result of the Barbash experience, the cost of the control will drop in three to five years to about $1,000 and the size to that of a shoebox. But the job will be the same: to govern heat distribution automatically and assure maximum use of the solar energy provided by Sunpak. The Sunkeeper system divides the Barbash home into five heat-control zones. Sensors in each zone relay temperature data to the computer, which regulates heat flow accordingly.

For example, suppose the outside temperature drops from 55° to 27° Fahrenheit. Within a short time the temperature in the living room begins to fall. A series of sensors in that room immediately notes the drop and relays that information to the computer in the basement. The computer tells a pump to circulate hot water through the proper radiator coil in the living-room duct. The computer then starts the fan (at a low speed if the outside temperature is above 40°, at a high speed if it's below 40°), stopping it when the appropriate temperature in the living room has been reached.

Sensors also constantly monitor outside temperature, solar insolation, and storage-tank temperature. If the home needs more heat than the sun can provide, the computer control also actuates a system of valves and pumps that demand as much heat as needed from the propane heater.

Sunkeeper official Joseph Frissora is responsible for the development of this complex system, which he calls "electronic-energy management." He feels that only this method, coupled with the evac-

Heat storage is a major part of any solar heating and cooling system. This photo shows an experimental "barrel of heat" that uses Glauber's salt to store heat gathered by solar collectors. Tests have shown that the salt is a more effective storage medium than water. The salt stores heat as it melts and releases heat as it freezes.

General Electric Research and Development Center

uated-tube collectors, can successfully handle solar energy on a commercial basis.

"Solar energy," Frissora says, "is not an easy thing. You need high temperatures for adequate heating and air conditioning, and high temperatures cause problems. But we're well on the way to solving those problems."

## OTHER SUNPAK APPLICATIONS

Besides the testing of Sunship in Quogue, there are other and different applications of Sunpak now undergoing close examination for cost, performance, and reliability. Among these are a housing project in the Denver suburb of Aurora, a townhouse development near Chicago, the Terraset Elementary School in Reston, Virginia, a government building in Saginaw, Michigan, and an industrial building in Canóvonas, Puerto Rico. The last will produce only air conditioning, the equivalent of a 60-ton air-conditioning load.

## MAKING IT COMPETITIVE

With the proper development, Owens-Illinois feels that the Sunpak collector system for solar-energy conversion could be available to the average homeowner for less than $4,000 within five years. This is based on the rough estimate of an array size of 20 per cent of the total square footage of a home. Thus, a 2,000-square-foot home would need an array of 400 square feet. The total cost, installed, including the computerized controls and 'plumbing' could be in the $5,000 to $7,000 range. This, say those concerned, should pay for itself in about seven years.

Says Sunpak project manager Dr. John Woulbroun: "We see our immediate markets as commercial and institutional buildings where heating and air-conditioning needs could be satisfied with the Sunpak collector; industrial applications where large quantities of process hot water are needed; and, eventually, in a low-rise residential use. We hope to make the cost of the Sunpak collector directly competitive with existing fossil fuels in most areas of the country when high-volume production of the collectors is reached."

If so, there could be exciting times ahead for Sunpak and Sunkeeper—and a million more Sunships may dot the horizon □

SELECTED READINGS

*Designing and Building a Solar Home: Your Place in the Sun* by Donald Watson. Garden Way Publications, 1977.

*Homeowners Guide to Solar Heating and Cooling* by William Foster. Tab Books, 1976.

*Solar Home and Sun Heating* by George Daniels. Harper & Row, 1976.

"Solar houses" by C. P. Gilmore. *Saturday Review,* October 30, 1976.

Combining data on the earth's rock formations, magnetism, and gravity with what is known about probable recovery rates, geologists have been able to estimate and graph probable oil reserves in the world.

# WHEN WE'LL START RUNNING OUT OF OIL

## by Peter Nulty

A rare exhibition of price-cutting at the late-1977 meeting of the Organization of Petroleum Exporting Countries (OPEC) brought home the fact that crude oil is, at least for the moment, in glut around the world. This development has added to the confusion about the "oil crisis." President Carter argues that "we are running out of petroleum," while the United Nations says there will be a lot around for "a hundred years or more." Who's right?

The fact is that there is a lot more agreement among experts about how much oil we have than the clash of prophecies would lead anyone to believe. If world demand increases by even 2.5 per cent a year—well below the pace of the past—it will outrun the rate of production sometime between 1990 and 2010. The shortfall could be brought on even sooner by political decisions, such as an OPEC policy to hold down production. But there is very little anyone can do to delay the event much beyond 2010.

### ESTIMATES ON RESERVES LARGELY AGREE

At that point, alternative sources of liquid fuel will have to enter the market to satisfy even modest growth in demand. There is vast, untapped potential in shale oil, tar sands, and processes to produce liquid fuel from coal. Given the necessary technology and appropriate government policies, these resources will come to market—though no one is very sure how fast. What conventional oil remains may well last for many decades, and will tend to be channeled toward such high-priority uses as transportation and the production of chemicals from petroleum.

That geologists can evince much certainty about how much conventional oil is left in the world may strike skeptics as surprising. It is true that for many years they continually raised their estimates. In 1908, the chief geologist of the U.S. Geological Survey put the amount of oil recoverable in the United States at between 10,000,000,000 and 24,500,000,000 barrels. Today the figure is closer to 240,000,000,000. Between 1920 and 1959, estimates of the amount ultimately recoverable in the world rose from 43,000,-000,000 barrels to 2,000,000,000,000. But that's where the escalation stopped: most estimates have remained close to that 2,000,-000,000,000-barrel figure.

Why? When that 1908 estimate was made, the deepest well drilled in the United States went down less than 1,750 meters (approximately 5,700 feet). Today the deepest is almost 9,500 meters (31,000 feet), and in doing a lot more deep drilling we have found out a lot more about the resource. Even though some oil has been discovered below 5,000 meters (about 17,000 feet), we have learned that geothermal heat and pressure usually transform oil into gas at that depth, and that the weight of the earth reduces the pore space in potential reservoirs.

To estimate the amounts recoverable, geologists begin with the data accumulated over long experience in exploration and production. Even where they haven't drilled, they can use this knowledge to analyze the earth's major sediments, which have been mapped and measured by magnetic and gravity techniques. And the seismograph, which provides geologists with pictures of the structures that trap oil, has been greatly improved since the 1950s.

## THE MYSTERY OF RECOVERY RATES

The 2,000,000,000,000-barrel figure was reaffirmed in late 1977 when the World Energy Conference released a poll of twenty-nine authorities, including the seven largest U.S. oil companies, the U.S. Geological Survey, and prominent private consultants. Two thirds of those polled clustered around an estimate of 2,000,000,000,000 barrels. This total is not without its dissenters, of course. The highest estimate among those polled was 3,700,000,000,000, the lowest 1,600,000,000,000.

If anything, the 2,000,000,000,000 figure may turn out to be low. Technology is capable of extracting only a portion of the oil discovered, and no one is certain what will happen to this rate of recovery. The present

CONOCO

As onshore oil reserves are exhausted, the more difficult and more expensive recovery of oil from offshore reserves—such as from this platform off Dubai—will increase.

world average is estimated to be 25 per cent. The participants in the World Energy Conference poll were asked to assume that technological advances would raise the rate to 40 per cent by the year 2000. Some optimists believe this can be lifted to 50 per cent or more.

Ultimate world recovery can be divided into three parts. Since the discovery of oil, 361,000,000,000 barrels, or 18 per cent of the total, have been produced. An additional 652,000,000,000 barrels, or 33 per cent, are "proven reserves," oil that has been discovered and can be produced under the present economic conditions with present technology. The remaining 997,000,000,000 barrels, nearly half the total, are yet to be discovered. This includes the category of "probable reserves"—oil that a banker wouldn't count on but that the producers themselves are pretty certain they will get out.

With geologists generally agreeing that we still have at least four barrels of oil in the ground for every one we have consumed, the question arises as to why supply should be falling short of our needs in just 15 to 30 years.

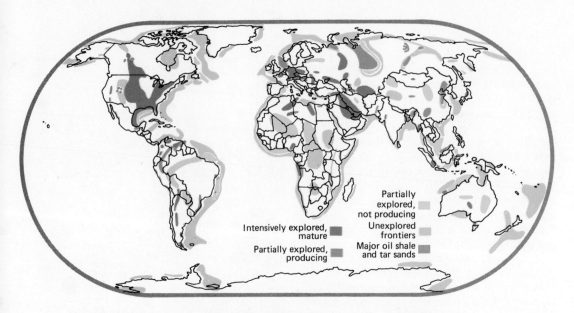

## ULTIMATE OIL RECOVERY BY REGION

Produced

Reserves

To be discovered

Ultimate recovery
(billions of barrels)

663
478
328
242
166
160
131
84

Middle East
Communist area
North America
U.S.
Latin America
Africa
Asia and Pacific
Western Europe

Most estimates show that the Middle East, the Soviet Union, and China may have one half of the yet undiscovered oil, and that another one third may lie in the oceans of other regions. The United States has already used up far more of its oil (46 per cent) than the rest of the world (15 per cent).

## PRODUCTION CURVE OF CONVENTIONAL OIL

Production of the world's "easy oil"—that is, conventional petroleum—is expected to peak around the year 2000. Even if the recovery rate is increased 50 per cent, the peak would probably be delayed only about ten years. On the other hand, a production ceiling set by OPEC could push the peak forward into this century.

The rainbow at the summit of the curve presents liquid fuels that might sustain growth as conventional oil levels off.

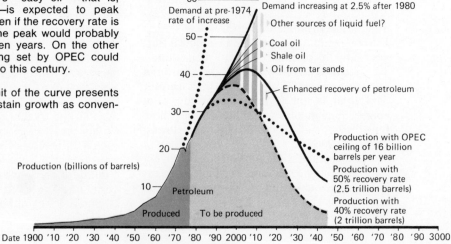

Demand at pre-1974 rate of increase

Demand increasing at 2.5% after 1980

Other sources of liquid fuel?

Coal oil

Shale oil

Oil from tar sands

Enhanced recovery of petroleum

Production with OPEC ceiling of 16 billion barrels per year

Production with 50% recovery rate (2.5 trillion barrels)

Production with 40% recovery rate (2 trillion barrels)

Production (billions of barrels)

Petroleum

Produced

To be produced

Date 1900 '10 '20 '30 '40 '50 '60 '70 '80 '90 2000 '10 '20 '30 '40 '50 '60 '70 '80 '90 3000

## NO MORE MIDDLE EASTS

For one thing, as we are passing the halfway point in discoveries, the rate of which we find oil is becoming increasingly difficult to maintain. Between 1950 and 1970, an average of 18,000,000,000 barrels of oil were discovered each year. From 1970 to 1975, the average fell to 15,000,000,000. Geologist Donald Eicher says, "There may be a few North Slopes out there, but we *know* there are no more Middle Easts."

Onshore, we are finding smaller and smaller fields, and many oilmen believe the best hope for adding big increments to reserves is in the offshore areas. "That," says one oil executive, "is the Great White Hope for the near future." Aggressive exploration could boost the discovery rate through the mid-1980s, but geologists believe it will fall off soon thereafter.

The level of reserves will begin to fall even sooner than that. With the world's proven reserves standing at 652,000,000,000 barrels and production at 21,000,000,000, today's reserve-production ratio (R/P) is 31 to 1. At projected rates of growth, production will pass additions to reserves by the early 1980s at the latest. If these trends continued until the year 2000, the reserve-production ratio would fall close to 9:1.

## UP AGAINST THE CEILING

At this point, production will face physical limits. Because of the need to maintain pressure, only a fraction of a field's reserves can be produced in any given year. The United States is now producing at a rate that brings the R/P ratio down to 7:1, close to what some geologists consider the lower limit. The average that could be maintained worldwide is estimated to be close to 10.1.

Declining discoveries and the limits imposed by the R/P ratio will inevitably cause production of conventional oil to peak in the next 25 to 30 years. This will happen even though 50 per cent or more of the world's recoverable oil will still be in the ground. As John J. Schanz, Jr., an economist at Resources for the Future, puts it, the limits of the R/P ratio and the peak in production are the "unavoidable realities that make us uneasy."

Even if tremendous fields are discovered and we unexpectedly double our reserves, Schanz says, that would delay the peak for only perhaps fifteen years. "A fifteen-year delay could be critical to making a smooth transition to other energy sources," he says, "but we still face that transition."

To supply our needs as we approach that transition, we will doubtless have to pay higher and higher prices. According to one estimate, excluding the Soviet Union and China, two-thirds of the undiscovered oil lies in offshore areas. The costs for recovering offshore oil are much higher than those for on-shore recovery: one oil company estimates that offshore oil is four to five times more expensive to produce than oil on land.

## GOVERNMENTS TAKE THE BIGGEST BITE

One of the hopes for expanding onshore reserves is to enhance recovery by injecting steam or gas into the wells. In 1975, a study for the U.S. Federal Energy Administration estimated that if the price of oil from enhanced recovery were freed from the controlled level of $5.25 per barrel, it would rise to $11 per barrel, costing the consumer an extra 2 cents per gallon of gasoline. The study added that the higher recovery rates would increase U.S. proven reserves by 10,000,000,000 barrels, or 27 per cent.

Despite such price rises, producers believe that most of the conventional oil remaining could be produced for less than the 1976 average selling price of $12 per barrel. Production costs now range from about 25 cents a barrel in some Middle Eastern fields to $6.50 or more a barrel in the North Sea. But this does not include payments to governments in the form of taxes, leases, and other payments. One study revealed that these payments average 49 per cent of gross revenues. They can, however, be more than 80 per cent.

## HOPE FOR THE FUTURE

The hope for the future of liquid fuel rests on unconventional sources. "Whether you are an optimist or a pessimist," says one expert, "depends on whether you are talking about oil or something oily." Oily liquid fuel can be produced from oil shale, coal, and tar

Oil from tar sands may total more than most estimates of liquid oil, but much of the tar sand reserve cannot be exploited by present technology. The photo at right shows tar sands as recovered from the ground and then when the oil is scrubbed out.

Sun Oil Company

sands. These resources are vast and hold the promise of satisfying the growth in demand for liquid fuel well into the twenty-first century.

## NO EASY ANSWER

The transition to new sources of liquid fuel will certainly not be easy. The chart on page 166 which shows alternative fuels making up for the shortfall in conventional oil supply in the early 1990s may be overly optimistic. For one thing, it assumes that growth in the demand for liquid hydrocarbons will rise 5.5 per cent annually between now and 1980, and only 2.5 per cent after that (compared with 7.7 per cent in the 1960s). This slow growth rate depends in part on a tremendous increase in the production of nuclear power up to 17 per cent annually, requiring 54 new plants by 1990, which will lessen the need for oil as a boiler fuel for electric utilities. If nuclear power falls short and coal fails to make up the difference, the demand for oil will be greater and the peak in production could come earlier.

Political decisions could also exacerbate difficulties. Exxon estimates that the world will need some 16,000,000,000 barrels of OPEC oil a year by 1990, a production increase of 60 per cent over the 1975 level, and more than half of that will have to come from the Arabian peninsula. If OPEC sets a lower production ceiling, the world supply would level off in the early 1990s, and fall short of "desired demand" even earlier.

Finally, there is no certainty that alternative sources of liquid fuel will enter the market in time or in the necessary quantities. Oil available from tar sands may total 2,000,-000,000,000 barrels worldwide, more than most estimates of conventional oil. But only 5 to 10 per cent of this is near enough to the surface to be exploited by present technology.

Oil shale could yield 3,000,000,000,000 barrels according to preliminary estimates, but only about 210,000,000,000 are retrievable with the techniques we have today. Coal, of course, is the world's largest resource of fossil fuel, with an estimated 12,-000,000,000,000 barrels of oil equivalent recoverable, but methods of liquefying it have yet to be perfected.

Environmental problems, high costs, and long lead times make it unlikely that these fuels will be available in quantity be-

A bucket-wheel being used to strip mine a region rich in tar sand deposits.

Sun Oil Company

fore the 1990s. Present estimates of their price range up to $27 per barrel, too high to make them competitive with conventional oil now. The lead times for production vary from seven to ten years for shale and coal conversion, and from six to nine years for tar sands.

The Athabasca tar sands in Canada are the first to be exploited. A plant operated by Great Canadian Oil Sands Ltd. has been in operation since 1967 and turned a profit for the first time in 1974, producing 47,500 barrels per day. A second plant is to be completed in 1978 by Syncrude Canada Ltd., a consortium including Exxon, Cities Service, and Gulf, at a cost of $2,400,000,000. It will produce 125,000 barrels per day, or only 0.7 per cent of U.S. consumption last year.

## A QUESTION OF WISDOM

Unconventional fuels could begin to enter the market in quantity in the late 1980s, and according to at least one estimate they may contribute 1 per cent of the world's energy supply by 1990. If the new sources don't come on stream as needed, though, a gap will inevitably materialize between the supply of liquid fuel and the amount needed to sustain economic growth.

The critical question is not whether we have the necessary geological resources to prevent such a chilling of the world economy. Clearly we do. Rather it is whether we have the wisdom and the will to adopt policies that will encourage development. Anything that discourages the development of new sources will only delay the pain and increase the agony when it finally comes. This is what the so-called energy crisis is really all about □

 SELECTED READINGS

"Days dwindle down for precious fuel." *Science Digest,* October 1977.

"How much more oil?" by P. H. Abelson. *Science,* November 4, 1977.

"Invisible crisis" by J. Cook. *Forbes,* July 15, 1976.

"When the oil runs out" by G. Rieger. *Field & Stream,* September 1977.

Brazil has had long experience with gasoline-alcohol blends and now, faced with the high price of imported oil, is exploring the possibilities of adding higher percentages of alcohol to its gasoline and of burning pure alcohol in automobiles. The photo at right shows an auto that runs on a 50 per cent water, 50 per cent gasoline blend.

Pictorial Parade

# ALCOHOL: BRAZIL'S ANSWER TO THE ENERGY CRISIS

## by Allen L. Hammond

WHILE many nations languish in protracted debate over synthetic fuels and other means of alleviating dependence on imported oil, Brazil has moved decisively in the direction of growing its own fuel. The Brazilian government has launched a bold program to replace much of that country's imported oil with ethyl alcohol produced from sugarcane and other crops. If successful, the alcohol program has the potential to establish Brazil not only as the world leader in renewable energy sources but also as the first developing country without large oil resources to find a path to energy independence—a path uniquely its own.

### TRYING TO BECOME ENERGY INDEPENDENT

An energy strategy based on biomass "is a natural for Brazil," says José Goldemberg, director of the physics institute at the Uni-versity of São Paulo and coordinator of an academic energy-policy group. "We have lots of land, lots of water, and an ideal climate for growth." Indeed, less than two per cent of the land area of Brazil could produce enough fuel to replace all imported petroleum.

Brazil imports more than 80 per cent of its oil, about 700,000 barrels a day, and finding the $3,000,000,000 annually to pay for this oil has seriously crimped the country's economic growth in recent years. A measure of the importance attached to reducing this dependence on imports is the amount of money—more than $400,000,000—that the Brazilian government has committed to the alcohol program since it began in November 1975.

The program has the personal backing of Brazil's President, General Ernesto Geisel, and is one of the few to have emerged unscathed from recent government budget cutting. Already proposed are more than 70 new distilleries and additional sugarcane plantings totaling about 500,000 hectares (1,250,000 acres), although only 15 projects have actually received funding. Nonetheless, the program appears to be rapidly gathering momentum, and few Brazilian observers now doubt that it is destined to play a major role in their country's future.

## WHY ALCOHOL?

A number of factors account for the rapid emergence of alcohol as a high-priority ingredient in Brazil's energy planning—not least that country's extensive prior experience with alcohol-gasoline blends as motor fuels. But three other factors stand out as having been of paramount importance. One was the demonstration that ethyl alcohol (ethanol) is superior to gasoline as a motor fuel, delivering liter for liter as much power with much less pollution in a properly tuned engine. A second was the realization that the manufacture of alcohol need not depend solely on sugarcane, which requires relatively good soils, but could ultimately use the far larger potential of manioc, or cassava, a root crop that grows in all parts of the country and for which Brazil is already the world's largest producer. A third and politically decisive factor was the role played by President Geisel in establishing a national program to exploit what is now widely described as Brazil's "fuel of the future."

The rapid establishment of an ambitious alcohol plan is apparently due in large part to Geisel's previous experience. Before becoming President he headed Brazil's national oil company, Petrobras, and he is described as uncommonly knowledgeable about energy matters for a national leader. In 1975 he stopped at a newly founded laboratory investigating alcohol as a motor fuel and was fascinated by the experimental results. He is said to have quickly grasped the possibilities, and a few months later a national alcohol program was established.

## LONG BLENDED WITH GASOLINE

Using alcohol as a fuel for automobiles actually has a long history in Brazil, dating

Dane Page, Photo Researchers

Brazil has abundant land, water, and cheap labor to grow the sugarcane and manioc necessary to produce the quantities of alcohol needed as a fuel. Here a sugarcane cutter is preparing to deliver cane to a mill for processing.

back to the 1920s. At that time the effort consisted of a few experimental vehicles, including one driven from Rio de Janeiro to São Paulo and back on pure ethanol. By the 1930s it was legal in Brazil to blend alcohol with gasoline, but really large-scale use did not begin until the late 1940s. Then, in an attempt to make the sugar industry more competitive, Petrobras agreed to purchase the growing quantities of alcohol produced as a by-product of sugar refining and blend it as a minor constituent in essentially all gasoline sold in Brazil. Depending on the region of the country, the alcohol content of Brazilian gasoline has ranged between 2 and 8 per cent in recent years—a level for which no adjustments to automobile engines are required.

## CLEAN, FLEXIBLE FUEL

Following the sharp rise in international oil prices that began in 1973, Brazil began a research effort to explore the possibility of blending much higher percentages of alcohol in gasoline and of burning pure alcohol. A

Carl Frank, Photo Researchers

São Paulo and other Brazilian cities have serious air pollution problems, caused largely by emissions from automobiles. An alcohol engine dramatically lowers the amount of pollutants emitted.

principal figure in the ethanol utilization effort has been Urbano Ernesto Stumpf, an aeronautical engineer who had devoted years to exploring the properties of alcohol as a fuel.

Stumpf and his colleagues were rapidly able to show that ethyl alcohol, despite its low heat content compared to gasoline, is a competitive fuel when burned in a properly designed engine. One reason for this is that an alcohol engine ideally operates at a higher compression ratio than a gasoline engine. Stumpf's data indicate that, with appropriate engines, pure alcohol delivers 18 per cent more power per liter than gasoline and is consumed at a rate between 15 and 20 per cent higher. The two factors effectively cancel, leaving neither fuel with a clear advantage from an energy standpoint.

Moreover, because an alcohol engine can be tuned to run much leaner than a gasoline-burning motor, the fuel is more completely combusted, giving alcohol a slight practical edge in the kilometers-per-liter figures. An alcohol engine also dramatically lowers the amount of pollutants emitted—by as much as 50 per cent for carbon monoxide and oxides of nitrogen. Since alcohol does not contain hydrocarbons and does not need tetraethyl lead additives to boost its octane, emissions of these substances are eliminated altogether.

Stumpf has also shown that alcohol is a far more flexible fuel than gasoline, since it can be used (although less efficiently) in motors designed for gasoline and can be blended with gasoline in proportions as high as 20 per cent with no adjustment to ordinary automobile engines. Alcohol can also be burned in a 50-50 mixture with diesel fuel in truck and bus engines through use of an ingenious double-carburetion system and seems to be an ideal turbine fuel for use in electric generating plants. To illustrate these virtues, the Brazilian Commerce Ministry equipped three automobiles to run on hydrated alcohol (95 per cent alcohol and 5 per cent water) and toured them all over Brazil, accumulating more than 100,000 kilometers of use in 1976.

The publicity stunt and the research data behind it have attracted considerable attention in Brazil and eliminated or at least muted the initial skepticism of automobile manufacturers. Last November, for example, the supervisor of motor engineering for Chrysler-Brazil announced that the company was demonstrating a high-compression engine suitable for pure alcohol. He also said that existing Chrysler motors could operate with up to 20 per cent alcohol without retuning.

Petrobras is reported to have been conducting large-scale tests of a 20 per cent alcohol-gasoline blend by the simple means of increasing the admixture in the gasoline delivered to particular localities. The city of São Paulo, where air pollution is a serious problem, is planning to test a 300-car fleet operating on pure alcohol this year.

PRODUCING THE ALCOHOL

Producing enough alcohol to make a major contribution to Brazil's energy supply is a more difficult problem. Some 800,000,-000 liters (more than 200,000,000 gallons) of alcohol are now produced annually from sugarcane, and the technology and economics of the distilling process are well established. Cane production can clearly be expanded and all but two of the proposed new distilleries are to be based on cane. If they are funded, they will nearly triple the current output of alcohol. But cane can be grown in only a few parts of Brazil, and much of the ideal land is already under cultivation. Therefore a 50-fold increase in alcohol production—which would be required to essentially eliminate oil imports—could probably not be based on cane. Cane, moreover, is a seasonal crop with a harvesting period of at best 160 days and, once cut, must be quickly processed before the sugar content degrades. The distilleries would thus stand idle more than half the year.

Hopes for really large-scale production of alcohol seem accordingly to rest on manioc. With an estimated 2,000,000 hectares (almost 5,000,000 acres) already under cultivation, largely for food, manioc is already a major crop in Brazil. The root of the plant contains between 20 and 40 per cent starch, depending on the variety, and it is from this material that alcohol is made.

Commercial production of the enzymes needed to convert the starch into alcohol has begun, and Petrobras has built a pioneer manioc distillery.

Large-scale production of alcohol from manioc remains in the future, however. Manioc is now grown almost exclusively in backyard plots and the agricultural structure for commercial cultivation will have to be built from scratch. Government officials argue that this is an advantage, since modern techniques for both cultivation and distillation can be introduced from the start. Nonetheless, skepticism abounds among Brazilian observers not directly connected with the alcohol program. Cane distilleries are often self-sufficient in energy, generating heat and electricity by burning the fibrous residue of the cane. Manioc residues have too high a water content to burn, however, and so an additional energy source will be needed to operate the distilleries.

More crucial to the ultimate feasibility of obtaining alcohol from manioc is the question of the net energy output from this crop when fertilizers and other energy-intensive inputs of large-scale cultivation and production are included in the balance. No

Gasoline stations in Brazil, like this one in Rio de Janeiro, may soon be selling gasoline-alcohol blends in which the alcohol content is 20 per cent or higher. Blends with 2 to 8 per cent alcohol are already widely available throughout the country.

detailed assessment of this balance has yet been published and, although government officials assert that making alcohol from manioc is feasible, the subject is hotly debated by Brazilian energy scientists.

## HOW MUCH IS NEEDED

Officials of the national program estimate that about 4,000,000,000 liters (approximately 1,000,000,000 gallons) of alcohol per year will be required to substitute for 20 per cent of gasoline consumption by the early 1980s. This level of production would require either 1,300,000 hectares (3,200,000 acres) of cane or between 1,000,000 and 2,000,000 hectares (2,500,000 and 5,000,000 acres) of manioc. The prospect of opening this amount of land to a new crop does not seem insuperable to the planners, however. There is plenty of readily accessible arable land in Brazil and an abundance of cheap agricultural labor.

As a result of the cheap labor and high gasoline taxes, alcohol is already competitive with petroleum products: it sells for about $1 per gallon, a price fixed by the government, compared to $1.50 per gallon for gasoline. Despite their inefficiencies, existing distil-

Starch, from sugarcane or manioc, is converted into alcohol through the action of enzymes. The Brazilian government and private enterprise will have to provide the facilities for large-scale commercial production of the necessary enzymes and for distilling equipment if Brazil is to find alcohol the answer to its energy crisis.

Manchette, Pictorial Parade

leries operate profitably under these conditions. To stimulate production even further under the alcohol program, new distilleries can be financed with government loans at low interest rates, and Petrobras guarantees that it will buy all alcohol delivered to it.

## BROAD IMPACT ON BRAZIL

The alcohol program seems likely to have an unusually broad impact on Brazil. In addition to providing what is potentially a major and inexhaustible source of energy and reducing the disastrous economic effects of importing foreign oil, it may have equally profound effects in other areas. Even a partial switch from gasoline to alcohol could substantially reduce the air pollution that in large Brazilian cities is already a substantial health hazard.

The alcohol program is also expected to create between 25,000 and 1,000,000 new jobs, primarily agricultural, in coming years. The availability of jobs in rural areas will, it is hoped, help to slow the migration to the cities that is overwhelming Brazil's major urban areas.

The proliferation of distilleries is also expected to stimulate other industries. A complete chemical industry based on alcohol rather than oil could, for example, be developed.

National self-confidence would also be bolstered. The psychological impact of successfully developing a Brazilian solution instead of copying an imported model would be enormous. Brazil would stand to gain substantial international prestige from securing its energy independence, not to mention a market for its alcohol expertise in other energy-poor but land-rich tropical countries. Finally, many scientists believe that the success of the alcohol program would establish the value of research to Brazilian industry.

## TOO SOON TO JUDGE

Despite its enormous potential, it is too early to judge the alcohol program a certain success. It requires, for example, a degree of cooperation among several different government ministries, and delays in approving financing for new distilleries have given rise to concern. There is also thought to be some opposition by entrenched and powerful economic interests.

Although alcohol forces clearly seem to have won at least some of the initial battles, the program has some way to go before it can significantly contribute to Brazil's energy supplies. But the Brazilian alcohol venture is just beginning, its potential is enormous, and it may yet become a model for an energy-hungry, and increasingly oil-poor world □

 SELECTED READINGS

"Methanol conversion for your car?" by E. F. Lindsley. *Popular Science,* August 1977.

"They turn to alcohol to cut oil imports." *Farmers Journal,* January 1977.

"We've been asked about using alcohol as fuel for automobiles." *U.S. News & World Report,* June 16, 1978.

# SHELTERBELTS

## by Fred J. Nisbet

TOO few homeowners in many areas, including the northeastern United States, have given much thought to shelterbelts and windbreaks. As energy problems in the United States and elsewhere worsen, it is time to change our way of thinking. It is surprising what screens of plants can do to save fuel and still keep us comfortable.

We know of their value and abundant use in the U.S. Great Plains, where, for the survival of both people and animals, it has been necessary to temper the frigid winter winds. In addition, plant screens trap enough snow to supplement the scant rainfall (30 to 35 centimeters, or 12 to 14 inches, per year) that falls there and make a few crops, especially winter wheat, feasible.

Up to the present, most research on the subject of shelterbelts has been conducted on the Great Plains and on the Soviet steppes, under conditions quite dissimilar from those that prevail in other areas such as the northeastern United States. Despite all the unknowns, however, one fact shines through: wind barriers can have a significant fuel-saving effect in many regions.

One favorable factor in the U.S. Northeast is plentiful rainfall: there is usually 85 to 110 centimeters (approximately 35 to 45 inches) a year. This not only speeds the growth of the plants but also allows the use of many plants that are more effective, more attractive, and longer-lived than those that are tough enough to withstand harsher conditions.

Another factor is terrain. Although the U.S. Northeast has areas where the winds are concentrated and sweep down with considerable fury, there is not, for the most part, wide-open, flat country where no natural protection is afforded.

### SAVING FUEL

How much fuel can be saved by planting wind barriers depends on many factors, and research on the subject is so new and complex that no one answer can be given. But in general terms, if a good wind shelter is raised between your house and the prevailing winter winds, you can expect an overall reduction of fuel needs of about 12 to 15 per cent. If, on the other hand, you have shelters on two sides (pick the worst two in your locality), the savings can soar to 25 to 30 per cent. Interestingly, shelters on the northeast side of the house seldom increase the savings much further, unless the house is on or near the coast. For special problems of wind protection, get in touch with your local Soil Conservation Agent, the county foreman of your highway department, or the U.S. Army Cold Regions Research and Engineering Laboratory, in Hanover, New Hampshire.

Let us take an example. If you raise a

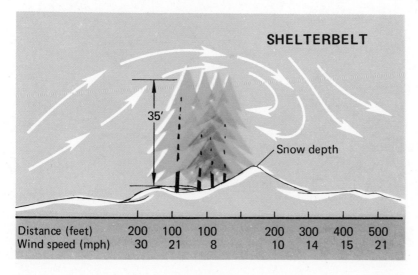

**SHELTERBELT**

35'

Snow depth

This simplified drawing shows the sheltering effect of a windbreak. Wind speed is considerably lower on the leeward side of the shelter.

| Distance (feet) | 200 | 100 | 100 | | 200 | 300 | 400 | 500 |
|---|---|---|---|---|---|---|---|---|
| Wind speed (mph) | 30 | 21 | 8 | | 10 | 14 | 15 | 21 |

shelter directly against the prevailing winter wind, the modifying effect will be greatest on the shelter's lee side up to three to five times the height of the barrier. Obviously, the protected distance increases as the plants grow. The effect will be moderate from ten to thirteen times the height of the shelter and will be detectable up to twenty times the height of the barrier.

The desired density in your shelter is 50 per cent, which will reduce for a distance of approximately three times the height of the barrier a 25-kilometer per hour wind to about 8 kilometers per hour, or a 15 mile per hour wind to a 5 mile per hour wind. At −1° Celsius (30° Fahrenheit) this will amount to a fuel saving of about 20 per cent; at −18° Celsius (0° Fahrenheit) the saving would be about 25 per cent.

## SCREEN DENSITY

The density of the screen requires a bit of explanation. Wind shelters are effective not because they stop winds, but because they slow them down. A screen with a density of less than 50 per cent does not give maximum benefit. On the other hand, greater densities, which block rather than filter the wind, create turbulence on the lee side of the barrier. In fact, a solid board fence will create much higher velocities in the range of one to five times the height of the barrier than will exist over an open field and can

often cause enough "swirl" to be destructive.

A point often overlooked is that a good windbreak decreases the wind velocity appreciably for two to three times the height of the barrier on the windward side of the barrier as well. Because of this effect, snowdrifts on the windward side will be fewer than on the lee. This can be a fine way of diverting heavy snow accumulation from well-traveled areas. But if your shelter is on your property line, it most certainly could cause strained relations with your windward-side neighbor, especially if the drift zone includes his driveway. Fuel-cost reductions from this effect are apt to be on the slim side, in any event.

## STAGGER THE PLANTS

A typical shelterbelt consists of two, or sometimes three, rows of trees, usually with the taller ones on the windward side. Two or even three rows of fairly large, dense shrubs are then placed on the windward side of the trees. If sufficient space is available, a row of tall shrubs is placed on the lee side as well. Staggering the plants in adjoining rows increases the efficiency of the planting as a windbreak.

If there is not enough space for such a wide planting, you can use a windbreak that consists of only two rows of trees. This is less efficient but far better than nothing. The rows are planted close together, trees staggered in the rows.

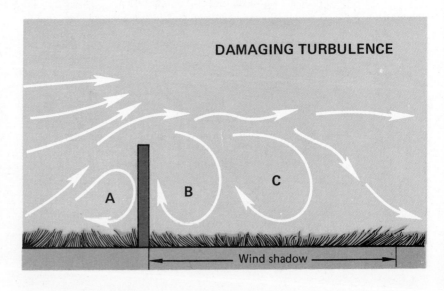

**DAMAGING TURBULENCE**

The turbulence that develops on both sides of a solid barrier may well create wind problems instead of solving them. The turbulence, or motion, is characterized by relatively large eddies. A is a pressure eddy; B, a suction eddy; and C a turbulence occurring in the wake of the eddies.

A    B    C

Wind shadow

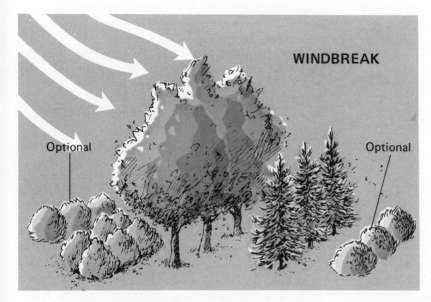

**WINDBREAK**

Optional

Optional

Drawing showing a typical windbreak using trees and shrubs of varying heights.

## EVERGREENS THE BEST

Evergreens are most efficient in slowing winds, especially during the winter when they are needed most. Unfortunately, they are much slower growing than many deciduous trees, which are most effective—and least needed—when in full leaf. Because of this, many windbreaks are planted with evergreens on the lee side and faster-growing deciduous varieties on the other. As the evergreens gain sufficient size, the deciduous row is cut out. The two-row protection can be salvaged to some extent by replacing the cut trees with dense shrubs that grow fairly high, or other evergreen trees. These plants must be strong-growing varieties as they will have to compete with the established trees. They will need extra attention in watering, fertilizing, and weed control for two or three years until they are well enough established to make it on their own. A mulch is a big help here.

Russian olive is one of my favorites if shrubs are indicated, but if trees are to be used it is hard to beat the better pines. If space is available, grow the replacement evergreens somewhere nearby while the main windbreak is becoming established. When the fast-growing trees are cut, the replacements will be quite large. An experienced backhoe operator can dig the holes and move the balled replacements very quickly—burlapping is not necessary for such a short, quick move.

Choosing the deciduous trees must be a compromise. The faster-growing varieties, to a great extent, have more brittle wood, increasing the danger of damage by wind, ice, or snow. This is especially true of poplars and willows. Red maple, though, is relatively fast growing and very strong, while sugar maples and oaks are too slow growing to consider.

## PLANTING

In first planting a windbreak, the rows must be properly spaced so that the evergreens can attain an effective size without crowding from the deciduous trees; otherwise the lower branches will die. If this happens, the actual wind velocity under the remaining branches will be greater than that in open fields, and the desired effect will be lost. Spruces are especially bad in this respect, as they often lose their lower branches as they grow older. Pines and red cedar are much better choices. When loss of lower branches is first seen it can be minimized by heavy pruning of the deciduous trees on the side facing the evergreens. Columnar trees reduce this problem; even Lombardy poplars may be used, in spite of their other faults.

Spacings between trees or shrubs in a

wind barrier are much closer than for ornamental plantings, but those who suggest planting trees 1.2 to 1.8 meters (4 to 6 feet) apart in rows only 90 to 120 centimeters (3 to 4 feet) apart are overdoing it. The rows in a shelterbelt should be at least 1.5 to 2 meters (5 to 7 feet) apart.

Even under the best of circumstances, plant screens take a back seat to fiber glass or rock wool insulation in the walls of your house: they take time to become effective. But there are ways of reducing this time lag. First, start with the largest plants you can afford. State forestry nurseries have plenty of very cheap plants, but they are generally quite small. Larger plants from commercial

# TREES FOR WINDBREAKS

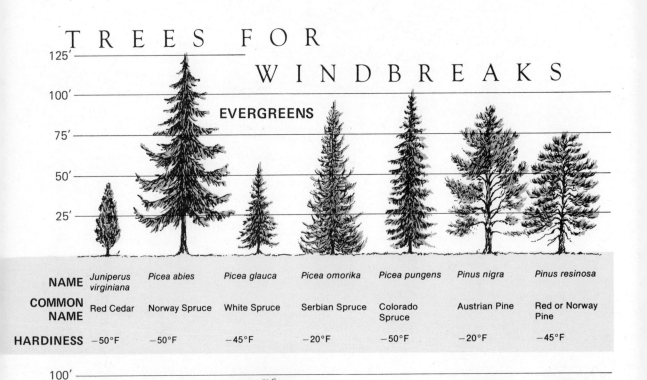

## EVERGREENS

| NAME | *Juniperus virginiana* | *Picea abies* | *Picea glauca* | *Picea omorika* | *Picea pungens* | *Pinus nigra* | *Pinus resinosa* |
|---|---|---|---|---|---|---|---|
| COMMON NAME | Red Cedar | Norway Spruce | White Spruce | Serbian Spruce | Colorado Spruce | Austrian Pine | Red or Norway Pine |
| HARDINESS | −50°F | −50°F | −45°F | −20°F | −50°F | −20°F | −45°F |

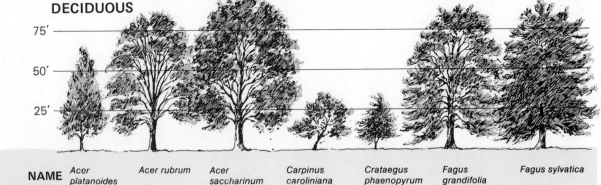

## DECIDUOUS

| NAME | *Acer platanoides* | *Acer rubrum* | *Acer saccharinum* | *Carpinus caroliniana* | *Crataegus phaenopyrum* | *Fagus grandifolia* | *Fagus sylvatica* |
|---|---|---|---|---|---|---|---|
| COMMON NAME | Norway Maple | Red Maple | Sugar Maple | American Hornbeam | Washington Hawthorn | American Beech | European Beech |
| HARDINESS | −35°F | −35°F | −35°F | −45°F | −20°F | −35°F | −20°F |

nurseries cost more but can cut years from your program. If you are now living in your home year round, your budget will be the limiting factor. If you have a summer home to which you expect to retire in a few years, you can make substantial savings by starting with smaller (and cheaper) plants.

Either way, give your plant screens plenty of attention so that they will attain maximum growth. Plant trees or shrubs in large holes with some superphosphate dug into the bottom. Then fill around the roots with a combination of equal parts of good topsoil, compost or peat moss, and sharp sand. Firm this with your fingers until there are no air holes left. Then water well and add

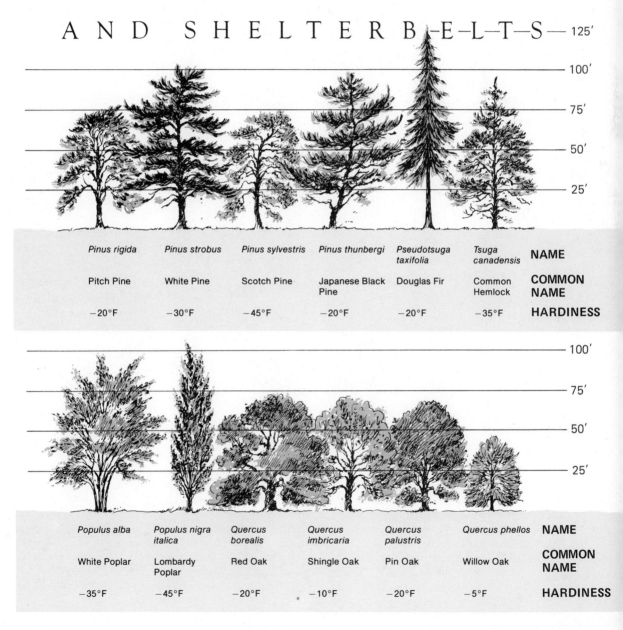

A N D   S H E L T E R B–E–L–T–S— 125′

| *Pinus rigida* | *Pinus strobus* | *Pinus sylvestris* | *Pinus thunbergi* | *Pseudotsuga taxifolia* | *Tsuga canadensis* | **NAME** |
|---|---|---|---|---|---|---|
| Pitch Pine | White Pine | Scotch Pine | Japanese Black Pine | Douglas Fir | Common Hemlock | **COMMON NAME** |
| −20°F | −30°F | −45°F | −20°F | −20°F | −35°F | **HARDINESS** |

| *Populus alba* | *Populus nigra italica* | *Quercus borealis* | *Quercus imbricaria* | *Quercus palustris* | *Quercus phellos* | **NAME** |
|---|---|---|---|---|---|---|
| White Poplar | Lombardy Poplar | Red Oak | Shingle Oak | Pin Oak | Willow Oak | **COMMON NAME** |
| −35°F | −45°F | −20°F | −10°F | −20°F | −5°F | **HARDINESS** |

# SHRUBS FOR SHELTERBELTS

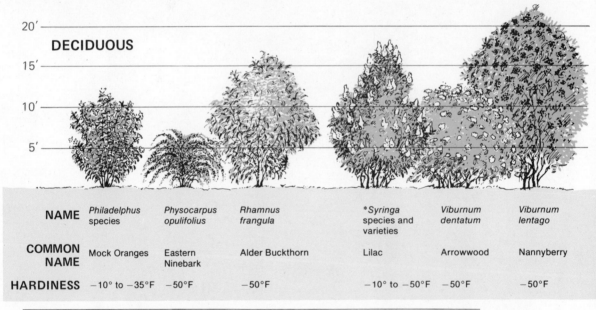

| | | | | | | |
|---|---|---|---|---|---|---|
| **EVERGREENS** | | | | | | |
| **NAME** | *Elaeagnus angustifolia* | *\*Juniperus chinensis* | *Juniperus communis* | *\*Taxus cuspidata* | *Taxus media* | *\*Thuja occidentalis* |
| **COMMON NAME** | Russian Olive | Juniper varieties | Common Juniper | Japanese Yew | Anglo-Japanese Yew | Shrubby American Arborvitaes |
| **HARDINESS** | −45°F | −15° to −20°F | −50°F | −20°F | −20°F | −20°F |

| | | | | | | |
|---|---|---|---|---|---|---|
| **DECIDUOUS** | | | | | | |
| **NAME** | *Philadelphus species* | *Physocarpus opulifolius* | *Rhamnus frangula* | *\*Syringa species and varieties* | *Viburnum dentatum* | *Viburnum lentago* |
| **COMMON NAME** | Mock Oranges | Eastern Ninebark | Alder Buckthorn | Lilac | Arrowwood | Nannyberry |
| **HARDINESS** | −10° to −35°F | −50°F | −50°F | −10° to −50°F | −50°F | −50°F |

\*Many fine varieties with a range of color and shape are available. Ask nurseries in your area for recommendations.

some soluble fertilizer. A good, fluffy mulch is always a help in getting the plants growing rapidly and keeping them in good shape later. Prune heavily the first few years to make the plants bushy at the base.

If rainfall doesn't average 2 or 3 centimeters (about 1 inch) a week, water thoroughly once a week. After the plants have made some root growth—in about six weeks or so—fertilize lightly. Fertilize again about six weeks later. Foliar fertilizers can be used until September in most areas, especially if they are not too high in nitrogen.

One final word on pruning. Deciduous plants and scaly-leaved evergreens are normally pruned in late winter or just as growth

# O R  G A P S  I N
# W I N D B R E A K S

**DECIDUOUS**

| | | | | | | |
|---|---|---|---|---|---|---|
| *Acanthopanax sieboldianus* | *Aronia arbutifolia* | *Berberis thunbergii* | *Cornus mas* | *\*Ligustrum* species | *\*Lonicera* species | **NAME** |
| Five-leaved Aralia | Black Chokeberry | Japanese Barberry | Cornelian Cherry | Privets | Honeysuckles | **COMMON NAME** |
| −20°F | −20°F | −20°F | −20°F | −20° to −35°F | −20° to −45°F | **HARDINESS** |

Grant Heilman

A dense cluster of trees and shrubs, of various heights, helps to protect this homesite from the chill Colorado winds.

starts. Needle-leaved evergreens, which have a single terminal leader, should not be pruned until the new "candles" are half to two-thirds grown, depending on how close you wish the whorls of growth to be.

If you make good selections for your area, get strong, healthy plants, and give them the best of care, your savings in fuel will eventually pay off and you will be more comfortable in the meantime□

### SELECTED READINGS

"Shelterbelts: farmer's friend or foe?" by L. Palmer. *Farmer's Journal*, February 1977.

*Windbreaks and shelterbelts* by World Meteorological Organization. Unipub, 1964.

Many nations are choosing nuclear power as an energy source. At right, a nuclear power plant in Switzerland, one of several Swiss plants that supply a total of 18 per cent of that country's electric power needs.

General Electric

# IS THE NUCLEAR POWER DREAM FADING?

## by David F. Salisbury

AFTER two decades of loudly touted growth, the giant nuclear-power industry is grinding to a halt.

Since President Eisenhower's Atoms for Peace program provided the impetus for commercializing atomic power, the nuclear industry has steadily grown until today it has assets approaching $100,000,000,000 and more than 300,000 employees. In 1977 its 67 operating reactors churned out more electricity than U.S. hydroelectric dams.

But economic and environmental obstacles now threaten to block further expansion. Orders from utility companies for new nuclear-power plants are plummeting. Since 1975, orders have been running at three or four annually, far short of the 16 new plants the industry says it needs to sustain business.

### A POST-EMBARGO QUIRK

Ironically, the turbulent energy economics since the 1973 Arab oil embargo are primarily responsible for this stagnation. While the rising price of petroleum would

seem to favor the nuclear option, the nation's utilities have been financially weakened, and raising enough capital to build a large power plant of any type is more difficult now than it used to be.

The recent recession also saw a significant drop in demand for electricity. As a result, reserve generating capacity skyrocketed from 22.5 per cent in 1970 to almost 45 per cent in 1976—and the utilities' need for new plants thus decreased.

With economic recovery, demand for electricity has begun creeping up again, drawing on utilities' reserve capacities, which, according to U.S. government estimates, will drop below 25 per cent by 1980— prompting another round of power-plant buying.

In the meantime, manufacturers of reactors and their components face a difficult few years. Westinghouse, which dominates the industry, has a backlog of orders that will enable it to keep going for several years. However, analysts feel that a prolonged period of financial losses would force at least one of the four U.S. reactormakers out of business.

## ENVIRONMENTAL OBJECTIONS

The industry's problems are not solely the result of economic pressures. Opponents of nuclear power have waged well-organized campaigns to draw attention to social and environmental costs: the dangers of accidental leakages of radiation and problems of storing and disposing of toxic atomic wastes. Adversaries also argue that energy conservation, increased reliance on coal, and advanced techniques such as generating electricity on site and using waste heat for other purposes can eliminate the need for more nuclear-power plants.

The Department of Energy, however, sides with the advocates of nuclear power on this issue. Assistant department administrator Jack O'Leary estimates that failure to revitalize the nuclear option could cost the United States an added 10,000,000 barrels of imported oil per day in the year 2000.

Although nuclear power continues to dominate federal energy funding, it does not do so to the same extent as has been true in the past. This year, nuclear programs account for 50 per cent of the Department of Energy's spending. The proposed Carter budget would pare this to 43 per cent for 1979.

The most dramatic change in emphasis in the nuclear program continues to be President Carter's attempts to phase out the Clinch River breeder reactor project. Funding, for nonbreeder nuclear research, in contrast, would increase 22 per cent. A higher priority is given to nuclear waste storage efforts and study of alternative fuel cycles.

Also, intervention by opponents of nuclear power, especially during the expensive five-year construction period, can double the cost of a nuclear reactor, utility executives say.

Changes in federal requirements and standards—many of which entail extremely costly alterations—also represent a bottomless pit for many utilities with tight finances. Although the Carter administration has drafted licensing reform legislation, industry

Rochester Gas and Electric Corp.

Technicians load nuclear fuel rods into a reactor. The storage and disposal of spent, but still hazardous, fuel rods is one of the problems associated with nuclear power.

spokesmen claim it has been seriously weakened by nuclear critics within the executive branch.

## UNCERTAINTIES HURT

Uncertainties in uranium supplies and the handling of burned-up fuel by the government also increase utilities' reluctance to go nuclear.

"If government policies were just predictable there would be a totally different atmosphere," Francis M. Stazesky of Boston Edison says.

In view of the faltering growth of the nuclear power industry, the crucial question is whether alternative sources of electricity can be developed fast enough and whether conservation efforts prove effective in reducing U.S. dependence on foreign petroleum.

But as David Rose, a professor of nuclear engineering at the Massachusetts Institute of Technology, observes, many of nuclear energy's problems have been "self-inflicted." As examples, he cites lackadaisical efforts to come up with a satisfactory method to dispose of nuclear wastes and the Atomic Energy Commission's de-emphasis of safety research in the 1960s.

Major issues facing the nuclear power industry include breeder reactors, uranium supplies, reprocessing, and waste disposal.

ENERGY **183**

U.S. Dept. of Energy

A breeder reactor, such as this one in Idaho, produces, or "breeds," more nuclear fuel than it consumes. Such reactors can double their fuel supply every 10 years.

## BREEDER REACTOR

The controversial "breeder" reactor can squeeze 30 times the energy out of uranium that ordinary reactors can. It does this by transmuting the most abundant form of uranium, which does not "burn" in a reactor core, into plutonium, which will burn.

However, the prospect of producing, shipping, and processing large amounts of plutonium—which is highly toxic and inflammable, and the stuff from which atomic bombs are made—raises serious safety questions.

To strengthen international nonproliferation efforts, and backed by an assessment that there is still time before a decision must be made to develop the breeder, President Carter has opposed a pilot plant that would have been built in Tennessee. There is still a chance, however, that Congress will authorize $80 million to keep the project alive and on the licensing path.

The Clinch River pilot plant in Tennessee is one type of breeder. It converts uranium into plutonium with "fast" neutrons and uses liquid sodium to carry away the heat. This type of breeder is also being developed in the Soviet Union, France, and Great Britain.

Other breeder technologies, rejected by the earlier Atomic Energy Commission, now are being reconsidered by the Department of Energy. One concept is a reactor that transmutes thorium into a fissionable form of uranium. Unlike plutonium, this uranium gives off lethal doses of radiation, making it harder to steal and easier to trace. Such a reactor is more difficult to engineer and the cost and hazards of handling the fuel are great.

Another type of reactor, under study at Oak Ridge National Laboratory, would dissolve nuclear fuel in molten salt. In this case, plutonium would be produced but it would be "burned" right in the reactor vessel. The main problem with this concept is finding the proper materials to contain this extremely radioactive solution.

Oak Ridge scientists have developed alloys that they think can contain the mixture, but these have not been produced in large quantities, nor have techniques for fabricating them been perfected.

All these alternative breeder concepts would require at least 25 years to develop, says Saul Levinson of the Electric Power Research Institute. But whether there is time to develop such concepts—indeed, whether breeder technology is needed or not—depends in large measure on the rate of growth of electric demand and the size of U.S. uranium reserves.

## U.S. URANIUM SUPPLIES

The current status of U.S. uranium is "like an overly ambitious first novel," according to one person knowledgeable in the field. It "has so many subplots that even a close observer has trouble following the story line."

Despite extensive prospecting, there is an extremely wide spectrum of opinion on how much recoverable domestic uranium ore exists. National Academy of Science geologists have concluded that there may be serious supply problems by the mid-1980s. But using the same basic facts, a report issued by the Ford Foundation finds that U.S. uranium supplies "will probably be adequate well into the next century."

The government is conducting a national survey to evaluate domestic reserves better. Since 1975, official estimates of the uranium oxide recoverable at a cost of about $30 per kilogram ($15 per pound) have shrunk by 21 per cent. But the Energy Department now is including uranium that can be mined at $100 a kilogram (about $50 a pound), three times the present price, so total reserve figures have increased from 650,000 to 750,000 metric tons.

At the same time, progressive trimming of federal forecasts of nuclear energy growth has lead to lower estimates of uranium requirements. Taking these lower requirements together with estimates of uranium available at higher prices helps the administration to argue that sufficient uranium will be available for some time and thus that breeder development can be delayed.

## REPROCESSING

Next to each nuclear reactor core there is a "swimming pool" where burned up fuel elements are stored. In the original scheme of things, these pools were intended as temporary storage facilities for spent fuel bundles. The water cools the hot fuel and shields workers from its lethal radioactivity until it dies down in intensity.

After a few years, the fuel was to be sent to a reprocessing plant where the valuable uranium and plutonium were to be separated from the radioactive wastes and mixed into fresh fuel. Experiments to test fuel made of mixed uranium and plutonium were halted by court order in 1975. First President Ford and now President Carter decided to defer reprocessing indefinitely because the plutonium it purifies might be used to make clandestine atomic bombs.

In the last 20 years spent fuel has been piling up in the on-site pools. It now has reached a point where a number of plants must find somewhere to unload their old fuel—or shut down.

The administration has offered to take spent fuel off utilities' hands, but the government intends to charge a fee to cover the costs. Preliminary estimates put this figure at 1/40th of the cost of the electricity the fuel produces.

Utilities that have considered the uranium and plutonium in their old fuel a valu-

This "tank farm" for the storage of radioactive wastes is being "mined" for its valuable radioisotopes that can be reprocessed for use in a variety of research and industrial projects.

able asset—not a financial liability—are not happy with this offer. The industry had hoped that this material would be reprocessed and recycled, which would have meant more efficient use of the energy in uranium and decreased fuel costs. It appears the government is leaning toward a "throwaway" fuel cycle, where burned-up fuel will simply be disposed of.

Two other possibilities also are being studied. One involves feeding old fuel from U.S.-designed reactors to Canadian reactors, which do not require enriched fuel. This might produce 50 per cent more energy, and would involve redesigning fuel elements in both types of reactors to be compatible, or reshaping the highly radioactive spent U.S. fuel elements to fit the Canadian configuration.

The other alternative is called co-processing. As in reprocessing, uranium and plutonium would be chemically removed from the spent fuel. They would not be separated, however, before being mixed into fresh fuel.

## WASTE DISPOSAL

In a number of states where federal government officials have shown interest in storing the radioactive byproducts of military or commercial activities, they have

A portion of an abandoned underground salt mine near Lyons, Kansas, was tested as a possible storage area for high-level radioactive wastes. Since salt formations are stable for long periods of time, they have been suggested as possible storage areas for radioactive materials, but the suggestion has not been implemented.

U.S. Dept. of Energy

been told in no uncertain terms that nuclear wastes are not welcome. This has occurred in Michigan, Louisiana, South Dakota, South Carolina, and Georgia.

Only three states, New Mexico, Washington, and Nevada, which have had major nuclear facilities for a number of years, appear receptive to the idea. Public hearings in New Mexico on a proposed pilot storage facility have generated no significant opposition, according to officials at Sandia Laboratories who are managing the program.

Federal efforts to come up with a satisfactory solution to the problem of radioactive wastes are centered at a site 40 kilometers (25 miles) from Carlsbad, New Mexico. Some 600 meters (2,000 feet) below the surface of the site are thick layers of salt. The idea is to carve out underground chambers for storage of high- and intermediate-level nuclear wastes.

Placing radioactive wastes in salt formations was proposed in the 1950s by a National Academy of Science review committee. The formations are stable over very long periods of time and would seem to be an appropriate place to put waste that will be radioactive for thousands of years. But the recommendation was soon rejected as being unduly expensive.

A draft environmental-impact statement on the pilot waste storage plant is scheduled for completion in 1978. If all goes according to plans, the plant should accept nuclear waste in the mid-1980s.

The first radioactive garbage the facility handles probably will come from the Hanford Reservation in Washington state, where more than half of the wastes generated by the weapons program are stored. In September 1977 the Department of Energy estimated that the cost of processing and shipping all the Hanford waste to an off-site repository could run as high as $27,000,000,000.

Many experts think that waste from the military program substantially outweighs that which commercial nuclear reactors have produced so far. But according to a recent analysis by Princeton University scientists, this is true only if the total volume of the waste is considered, since power-plant wastes are 100 times more concentrated, they say. So, in terms of total radioactivity, commercial wastes already are comparable to those generated by the weapons program □

📖 SELECTED READINGS

"Great nuclear power debate" by J. H. Douglas. *Science News*, February 21, 1976.
"Nuclear power debate: signing up the pros and cons" by P. M. Boffey. *Science*, April 9, 1976.
"Nuclear power—where do we go from here?" by P. W. Sturm. *Forbes*, May 15, 1977.
"Slowdown." *Scientific American*, March 1976.

A system of satellites beaming power collected from the sun to the earth is one possible answer to the increasing demand for energy. Each satellite, positioned so that it is always above the same spot on the earth's surface, could provide almost continuous power— and at a lower cost than land-based solar collectors.

Grumman Aerospace Corp.

# ENERGY FROM OUTER SPACE

## by Richard F. Dempewolff

THE year is 1999. You stand on a hillside looking southward at the night sky. Another glittering "star" has just been added to a growing line of them that soon will reach from horizon to horizon like a super Orion.

Each of these "stars" is a manmade satellite occupying about 5,700 hectares (22 square miles) of space. Each hovers in a geosynchronous orbit above the equator—that is, in an orbit that is in perfect time with the earth's rotation so that the satellite is always above the same spot on the earth's surface. Each of these "stars" beams power it collects from the sun to the earth, some 10,000 megawatts of electricity—enough to power a city the size of New York. The power is picked up by huge rectennas and fed into a power grid.

### A DREAM?

Cloud nine dreams and schemes?

Not according to the people now involved in actual development of the mind-boggling concept. They all seem to agree that the technical difficulties involved—great though they may be—are not insoluble and

Artist's conception showing construction of a solar power satellite in low earth orbit. Cargo is carried into orbit by special launch vehicles and space shuttles.

that solar power satellites might be operational before the end of the century.

S. V. Manson, U.S. National Aeronautics and Space Administration's (NASA's) manager of Satellite Power Systems, says that "Studies to date indicate that satellite power systems are potentially competitive economically with earth-based systems."

The idea of orbiting great solar collectors 35,700 kilometers (about 22,300 miles) in space, converting their gathered energy into electricity, and transmitting it earthward via microwave or laser, was suggested as early as 1968 by Dr. Peter Glaser of Arthur D. Little Company in Cambridge, Massachusetts. Reactions then were instant and skeptical. Today, all that has changed.

## TWO APPROACHES

Since Dr. Glaser first made his startling suggestion, design studies have been under way, and details of two separate approaches have been worked out meticulously.

One, developed by a group headed by the Grumman Aerospace Corporation and the Arthur D. Little Company, is the Solar Satellite Power System. Known as the SSPS, this approach uses a photovoltaic process in which solar cells convert sunlight directly to usable electric power in the same way they've provided power for nearly every spacecraft and satellite to date.

The other approach—"Powersat"—explored by NASA and Boeing Aerospace Corporation researchers, uses a thermal concentrator and heat engine system. This involves arrays of gigantic hexagonal bowl-shaped reflectors, each almost five kilometers (three miles) from rim to rim, that focus sunlight on a receiving cavity mounted high above the bowls. There the intense heat turns a fluid to steam and drives a mechanical turbogenerating system.

## WHY IN SPACE?

Why bother putting all that stuff in space when solar powerplants could just as well be located on sun-drenched deserts? The output of a solar collector in space is about six times what it would be at the best location on earth. A satellite in geosynchronous orbit is exposed to continuous sunlight more than 99 per cent of the time, and power could be beamed wherever it is needed. The only inactivity would involve minutes when the collectors would pass through earth's shadow.

## ABOARD AN SSPS

To comprehend even remotely the vastness of these gigantic space islands, you'd have to climb aboard one and look around. From one end of an SSPS, the view would reach out across a seemingly endless distance of glaring reflective corrugations, diminishing into star-studded blackness. Out there, other islands in the great energy archipelago would shine like links in a golden chain, disappearing where it curled behind earth's rim.

Activate your jet backpack and levitate yourself 30 meters (100 feet) or so above the surface of the vast solar panel, and you'll see that the station itself actually is made up of two rectangular panels. Each panel is about 5.5 kilometers (3.5 miles) long by 4.8 kilometers (3 miles) wide, and 180 meters (600 feet) deep. The panels are connected by a few main girders and a great mast. Located between the panels is the 800-meter (0.5-mile) disk of the adjustable microwave transmitting antenna.

Mounted on each huge panel, reflective ridges march away like waves, giving the panel the appearance of a shiny metal washboard. Oriented to face the sun in perpetuity, endless arrays of solar cells lie along the surface of each depression in the washboard. Slopes of the ridged corrugations are covered with reflectively coated sheet plastic. The solar cells are bathed in direct sunlight as well as the concentrated light that is focused on them by reflectors, more than doubling the solar energy impinging upon them.

Through a photovoltaic process, each solar cell converts the energy into direct electric current. The current flows through the metal frame of the space island and its mast to the huge movable antenna. There it is converted to microwave energy and is transmitted to a ground-based receiving rectenna. The rectenna reconverts it to electrical energy, changes it to alternating current, and feeds it to the power grids.

### ABOARD POWERSAT

Equally staggering is Boeing's "Powersat" space station, made up of four huge bowl-shaped solar concentrators, each with about 1,200 hectares (3,000 acres) of a reflective plastic film stretched over a light metal framework. Together they comprise a satellite cluster about 14 kilometers (9 miles) long, weighing 100,000 metric tons.

Sunlight is focused by each huge bowl into a "cavity absorber" centered above it on a spidery girder arrangement. Here, the concentrated heat is transferred to helium gas in a specially designed engine to drive turbogenerators. Waste heat, dumped into the deep-freeze of space by two huge radiator wings, completes the cycle. Electricity is routed through the framework to a transmitter at one end of the satellite. There it is converted to a microwave beam and directed to an earth-based rectenna.

### WHY MICROWAVE TRANSMISSION?

Microwaves are used to transmit the energy for several reasons: a microwave beam loses little energy in transmission; its power is

Grumman Aerospace Corp.

Artist's conception of a prototype Solar Satellite Power System that could be used to demonstrate energy transmission to earth and to develop space construction-technology.

generated at frequencies that preclude interference with other radio-frequency bands; the beam penetrates any weather factor; and lastly, it's safe. Other proposed transmitting agents like lasers or mirrors do not have all the advantages of microwaves.

### GIANT RECTENNAS

For both Powersat and SSPS, the receiving system would involve a giant rectenna sited either offshore or on low-value land near large metropolitan areas. The land-based rectennas would be elevated, allowing the land beneath to be farmed. Birds flying through the beam would be unharmed; air passengers would be shielded by the plane's metal skin. Since the rectenna will absorb more than 90 per cent of the energy, people working beneath the structure would be unaffected.

### SPACE FREIGHTERS

All very well, but how do you get an 18,-000,000 to 27,000,000 kilogram (40,000,000 to 60,000,000 pound) manmade satellite, a little larger than Manhattan Island, into orbit? Both the Powersat and SSPS concepts

NASA

Artist's concept of rectenna that would be used to receive microwave energy from orbiting power satellites.

call for a "Heavy Lift Launch Vehicle" (HLLV).

Plans for a reusable, low-cost "space freighter" capable of boosting 250 metric tons of material to low orbit have been made. The giant payloads of the space freighters would be delivered to a low earth-orbit assembly station, where several hundred workers would build the power satellite.

Once assembled in low orbit, electric rockets, drawing power from already operating solar generators, would propel each module to geosynchronous orbit. There, they'd be assembled into four-module clusters that are capable of pouring some 10,000 megawatts of energy into the power grids.

Proponents of solar-power satellites look to the U.S. Space Shuttle—due for operation in the early 1980s—as a transporter-to-orbit of materials for experimental modules. By using the Shuttle, 80-metric-ton payloads of basic material for a test prototype could be ferried to orbit, they note.

Later, a single-stage HLLV, with a 200-metric-ton capacity, would carry materials and manufacturing modules to low earth orbit for construction of the satellite.

## FLYING CRANES

Manufacturing and construction in space will call for pretty far-out equipment. For example, flying cranes powered by jet

thrusters and guided by operators in pressurized cabs will hold and manipulate structural elements, grabbing collapsed components and unfolding and positioning them for attachment to the huge frameworks that will support fields of solar cells.

Other vehicles will ride the horizontal and vertical members of the structure, with manipulating arms drawn up like gargantuan grasshopper legs, fitting and fastening components. Up top, beam crawlers will ride the open framework like railroad work cars, unrolling ribbons of reflective plastic.

Once built, the vast platform would be moved to stationary orbit with a gentle but steady push from an ion jet system.

## MAINTENANCE

Maintaining the space islands during their estimated 30-year useful life would be handled by small transient crews. The SSPS, having no moving parts, would need only occasional repairs and replacement of solar cell blankets. One plan calls for fabricating the cells in a triple layer of material. Every 10 years, the top layer would be peeled away to expose a fresh array. Maintenance crews handling that work, along with repair of meteoroid damage and other deterioration, would live in the work modules used by the construction workers.

Boeing's thermal engine concept, with its many moving parts, would see a constant bustle of activity. Rotating crews would live in cylindrical "hotels" located on the satellites' great structural arms.

## WOULD PAY OFF

Wouldn't the cost of this gigantic enterprise far outweigh the returns in energy? Most scientists who have studied the systems think it would pay off. Boeing scientists point out that six Powersats would fill all the present electrical needs for all of Japan. About 35 of them would provide the whole baseload for the entire United States.

"A program which adds one Powersat per year for 30 years would pay for itself if its electricity was sold at the point where it enters the nation's power grid for a price that is less than some producers get now for their electricity at the grid junction □

In the worst oil spill in history, the tanker L'amoco-Cadiz grounded on cliffs off the coast of Brest, France, creating an oil slick many kilometers long and intensifying research on ways to prevent and control oil spills in the future.

# THE ENVIRONMENT

## contents

# THE ENVIRONMENT

## review of the year

UPI

As part of a program to minimize the presence of toxic substances in the environment, technicians draw water samples to test. Analysis will reveal if water treatment programs are effective in purifying water.

James E. Carter came into office as President of the United States with a strong commitment toward the preservation of natural resources. In a comprehensive "Message on the Environment" to the U.S. Congress on May 23, 1977, he proposed actions to control pollution and protect health, wildlife, and other natural resources; preserve the national heritage; affirm the U.S. concern for the global environment; and improve implementation of environmental laws. By year's end, however, the results were somewhat disappointing. Congress enacted somewhat weakened strip-mining, air-pollution, and water-pollution measures but left for 1978 proposals to regulate offshore oil development, measures to protect non-game wildlife, and other programs. The President was rebuffed in his attempts to improve water-control projects. He was, however, able to choose the least damaging route for the transport of Alaska gas. At least part of the difficulty stemmed from uncertainties and delays in establishing a new energy department, in government reorganization plans, and in getting the new administration into motion.

**Toxic substances.** When the Toxic Substances Control Act (TOSCA) was passed in 1976, the federal government had, for the first time, a means for evaluating, assembling, and, where needed, controlling the development, production, and marketing of the ever-increasing number of manmade chemicals. TOSCA enables the government to stop production of chemicals that may present unreasonable risk to human health or to the environment. It provides for the establishment of testing requirements, record keeping, and the disclosure by a manufacturer or producer of health reactions to dangerous chemicals. Manufacturers must also inform the Environmental Protection Agency (EPA) ahead of time of intent to produce a new chemical and the EPA may require particular tests of the compounds.

Proper use of land is an environmental concern of increasing importance. Photo below shows land that was the site of a coal strip mine reclaimed and converted for use as a recreation area.

There are some 70,000 chemicals in commercial production. During 1977 the EPA's major effort was to develop mechanisms for "focusing, coordinating, and otherwise improving research on potential hazards." The assembling of accurate technical data is a monumental task and requires extensive interagency cooperation. Most of the basic tools needed to implement TOSCA have now been created but the continuing coordination of research, establishment of regulatory mechanisms, and the management of data will not be easy. Many hazardous residues are still with us and will require time and innovative technology to eliminate. It will also require considerable diligence to test, monitor, and eliminate new hazards. ■ TOSCA also requires that uses of the persistent chemical PCB (polychlorinated biphenyls) be phased out.

Peabody Coal Co.

The U.S. Occupational and Safety Health Administration proposed new rules for the identification, classification, and regulation of toxic substances that present occupational-cancer risks. The chemical industry opposes such regulation. Hearings on the proposal began in 1977.

**Pesticides.** Progress in the re-registration of the roughly 45,000 brand-name pesticides for use in the United States has moved very slowly. At fault is the enormous technical complexity of the task, confusion about the law, legal battles, and bureaucracy. The picture has been further clouded by the discovery that much of the existing safety-testing data is of questionable value. In an effort to speed up the re-registration or licensing process, President Carter ordered the EPA to work closely with Congress to develop amendments to the Federal Insecticide, Fungicide, and Rodenticide Act to permit the EPA to focus on the 1,850 basic active ingredients contained in pesticides rather than on the 45,000 or so brand-name products.

In 1977 the EPA issued a "rebuttable presumption against registration" for 11 products. This is a process through which the EPA finds sufficient preliminary evidence of serious danger which must be refuted by the manufacturer or user in order for the EPA to re-register the pesticide in question. Of the 11 products so challenged, the proceeding for Kepone is the only one to be completed. EPA's "presumption against" was not challenged. ■ The EPA is also continuing cancellation hearings on Mirex, heptachlor, and chlordane, all of which are suspected of causing cancer in humans. Rulings are expected in 1978.

**Solid-Waste Management.** At the end of 1977 environmentalists were mounting a "Containers to Carter" campaign to urge greater Administration involvement in the enactment of national deposit legislation pending before Congress. So far, the President's Interagency Resources Conservation Committee has not come out with recommendations on bills to encourage waste reduction and recycling of materials.

**Water and Air Pollution.** All 40,000 of the U.S. community water systems were brought under national drinking-water standards during 1977. However, too little is still known about the toxicity of many materials and about water-borne diseases for completely effective safeguards to be planned and enforced. ■ While most of the 4,000 major industrial polluters met cleanup deadlines in 1977, the municipalities did not. In the case of sewage treatment, only 4,150 of 12,500 cities met the government standards for secondary treatment of all sewage. Partially as a result, the EPA shifted its policy and is now emphasizing land treatment of sewage as an alternative to conventional sewage-treatment plants. Land treatment recycles nutrients as well as water and is often cheaper to build and operate than conventional sewage treatment facilities. ■ The biggest water-pollution problem remains, however—namely, non-specific runoff from agricultural and urban areas which accentuates soil loss by erosion.

Clean-air standards are also not being met. Some 4,000 deaths and 4,000,000 sick days annually are attributed to auto emissions alone, and as many as 21,000 persons in the eastern United States alone die prematurely because of air-borne power-plant pollutants. With a swing to coal as a source of energy, the air-pollution problem is expected to mount because only 120 of the 970 fossil-fuel-fired power plants have scrubber facilities to cleanse air emissions. ■ In one important advance, U.S. agencies are banning ozone-depleting fluorocarbons in aerosols.

Louis S. Clapper

Soil Conservation Service

The biggest water-pollution problem is runoff that creates gullies and soil erosion such as that shown in the above photo.

Solid waste management is a growing problem for all population centers. The city of Milwaukee, Wisconsin, and Americology, a division of the American Can Company, are now operating a joint venture in which some 250,000 tons of refuse a year are recycled at a new fully automated plant, part of which is shown below.

UPI

EPA Documerica

Is this all-too-common scene yet another source of environmental pollution? Many scientists now suspect that electromagnetic radiation may harm living things.

# ELECTROMAGNETIC POLLUTION

## by Robert O. Becker and Andrew A. Marino

THE landscape of the United States and that of some other heavily industrialized and urbanized countries would be unfamiliar were it lacking high-voltage transmission poles standing like metal skeletons strung with high-tension wires. These and other products of modern power and communications industries, such as radio, television, and radar, all operate in the electromagnetic spectrum. Electromagnetic waves—produced both naturally and artificially—are present in our environment. Except for light waves, however, we cannot hear, see, feel, or otherwise detect them with our senses without the use of special instruments.

Until recently, scientists believed that electromagnetic radiation had no effect on life. No obvious diseases had been identified

as having been caused by such energy. Expert opinion held that there was little or no connection in nature between electromagnetic radiation and biological tissue, other than gross heating effects from high doses. Industry has gone ahead expanding its use of electromagnetic waves with the assurance that no danger exists. We now live submerged in a sea of unperceived electromagnetic radiation.

### WHAT IS ELECTROMAGNETIC RADIATION?

The electromagnetic spectrum extends from wavelengths of millions of meters to ultrashort cosmic rays. Light is a special case. It is the only part of the spectrum which we can actually perceive directly. The others, like the long wavelengths used in seismic exploration, are masked from our direct perception. Clinical medicine uses the very short wavelengths in X rays and industry exploits the largest share of the spectrum—that which lies between one hertz and one hundred gigahertz, or between one cycle per second and 100,000,000,000 cycles per second. The most commonly used frequency—60 hertz—is used by electric power systems.

Only part of our electromagnetic environment occurs naturally. Most of it is artificially produced. Naturally occurring long-wavelength electromagnetic radiation in the earth's atmosphere primarily results from geophysical processes and from lightning. Extraterrestrial sources, such as radiation from the sun, account for the short wavelengths.

Within the last hundred years, human activities, particularly power and communications system activities, have profoundly changed the natural electromagnetic background waves which have prevailed since the beginning of evolution.

BIOLOGICAL EFFECTS

Recent research on the properties of biological tissue now offers us some new and troubling clues about the interaction of life with very weak electromagnetic radiation waves. A number of scientists have begun to report that exposure to these waves can have biological effects.

In some cases, investigators have succeeded in identifying the biological significance of naturally occurring nonionizing electromagnetic radiation. Other reports describe some responses of organisms exposed to artificial radiation.

First, there is the finding that at least some birds use geomagnetic clues in their orienting processes and that disturbances in the magnetic environment disrupt this ability. Another link between life and electromagnetic energy can be found in the work of James D. Hays and Neil D. Opdyke of the Lamont-Doherty Geological Observatory in New York City. They studied oceanic sediments, and claim that in those geologic periods during which the earth's magnetic field reversed its direction, an unusually large number of organisms died and some species of marine life became extinct. Frank A. Brown of Northwestern University has shown that living organisms exhibit changes in their behavior and physiology relating to corresponding periods in the earth's electromagnetic environment. In still another series of experiments—this time on humans—

AT&T

Placing all cables underground would remove the possible health hazard, eliminate the possibility of storm damage, and be more attractive. There is one serious problem, however: it is very expensive.

Researchers Milton Zarat (upper photo) and Frank A. Brown (lower photo) have found in separate experiments, involving different organisms, that electromagnetic radiation affects biological tissue.

Rutger Wever of the Max Planck Institute in Germany found that circadian, or daily, body rhythms are affected by the existing atmospheric electromagnetic environment.

Other laboratory experiments in which animals and humans were exposed to artificially produced electric and magnetic fields further suggest the connection. In 1973, Dietrich E. Beischer of the Naval Aerospace Medical Research Laboratory, using ten subjects, reported that humans exposed to certain levels of artificially produced magnetic field showed elevated serum triglyceride levels. A high level of triglycerides in blood serum is one factor believed related to arteriosclerotic disease. James H. McElhaney of West Virginia University showed that certain levels of low frequency electric fields can cause bone tumors in rats, and Gordon Marsh of the University of Iowa found that even lower doses can interfere with the growth pattern of flatworms. James R. Hamer of the University of California at Los Angeles reported that an electric field about one hundred times weaker than that used by Marsh can affect animal reaction-time performance. In the microwave region, Milton M. Zarat of New York University and others reported that exposure even to very low levels that produce no temperature changes could cause cataracts in mammals.

In our laboratory, we found that rats exposed to a 60-hertz electric field for one month exhibited hormonal and biochemical changes similar to those caused by stress. In our study we used an electric field comparable in strength to that produced at ground level by a typical high-voltage transmission line. In another experiment, we continuously exposed three generations of rats to the electric field and found increased infant mortality and severely stunted growth. Our results appear to indicate that the applied electric field primarily affects the central nervous system and activates the stress-response mechanism. Chronic stress is known to produce a wide variety of diseases and pathological conditions.

## HEALTH HAZARDS?

Now that abundant evidence establishes that both natural and artificially produced nonionizing electromagnetic radiation can produce some biological effects, serious questions about possible health hazards for humans are being raised. Nonetheless, the U.S. Environmental Protection Agency and state health and environmental agencies have not as yet significantly supported the research necessary to establish safe exposure levels. Until now, on the assumption that the

The Soviets bombarded the U.S. embassy in Moscow (shown at left) with microwave radiation that may be high enough to cause harmful biological effects.

Tass from Sovfoto

fields and energy levels associated with power and communications systems could not produce nonthermal biological effects, Western nations have evolved no standards to protect populations from excessive exposure. The Soviet Union does, however, have stringent regulations governing human exposure at both the low and high frequency regions of the spectrum.

## A SOVIET EXAMPLE

This odd discrepancy emerges in the current diplomatic squabble between the Soviet Union and the United States over Soviet bombardment of the U.S. embassy in Moscow with microwave energy. The intensity level being used by the Soviets is lower than the U.S. safety level, which is based solely on the possibility of inducing tissue heating, but greater than the level which the open Soviet scientific literature indicates can cause biological effects. As a consequence, the U.S. government has no formal basis upon which to claim embassy employees may be suffering hazards to their health.

A recently released U.S. Defense Intelligence Agency report suggested that nonthermal levels of microwaves might have offensive weapons applications. The report found that Soviet scientists are aware that chronic exposure to nonthermal microwave energy has great potential for development as a means of disrupting behavior patterns and for use as an interrogation tool. It has been reported that the Soviet bombardment of the U.S. embassy, which occurred be-

tween October 1975 and January 1976, was highest at 18 microwatts per square centimeter, or about 115 microwatts per square inch. In contrast, the U.S. microwave oven emission standard is 1,000 microwatts per square centimeter (6,500 microwatts per square inch), and the U.S. occupational exposure standard is 10,000 microwatts per square centimeter (65,000 microwatts per square inch). The Soviet exposure standard is 10 microwatts per square centimeter (65 microwatts per square inch).

## NEED TO STOP AND STUDY

The use of electromagnetic energy in the United States continues to expand. The generation of high-voltage transmission lines currently being constructed will operate at 765,000 volts, as compared to the present maximum of about 500,000 volts. The electric utility industry has begun developing the technology to operate at more than a million volts. The U.S. Navy has proposed to build a gigantic antenna in Michigan which would radiate at very low frequencies. Communications facilities at all frequencies continue to proliferate.

Recent scientific evidence on the biological effects of nonionizing radiation requires that we know whether or not chronic exposure is hazardous to health. This may be the right moment to halt those technologies which may result in further electromagnetic pollution until scientific studies establish safe levels not only for humans but for the entire ecosystem□

# DOOMED JUNGLES

## by Peter Gwynne

IN the tropical island chain of Indonesia, stretching 4,800 kilometers (3,000 miles) across the western Pacific, the amount of timber felled for export by U.S. and Japanese logging companies boomed more than twentyfold between 1966 and 1970. Since then, mechanized cutting operations have been chewing up the archipelago's rain forests at an even faster clip.

In the jungles of Rwanda, in the heart of the African continent, over-population has vastly intensified local slash-and-burn agriculture. Thousands of hectares (acres) of forest have become wasteland. The inexorable onslaught of more and more farmers, plundering one area after another, has put the mountain gorilla on the brink of extinction.

In Brazil, the government is pushing ahead with an ambitious plan aimed at developing the huge, steamy "green hell" of the Amazon basin. It plans to people the region with 18,000,000 farmers and industrial workers, converting entire regions into grassland for cattle ranching or otherwise destroying forest areas in what is known as one of the most inaccessible regions on earth.

In southern India and Malaysia, extensive clearing of the tropical forest seems to have altered patterns of rainfall. Now there are very heavy bouts of precipitation at longer intervals than normal—and indications that the annual rainfall is decreasing.

These activities are symptoms of one of the most significant, long-lasting, and irreversible changes that the face of the earth has ever undergone—the pell-mell devastation of the planet's tropical rain forests. Just a quarter of a century ago, a composite satellite photograph of the earth would have revealed a broad belt of greenery around the equator that was broken only by the oceans—a belt that had remained essentially unchanged for some 50,000,000 years.

### MOST THREATENED ECOSYSTEM

Today, the picture is strikingly different. Photographs from space now show that the girdle of green is broken in many places, and reduced in area throughout its width. Pressures from industry, farming, and soaring populations are tearing into its very fabric. "The tropical rain forest is by far the world's most threatened ecosystem," warns Tom Kimball, executive vice president of the National Wildlife Federation. "The consequences of all the destruction now taking place may be far more costly to man over the long run than any short-term economic gains could possibly justify."

All indications are, however, that the rate at which the pristine jungle is disappearing is on the increase. "If unguided commercial and agricultural exploitation are permitted to continue at the present accelerating pace," asserts Thomas Lovejoy, staff scientist and program director of the U.S. World Wildlife Fund, "almost all these virgin rain forests will be eliminated in only 25 years."

## EVOLUTION AND CLIMATE CHANGES

The major concern of conservationists is the near certainty of losing most fauna and flora living in the jungles. According to Duncan Poore, senior ecologist of the International Union for the Conservation of Nature and Natural Resources (IUCN), "the tropical rain forest is the richest expression of life that has evolved on this planet." The 7,000,000 to 9,000,000 square kilometers (2,700,000 to 3,500,000 square miles) of tropical rain forests around the world are cradles of evolutionary diversity—gene pools whose continued health is vital to the productivity, climate, and quite possibly even the very survival of the earth as a whole. "Destruction of the rain forests," warns Lovejoy, "would mean the loss of an enormous wealth of genetic material, permanently altering the future of evolutionary options."

Many scientists caution that the current worldwide massacre of rain forests could have far more immediate consequences, as well. Chief among these is the dramatic alteration of climatic conditions that will almost certainly result from the transformation of immense areas of jungle into deserts.

## VERY COMPLEX RELATIONSHIPS

To conserve the rain forests, however, scientists must understand their ecology far better than they do now. Experts know that the forests extend in a band of varying width from the equator toward the tropics of Cancer and Capricorn and that the predominant fact of life inside them is rain. Few tropical forest areas receive less than 250 centimeters (about 100 inches) of rain per year, while the 1,000 centimeters (about 400 inches) of annual rainfall that deluges the Choco forest of Colombia is enough to make even areas thought of as damp appear as dry as a desert in comparison. It is this rainfall that facilitates many of the ecological relationships in the tropical forests—relationships that are often too complex to be understood on more than a superficial level.

Ecologists recognize that the popular picture of the rain forests as steamy regions of impenetrable undergrowth underlain by

Tropical jungles have the richest diversity of plant and animal life of any ecosystem in the world. Here we see just some of the many types of plants found in a small section of a tropical rain forest in South America.

The first impression of the tropical rain forest is generally one of monotony rather than diversity. The trees all seem very much alike and few animals hove into view, apart from an occasional bird, butterfly, or lizard and numerous ants, flies and ticks. Only rarely is there a glimpse of the forest's splendor, in the form of a startlingly red land crab, an anteater curled up asleep in a hollow tree, an elephant or leopard viewed at a distance, or a tall, pink-flowered wadara tree surrounded by a swarm of hummingbirds.

## ASTONISHING DIVERSITY

More thorough studies, from the tops of trees and from specially mounted 30-meter (100-foot) towers, reveal the true extent of the jungles' riches. In fact, no other ecosystem in the world has such a diversity of plants and animals. A hectare (2½ acres) of rain forest in Malaysia, for example, contains between 100 and 150 different kinds of trees exceeding 30 centimeters (1 foot) in girth and 20 meters (65 feet) in height. A 4.5-hectare (11-acre) section of the Mocambo Forest close to Brazil's 450-year-old Amazonian port of Belém features the astonishing total of 295 separate tree species. By contrast, even the richest forests in North America rarely contain more than a couple of dozen types of trees.

The diversity of birds in the tropical rain forests is equally astonishing. In a single Andean valley in Peru, naturalists have discovered more than 600 individual species of resident birds, while the tiny Barro Colorado island in the Panama Canal boasts 208 species in its nearly 1,700 hectares (6.5 square miles).

Trees and birds represent only a fraction of the fauna and flora in the tropical rain forests. The jungles contain large numbers of orchids, ferns, bromeliads (relatives of the pineapple), and other herbaceous plants, most of which grow on the trunks and branches of trees and not on the ground. The forests also hold literally hundreds of different species of vines, mosses, liverworts, lichens, fungi, and microorganisms too small to be visible to the naked eye.

The animal life of the tropical forests ranges from the largest mammals, such as elephants and hippopotamuses, downwards

Toucans and gibbons live in the canopy of the rain forest. Specially adapted to their treetop world, they move agilely from tree to tree—the gibbon swinging with its long arms—and feed on the abundant fruit and leaves.

masses of rotting vegetation, from which fabulous creatures of every imginable type and hue might emerge at any moment, is inaccurate. Close to the ground, the forests' vegetation is actually quite sparse. As a result of the jungles' extraordinarily efficient recycling of all their material—most nutrients are cycled locally within the vegetation and surface layers of the soil—the amount of dead leaves underfoot is less than that found in a normal temperate forest.

in size through the big cats—leopards, jaguars, and others—to snakes, lizards, and frogs. But the numbers of these vertebrate species are far exceeded by those of the insects.

Much of the animal life is in middle and upper forest levels where it cannot be sampled easily. Census methods are so inexact—they normally consist of nothing more sophisticated than sweeping a butterfly net through the forest undergrowth and identifying the creatures captured—that reputable scientists hesitate to say just how many species of animals make their homes in a single section of any tropical forest. Experts are content to assure us that the numbers are very large, and almost certainly exceed those to be found in similarly-sized areas in nontropical regions.

Just as impressive as the ecological diversity within individual jungles is the variation between tropical forests in different parts of the world. In the Kibale Forest of Uganda, the 1,500-meter (approximately 5,000-foot) elevation gives a definite chill to the morning air—a remarkable contrast to the normal pattern of heat and humidity morning, noon, and night. Nearly half of the roughly 25,000 species of plants that grow in the rain forests of southeast Asia are found nowhere else in the world.

The unusual environmental conditions that exist in the tropical rain forests have given rise to a number of remarkable relationships between plants, soil, and animals, one of which is the pollination of flowers of the durian tree of Malaysia by bats.

## COMPLICATED FOREST LAYERS

The major reason for the rather monotonous first impression of the tropical forest is that the leaves of most of the trees are superficially very similar in size, shape, and texture. But beneath the monotony is a forest structure of complicated layers. While the tallest trees of the forest climb to heights of 40 to 50 meters (about 130 to 160 feet), standing out above the rest of the forest like gigantic cauliflowers, the densest regions of vegetation in the jungles occur between altitudes of 14 and 28 meters (45 and 90 feet). This closely-packed region produces a natural barrier between the airy, well-lighted region above, often known as the canopy, and the gloomy, unchanging undergrowth below, illuminated only by passing sunflecks.

Another layer vital to the smooth functioning of the forests is the one below the

Nocturnal animals, such as this spectacled owl of South America, are frequent inhabitants of the somewhat dark shrub layer of the rain forest.

Tapirs commonly roam the rain forest floor, feeding on the small ferns and other plants found there.

Gunter Ziesler, National Audubon Society/PR

ground. German researchers who have investigated the Amazon forest have estimated that fully half of the total mass of animals supported by that jungle live in the soil. The subterranean creatures include not only insects but also such reptiles as blind lizards and burrowing snakes.

## HUGE RECYCLING CENTERS

The wealth of exotic creatures is not, however, the most astonishing aspect of the tropical forests. That distinction must go to the speed at which the forests use their basic resources of heat, water, minerals, and organic material. The jungles are really huge recycling centers that put their scarce resources to use the instant they become available. Most forest plants have tiny roots near the surface of the soil, ready to take in nutrients as soon as they reach the soil, and even the tallest trees put most of their roots within about one meter (3 or 4 feet) of the surface. As a result of this rapid turnover, the tropical rain forests normally accumulate negligible amounts of leaf litter and produce scarcely any topsoil.

## SOURCE OF MANY THINGS

What is the use of these jungles to people? Many species of trees in the rain forests produce valuable timber, nuts, gums, and fibers, as well as the tough, pliable stems of climbing palms (rattans) that are used in making furniture. The forests also contain the wild ancestors of some of the world's most useful crop plants, among them cacao, coffee, rubber, and oil palm. Some of the forest animals are in demand for zoos and laboratories, and medical research has benefitted from several forest plants. Beyond these current uses, experts are confident that the jungles will yield more compounds that will benefit mankind.

## RAPID EXPLOITATION

But these bright hopes are already being dimmed by the headlong rush—sparked by the powerful tools of modern technology—to exploit the forests' other resources. Whereas in years past a gang with axes and machetes would take a month or two to clear a hectare (about 2½ acres) of forest, a small team equipped with chain saws and bulldozers can now fell the same amount in a single hour. Nor are the modern lumbermen selective in their exploits. Two factories, one at Gogol in New Guinea and one in the Choco rain forest in Colombia, are now converting all the forests' trees, regardless of their timber value, into wood chips that will be exported for papermaking. Other tropical nations presently have plans for similar facilities.

The search for mineral reserves is also turning up finds that threaten to uproot more of the jungles. Tin mining in the Malaysian peninsula has been making inroads into the rain forest for years. Newly developed methods of surveying for minerals from airplanes and orbiting satellites have shown signs of iron ore and other resources in Amazonia that will inevitably be mined in the near future.

Large scale agriculture is also contributing to the devastation of the forests, as entrepreneurs and state agencies invest in "monocultural" projects of oil palms, rubber trees, and tropical pines.

Modern technology has planted another nail in the coffin of the jungles by making even the most remote tropical areas accessible to twentieth century man. In the past decade, air transport and modern methods of road construction have opened up almost all the vast region of the once-impenetrable Amazonia to the depredations of industrial nations. Land-hungry settlers by the thousands have made their way into the region. And while their efforts to grow crops and raise cattle have been uniformly disappointing to date, the Brazilian government still seems unshaken in its belief that, somehow, some day, modern agricultural technology will make the Amazon region productive.

It is not only modern agriculture that threatens the rain forests. Throughout the equatorial regions of the world, small farmers are using their axes to clear patches on which they can plant a crop or two of rice, manioc, sweet potatoes, or corn, before moving on to adjacent plots after the soil be-

Butterflies, like this Jezabel butterfly, are an abundant and colorful part of the animal life of a rain forest. They serve to pollinate many species of flowers and themselves serve as food for birds and larger animals.

comes too weakened to support even those poor harvests. Slash-and-burn agriculture of this type is hardly a phenomenon of the twentieth century, but the population of the tropical rain forests is increasing at such a rate that the primitive farmers are forced to return to forest plots before the soil has fully recovered. The result is that vast areas of jungle are cut down to produce insignificant quantities of food.

## ALL SELF-DEFEATING

In fact, just about every type of conventional use of the tropical forests is self-defeating. In contrast to the temperate northern forests, which grow back to be used again, forest removal in the tropics can wipe out the possibility for renewal. Intensive agricultural development, for instance, opens up the easily damaged soil to the intense heat of the sun, which bakes it as hard as concrete, and to the torrential rain, which washes away whatever nutrients are left in the soil. Usually, the soil is so denuded that it can support only two or three harvests of crops without the use of fertilizers; and with fertilizers in increasingly short supply, few agri-

cultural experts are likely to advocate their use in chronically infertile areas.

The monocultures of rubber plants, cocoa, and oil palms also suffer depredations unknown in the natural forests when pests concentrate their activities on one or two plants and multiply unchecked by the natural ecological balance. In similar fashion, tropical timber trees are often difficult to grow as pure stands because they fall foul of diseases that cause little apparent harm to the trees in their natural settings. Sometimes a lack of pollinators, which depend for their survival on plant diversity, will also spell doom for a single-species crop.

## EFFECT ON RIVERS

The destruction of the rain forests also threatens indirect harm to rivers and streams and the life they contain. In an undisturbed forest, of the type that still exists in parts of Amazonia, many rivers are relatively free of large amounts of soil run-off because the forests' ultraefficient recycling system leaves hardly any waste to be collected by drainage water. But when large clearings are cut in the forests, the situation changes completely.

Toby Molenaar, Alpha

Destruction or severe disturbance of a rain forest—such as that being caused by the construction of the Transamazon Highway—has serious effects not only on the local plant and animal life but also on the overall climate and ecology of the earth.

Frederick Ayer III, Photo Researchers

Whatever the use of rain-forest land, the result is all too often poor, eroded soil that, baked by the sun and washed away by torrential rains, becomes almost impossible to renew.

Surface erosion carries away large quantities of soil and its nutrient-rich organic material into the rivers, which become clogged with silt. The result is impoverishment of the soil, destruction of fish, elimination of other forms of river life, and frequent flash floods.

## FAR-REACHING EFFECTS

The effect of over-exploitation of the tropical rain forests is not restricted to the ten per cent of the earth's land area that they now occupy. If the forests are destroyed, as now seems likely, biologists believe that virtually all the plant and animal life that inhabits them will be doomed—including more than half of the earth's bird species and three fourths of all the world's tree species. Such carnage would inevitably reduce the earth's natural genetic diversity to a dangerously low level, and destroy the vast potential of the tropical forests to contribute to the good of mankind. "New and valuable uses of organisms are constantly being discovered in medicine, pest control, and in the breeding of economic plants and animals, and it would be blind and irresponsible to destroy the source of so much potentially valuable material," explains IUCN's Duncan Poore.

The forests are vital to mankind in another, more fundamental way. The fact that an enormous diversity of plants and animals live together in ecological harmony in the tropical rain forests indicates that there must be some kind of natural biological balance within them. If we could fully understand this balance, we might be able to learn lessons that are important for our own survival on this planet. But unless the felling of the forests is halted soon, the jungles will join the dinosaur and the dodo, and the great potential that they contain will disappear like the nutrients that are swept away from forest soil once its tree cover is removed□

SELECTED READINGS

*Jungles Long Ago* by Kenneth Anderson Allen. Unwin, 1976.

# MOUNTAINS BESIEGED

Ben Ami Altarazt, APF

## by Edward R. Ricciuti

PEOPLE have long associated mountains with things holy and undefiled. They have worshiped atop mountains and even designed sacred edifices in their towering likeness. Until now, mountains have always seemed pure, pristine, far removed from the turmoil below. Increasingly, however, that is no longer the case. Like other ecosystems the world over, mountains are suffering from a persistent problem: people.

These days, the high country is full of humans, most of whom are there for one of two reasons, neither of which has anything to do with the sacred. One reason is survival; the other, ironically, is fun.

In the tropics and subtropics, most mountains have been invaded by hordes of poor farmers and herdsmen, pressured by expanding populations farther below and desperate for land. In Mexico and Central America, farmers are hacking fields out of high cloud forests that shelter many plants found nowhere else. So close have farms come to the mountains of the Aberdare National Park in Kenya that a trench has been dug to separate livestock from wild animals. At the western end of the Himalayas, the sheep and goats of Pakistani villagers are stripping vegetation all the way up to the tree line. And in the center of the same range, Nepalese farmers with no place else to go are tilling slopes so steep that erosion starts almost at the touch of a plow.

Not even Nepal's 8,850-meter (29,018-foot Mt. Everest—the world's highest peak—has escaped the human tide. Trash is piling up on the lower slopes and it is not being dropped there by farmers. Thousands of tourists and climbers are the culprits, which underscores the other half of the mountain problem. For millions of people from the world's more affluent nations, the mountains have become prime fun spots. Skiers are schussing down the revered slopes of Japan's Mt. Fujiyama. The remote Altai Range in the Soviet Union is studded with winter sports resorts.

In the United States, second homes are sprouting in the Great Smokies, and dancers hustle and bump at night clubs in the heart of Rocky Mountain elk country. Mountainous parks such as Mt. McKinley in Alaska and Mt. Rainier in Washington have been forced to limit backcountry camping on a first-come, first-served basis. So many hikers are tramping through parts of California's Sierras that skittish bighorn sheep have hightailed it into desolate corners where forage is pitifully skimpy.

"You can't get away from people until you reach the snow line," says naturalist and author George B. Schaller of the New York Zoological Society, an authority on mountain animals. Adds Professor Jack D. Ives of the University of Colorado's Institute of Arctic and Alpine Research: "Two hundred million people depend directly on the mountains of the world for their livelihood."

## MOST SUSCEPTIBLE REGIONS ON EARTH

Ives believes mountains are "the most susceptible regions on earth" to environmental disturbance. His observation lends urgency to a United Nations panel's recent warning that people's impacts on mountains are producing critical situations at a faster rate than in many other ecosystems. The panel is talking about a huge chunk of landscape, for fully a quarter of the world's entire land surface is above 900 meters (approximately 3,000 feet), the level generally accepted as the boundary between lowland and highland. But mountains, Ives points out, are "really a matter of relief, rather than altitude." Plenty of 1,500-meter- (about 1-mile-) high land in Colorado is as flat as a platter, while there are sheer peaks in Puerto Rico that, solely in terms of altitude, would be considered lowland.

Because one person's mountain may be another's molehill, it is difficult to designate any one place as the most mountainous on earth. However, the nod probably goes to Tibet, with not a single tiny area under 900 meters (3,000 feet) and an average altitude over 4,500 meters (15,000 feet). Hawaiians might make a case for their islands, too, be-cause Hawaii consists of huge volcanoes rising from the sea. From sea bottom to peaks soaring almost 4,000 meters (13,000 feet) above the waves, Hawaii's two largest volcanoes—Mauna Kea and Mauna Loa—are higher than Everest.

## HOW MOUNTAINS FORM

As it happens, volcanic action is one of the three major forces that build mountains. Extruded through the earth's crust like a gob of toothpaste squeezed from a tube, lava and cinders pile up in a heap that becomes a mountain. Among the world's 10,000 volcanoes—about 600 of which remain active—are many noted peaks, including Mt. Kenya and Mt. Kilimanjaro in Africa, Mt. Rainier and Mt. Shasta in North America, Mt. Ararat in Turkey, and Mt. Fujiyama in Japan. Sometimes, the lava does not break through the crust, but pools underneath, arching the earth's skin into a giant blister. Eventually, the skin wears away, exposing the long-cooled lava "dome," such as the Abajo Mountains in Utah.

The other main processes of mountain building are "folding" and "faulting." A product of the first process is the Appalachian chain, formed 220,000,000 years ago when the crust was pushed into folds, like wrinkles on a rumpled tablecloth. About 25,-000,000 years ago, the jagged Sierra Nevada

James Pearce, APF

This busy ski resort scene contrasts sharply with the peacefulness and natural beauty of the mountains shown on the opposite page. Mountains all over the world are facing a problem: people.

John R. Clawson, Audubon/PR

Mountains have storied life zones, each with its characteristic vegetation and animal life. Here a view of the timberline in Colorado—trees become stunted as soils become increasingly poor.

Range got its present form from the second process. Faulting occurs when the rock cracks cleanly along a fault, or fracture, in the earth, and a block on one side of the break either rises or sinks.

Actually, while one of these three mountain-forming processes may be the principal cause of a particular range, all can play a role. And of course once the peaks have risen, they are continually sculpted by the abrasion of wind, water, and glaciers.

Today, the major mountain systems are arranged in broad belts called "cordilleras." The New World cordillera stretches from the Brooks Range of Alaska, through the American coast ranges and Rockies, down the Andes to the tip of South America. The influence of this immense mountain belt is felt far beyond even its vast limits.

## POWERFUL FORCE—YET FRAGILE

Consider the Rockies, for example. They form the Great Divide, the wellspring of mighty rivers and the origin of two continental drainage systems. There is no better example of the very important role mountains have as the source of water for lands below. Mountains also regulate rainfall patterns over the land around them, because they rob the winds of moisture. In northern California, for example, the High Sierras force winds blowing east from the Pacific to drop almost all their rain on the western slopes of the mountains. This leaves barely a sprinkle for the lands immediately beyond, which as a result are bone dry.

It is hard to imagine that such monumental creations represent ecosystems so fragile they can collapse like a house of cards. Yet mountain ecosystems have much in common with those of two other especially vulnerable environments, islands and rain forests.

Ecologically, many mountains really are islands because they differ so sharply from their immediate surroundings. Conditions atop the Great Smokies, for example, resemble those in Canada, not the surrounding areas of Tennessee and North Carolina. Like islands, mountains are havens for plants and animals that have evolved in isolation. Many organisms are especially adapted to life on a mountain—even on one particular mountain—but nowhere else. Typically, for example, 75 per cent of the plants of the Guiana Highlands grow only there.

## STORIED LIFE ZONES

From top to bottom, a mountain is girdled with life zones, much as the flora and fauna of a rain forest are stratified into layers, or "stories." Increasingly narrow and demanding with altitude, the life zones of a mountain create an extraordinary situation: they squeeze into one or two thousand vertical meters environmental conditions that would span thousands of kilometers on the level. Within the space of a little over a kilometer, for example, vegetation on Mt. Washington in New Hampshire changes from temperate deciduous forest to low tundra plants, like those of northern Canada.

The range of conditions is even more extreme in the tropics. Only 5,000 meters (16,400 feet) separate an alpinelike zone atop the Andes from the jungle at the bottom of the eastern slopes. The twin peaks of Mt. Kenya, on the equator, carry snow all year but, 5,200 meters (17,000 feet) below, the base sits on sun-baked savannah.

The progression of life zones is easily visible on mountains in equatorial Africa. Jungle normally comes first, then a forest with fewer vines but more tree ferns, next juniper, thick stands of bamboo, and then, at about 3,300 meters (11,000 feet), rolling moors flecked with white "everlasting" flowers and broken by groves of giant heath, resembling a medium-size conifer. On the highest African peaks, tundra follows and, finally, ice and snow caps.

## NARROW MARGIN FOR WILDLIFE

The vertical layering of life zones on a mountain is reflected in the distribution of its wildlife. From base to summit, the animals that live on a mountain decrease in kind and number. But even at the top, there is habitat for a few, such as the jumping spiders and springtail insects that skitter about the snows 6,600 meters (22,000 feet) up Mt. Everest. Finding enough to eat is the most critical problem, and few animals have solved it well enough to become full-time residents. Among these are many birds, which can quickly cover vast stretches in search of food. Hawks, eagles, condors, choughs, chaffinches, and even flamingos prosper above the timberline. Several large mammals roam surprisingly high on mountains—elk and

A marmot enjoys the peacefulness of its mountainous home range. Will it soon be forced to find another habitat?

Norman R. Lightfoot, PR

Some mammals, including some species of sheep, are very well adapted to life high in the mountains. Very surefooted, they can clamber over rocks and up cliffs.

Jeff Foott, Bruce Coleman

grizzly bear in the United States and elephants in Africa. In the giant heath of Kenya's Aberdare Range, elephants feed well above the 3,000-meter (10,000-foot) level.

Only a few big mammals, however, are specialized enough to spend most of their time on the highest, rocky reaches of mountains. Among them are many wild sheep and goats, the Rocky Mountain "goat" and its Eurasian cousin the chamois, the Asian yak, and the guanaco and vicuña of South America. These creatures can subsist on the scruffy plants of the crags, and manage the fancy footwork needed to get at them. But at best the conditions under which most of these creatures live are so rigorous that they have little maneuvering room, and additional pressure from people can shrink their margin of survival to the thinnest edge.

For many high-altitude animals, that margin during severe winter weather is the food and shelter of the timberline. When blizzards strike the high Rockies, for example, the white-tailed ptarmigan merely scoots downhill from the tundra to the tree line. This quick switch of surroundings contrasts sharply with the mighty migration of the snow bunting, which journeys more than 1,500 kilometers (1,000 miles) from the Arctic to the evergreens of southern Canada. If human activity interferes with the use of the lower slopes by alpine wildlife in rough weather, the animals can find themselves in a fatal crunch between inhospitable conditions above timberline and man below.

The importance of the timberline for animals is matched by its significance for people since melted snow from high altitudes is the source of water for irrigation, drinking, and hydroelectric power below. What happens in the mountains ultimately affects up to a third of the world's population.

## NOW: ROADS AND FARMS

What is happening in the mountains of the world?

For one thing, people are building roads into them, particularly in such politically-strategic regions as the Himalayas, where new military highways snake up the valleys. Roadways alter drainage patterns in mountains. Runoff from the pavement pollutes streams. And if the roads are built in valleys, they may prevent alpine animals from wintering there. All these things are happening in the Himalayas. Worse, soldiers traveling on the new Himalayan highways use their vehicles to ambush the wild goats and sheep that seek haven or forage in the valleys. According to George Schaller, uncontrolled shooting by the military "almost doomed" the stately Marco Polo sheep in the Karakoram region of Pakistan when it was opened by roads in the 1960s.

Even without roads, however, many mountain areas would still be inundated with people. Human beings are an enduring presence in Asia's mountains, despite their pristine image. Nepal has 12,000,000 inhabitants—1,500,000 in its capital, Katmandu, alone—and it is still growing fast. In

Nepal's mountains, a tillable piece of land the size of a suburban yard in the United States must feed more than a half-dozen people. Half of Nepal's mountain forests are gone and, although firewood is so scarce people burn dung, whole hillsides are torched to clear land for crops.

## SNOWBALLING EROSION

The danger of denuding mountains is that it paves the way for erosion. Natural erosion always occurs, but when a mountain is suddenly stripped of its plant cover, the process is greatly accelerated. The main reason mountains are so vulnerable, in fact, is that once serious erosion begins, it snowballs. "Given a steep slope and heavy rainfall," emphasizes expert Ives, "it is almost impossible to get a disturbed mountain system stabilized again." On gradual slopes well below timberline, however, deforestation is reversible, which is why low ranges such as Vermont's Green Mountains have recovered from it.

In the high mountains, says ecologist Erik P. Eckholm of the Worldwatch Institute, the situation is "self-defeating." As people try to squeeze more agricultural returns from high-altitude lands, they are creating problems with inestimable human costs. The erosion, landslides, flooding, and sedimenta-tion which result from denuding mountains may, in turn, result in a loss of food production, in both the mountains and the plains below. In many areas of the world, chronic malnutrition is the outcome. This sort of environmental degradation, Eckholm predicts, will continue to swell urban populations, miring millions more in poverty and further unsettling the world's precarious political order.

Unhappily, there is no let-up in sight. In Africa, Ethiopia's mountains are probably as heavily populated and denuded as the Himalayas. Farther south, people are pouring into the fertile highlands of East Africa, carving the vast lands of former colonial plantations into many small farms. Cultivation now rings the green ramparts of Ngorongoro Crater, in Tanzania, and Mt. Kenya. In North Africa, the livestock of Berber nomads is penned up in the high Atlas Mountains by government farms on the good lands below. The result, according to German scientist Horst Mensching, "is overstocking of herds in the mountains and an enormous increase of damage."

The central Andes, too, are thickly populated with farmers and herders up to nearly 5,000 meters (16,000 feet). Half of Peru's population and 90 per cent of Bolivia's people inhabit the mountains and, although

Nepalese farmers, with no other land available, are farming steep mountain slopes—and helping erosion. This trail leading to Mt. Everest winds through millet fields—not even the world's highest mountain peak has escaped the press of people and their activities.

M. Durrance, PR

some people have headed down to the cities to find work, the alpine birth rate keeps on booming. According to the United Nations panel, "overgrazing as a response to population increase appears to be producing rapid and irreparable damage to ecosystems."

## AND TOURISTS

While agriculture continues transforming the face of mountains in the world's developing nations, tourism is performing a similar disservice in more prosperous countries. This is especially evident in the Alps, where scrupulous management maintained a healthy balance between farming and mountain ecosystems for a century. The result was a pleasant patchwork of man-made meadows, manicured forests, peaks, and a few wisps of wilderness. It was the land of Heidi—not primeval, perhaps, but nevertheless green. Lately, however, Heidi has been growing up into a swinger. Dazzling resorts such as St. Moritz in Switzerland and St. Anton in Austria lure people from all over the world. Rural villages have become posh pleasure domes with the attendant problems of water pollution, smog, traffic congestion, and noise. Mountain land, owned by farm families or communally by villagers, has been sold, or the farmers have gone into the tourist business for themselves, changing the character of some mountaintops.

It is not just a matter of a few hotels perched on a mountain, although a resort may start that way. But one pleasure facility quickly begets another and soon the complex expands into a razzle-dazzle of nightclubs, hotels, ski lifts, and bars, linked by highways, power lines, and sewage systems. This is what is happening now around Vail, Colorado, once the site of a tranquil 16-kilometer- (10-mile-) wide ranching valley tucked in the Rockies 160 kilometers (100 miles) from Denver.

Since 1962, Vail has grown into a glittering spread characterized by some environmentalists as a "haven of affluent, alpine luxury," and by its proponents as a "reasonable development," conceived so sensitively that garishly lighted signs are banned. The snowflakes that bring Vail 785 centimeters (309 inches) of precious white powder annually fall on more than 60 restaurants and bars, half a hundred hotels, condominiums, and lodges, and 52 shops and boutiques. And that's just Vail. Other resorts are nearby.

"It's not getting bigger, it's getting better," says a promotional article about the ongoing expansion of Vail. Indeed, the people who gave the world Vail hope to build another huge resort, Beaver Creek, on a mountain only 16 kilometers (10 miles) away. Like much mountain land in the West, part of Beaver Creek is owned by a federal agency, in this case the U.S. Forest Service. Environmentalists opposed to the project hope the fact that it requires Forest Service approval will give them some leverage.

Environmentalists in Colorado and other mountain states view recreation and second-home development as the greatest specific threat to the mountains, much more so than industry and energy resource exploi-

James Pearce, APF

Recreation and second-home development is the biggest single threat to the Colorado mountains.

People going higher and higher into the mountains, bringing their daily turmoil into the "most susceptible region on earth."

Ben Ami Altarazt, APF

tation, which is generally considered the most serious overall problem for the entire region. "Resorts and second homes are built in valleys and they tend to take the best agricultural lands," complains Joan Nice of the *High Country News,* a crusading biweekly published in Wyoming. Environmentalists also charge that the Vail development, including the interstate highways that whisk vacationers to Vail from Denver, has destroyed the valley as a wintering ground for elk and mule deer.

The tourist tide is rising in the Himalayas and the Andes, too, bringing full circle the patterns of pressure on mountains. About 4,000 tourists annually trudge up the lower slopes of Mt. Everest, too many of them scattering litter along the way. One valley in Kashmir near K-2, the world's second-highest mountain, has in the past few years hosted six major climbing expeditions, totaling about 6,000 people, who have plucked it clean of firewood.

## WHAT CAN BE DONE

Although certain recreational activities take a heavy toll on mountain ecosystems, some might eventually help protect them. In Montana, conservationists are offering a recreational alternative to proposed "Ski Yellowstone" resort and second-home development they fear will destroy prime griz-

zly bear habitat. In place of the resort, the conservationists suggest setting aside more than 12,000 hectares (30,000 acres) for non-mechanized, low-key winter sports such as cross-country skiing, thus bringing needed tourist income to the region but minimizing disturbance to the grizzly.

In Pakistan, mountain wildlife might be saved by encouraging villagers to manage it for hunting, according to George Schaller, who envisions management units centered on individual villages. Residents of the villages could be paid as "wardens" to protect the game, and once it is replenished it could be hunted for meat by villagers, and for sport by tourists who would pay for the privilege. It would take years to establish such a program but with the help of an international organization, perhaps it could be done.

Clearly, something must be done—not only in Pakistan but all over the world—to preserve the mountain majesty that still remains□

### SELECTED READINGS

"Farming the edge of the Andes" by S. B. Brush. *Natural History,* May 1977.

*Life of the Mountains* by Maurice Brooks. McGraw Hill, 1968.

*The Mountain World* by David Costello. Crowell, 1975.

A deep fjord on Vancouver Island, Canada, provided an ideal site for studying minute ocean organisms. The waters are fairly calm, deep, and rich in plankton.

# PROJECT C E P E X

## by M. R. Reeve and M. A. Walter

*O what endlesse worke have I in hand*
*To count the seas abundant progeny*
*Whose fruitful seede farre passeth those in land.*

THE sea is so vast, and many of the important animals of the food chain which feed the fishes so small, that modern biological oceanographers can still feel that those words of Spenser from the *Faerie Queene* in the sixteenth century were written for them.

How is one to study or even to keep track of all those countless thousands of millions of minute single-celled floating green plants, which capture the energy of sunlight, and the millions of microscopic shrimplike creatures called copepods, which graze on them and, in turn, are fed upon by baby fishes? The oceans of the world, even the smallest bays and inlets, are all in constant motion. Their waters are driven by the tides, the winds, and other great planetary forces. Unlike the forests or meadows on land, or even the shallow grass flats of coastal waters, one can never hope to go back and find the same populations again in the same place. They have been swept far away, and in their place are new waters with new populations.

But these tiny organisms are vitally important to humankind. They are the meadows and the forests of the oceans, and most of the fishes and shellfishes people harvest ultimately depend on them. We need to know how they live their lives, how they live together as a community, how fast they grow, what makes them grow faster, and, equally important, what slows down their growth, or kills them. For, in the end, their fate will decide the fate of all the larger animals of the seas—the oysters, crabs, fishes, birds, and even the whales.

## NEED FOR REALISTIC EXPERIMENTS

To try to answer some of these questions, in 1972, the U.S. National Science Foundation asked an international group of marine scientists how to investigate the slow subtly harmful effects of the ever-increasing amounts and kinds of polluting materials that people are daily adding to rivers, estuaries, and coastal waters. Their suggestion was that in order to learn how all the creatures in the water column reacted to stress, whether manmade or natural, the experiments would have to be large enough to be realistic.

Basically, there are two ways to tackle the problem. One way is to bring these tiny plants and animals—the plankton—into the laboratory and grow them under carefully controlled conditions. This work has been going on for a long time, but it has its drawbacks. Usually, the organisms that tolerate laboratory conditions best have been likened to weeds. They are peculiar forms that are not particularly common in the sea under normal conditions and, unlike most marine creatures, they are resistant to stress of all kinds and so are not good examples. Besides this, aquariums in the laboratory are usually not large enough to support more than one or two species and so do not come very close to simulating conditions of the natural environment. Thus, the results from such experiments are often of doubtful significance.

Another way is simply to watch what happens in the natural environment by collecting specimens frequently. This involves going out in ships and taking samples with nets and other devices. Since it is never possible to find the same population twice, the causes of any changes can never be known for sure.

A researcher inspects the fabric to be used for huge polyethylene bags that will serve as "in-the-ocean test tubes," permitting scientists to study the effects of pollution on microscopic marine life.

Reeve/Walter

A gigantic bag is put into the water for the first time and submerged, using weights. When it is in place, the yellow collar is inflated with air. It then floats to the surface, filling the bag with water.

## GIANT AQUARIUMS

Over the past few years, scientists in several countries have been experimenting with a third alternative: giant aquariums, so large that the plants and animals in them are under conditions almost the same as if they were still in the ocean, but where the populations can be revisited time and time again, and where at least some of the many changing factors can be controlled or altered deliberately.

The simplest way to have an open-air laboratory aquarium is to use a natural body of water like a pond or lake. This has been done since the 1940s when Professor J. E. G. Raymont of the University of Southampton in England added huge quantities of fertilizer to a Scottish loch (a landlocked sea fjord) to investigate the effects of these nutrients in stimulating growth of the plankton and fishes.

Another solution is to construct a giant manmade aquarium. One of the earliest such attempts was a plastic sphere some 6 meters (20 feet) in diameter, moored off the laboratory of the Fisheries Research Board at Nanaimo, British Columbia. More recently,

German scientists have designed a "plankton tower" consisting of a rectangular steel framework that rests on the bottom of Kiel Bight.

## AN IDEAL SITE FOUND

The most extensive venture to date, however, is the Controlled Ecosystem Pollution Experiment (CEPEX), which began in 1973. This project, an outgrowth of the 1972 meeting and involving scientists from laboratories as far afield as Tokyo, Aberdeen, Miami, and Vancouver, was sited at Saanich Inlet, British Columbia, a deep clean fjord on Vancouver Island. The site was close enough to several fishery and oceanographic laboratories so that a great deal of information already existed on its populations and water currents. This site, provided by the Canadian Government, had several other advantages. The first was that it was a very rich area, with plankton in great quantities, as well as a salmon fishery. Secondly, being almost landlocked and surrounded by hills, its waters were usually much calmer than the open ocean, even though some of the animals in its depths were the same as could be found in the middle of the Pacific Ocean. In addition, the site is currently under development as a large new Canadian ocean science institute. Last but not least, close by in Victoria were the offices of John Case Laboratories, marine designers and engineers, which could supply original ideas and approaches.

Case designed a series of cylindrical transparent bags supported at the surface by flotation collars, which were moored by anchors to the bottom of the inlet. The bags themselves were only attached to the surface collars and were free to be pushed and shoved below as the currents and tides set first one direction, then another. This was because it would be almost impossible to make a rigid cylinder to withstand such tremendous natural forces and which would not be too expensive or difficult to maneuver. The giant plastic bag, on the other hand, is disposable and when it gets fouled can simply be replaced. The bags are open at the top, and end in a cone at the bottom from which a hose leads back to the surface. This hose can be used either to take out sediment or water from the bottom or to pump things in. The bag itself is clear polyethylene, with nylon mesh embedded in it. It is very strong and small puncture holes will not run.

## THE FIRECRACKER ASSIST

In the late summer of 1973, the researchers began learning how to work with "small" bags. These were about 2.5 meters (8 feet) in diameter by 16 meters (52 feet) deep, and held 68,000 liters (about 18,000 gallons). By the same time the following year, they had graduated to full-scale bags which were 10 meters (33 feet) in diameter by 24 meters (78 feet) deep, and held over 20 times more water, about 1,250,000 liters (350,000 gallons).

In the first trial in 1973, it took two or three days to pump three bags full of water. Pumps do not deal kindly with small animals in the water passing through them, however, and, worse still, the bags did not start off with identical populations because they were not filled at exactly the same time. This is essential in a controlled experiment, because otherwise the populations in the bags will be different and, therefore, develop in different ways, whether or not a pollutant is added to one of them.

Reeve/Walter

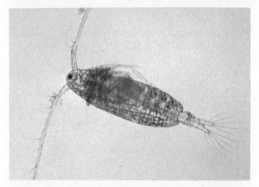

Reeve/Walter

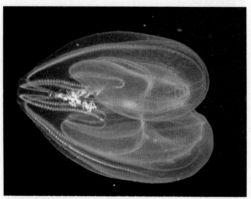

Reeve/Walter

The CEPEX researchers found that zooplankton—floating, often microscopic, aquatic animals—are the most seriously affected by water pollution. These small animals, including ctenophores, or comb jellies (top and bottom photos), and copepods (middle photo), provide an important food source for larger invertebrates and fish. The effects of the pollution are therefore passed along the food chain.

Reeve/Walter

The bags were enormous, so large that the plants and animals in them were under conditions almost the same as if they were still in the ocean.

The following spring, an ingenious way to avoid both of these problems was devised. A team of scuba divers took the bags down deep, held the mouths of the bags open, and on the signal from a special firecracker ignited in the water, all swam to the surface, causing the bags to fill simultaneously, by "capturing" the water column and the plankton in it. Within a few minutes the mouths of the bags reached the surface, and waiting helpers on the flotation collars grabbed the bags and tethered them to the collars.

## BAG MANAGEMENT SOLUTIONS

There were similar problems, although on a larger scale, with the full-scale bags. The first one, installed in late summer 1973, seemed to work just fine. But that was beginner's luck. When a real experiment with three of these monsters was started in May 1974, things began to go wrong. The flotation module was thought to be the largest acrylic structure ever fabricated. It had been manufactured from transparent acrylic, like the small-scale ones, and had 1.2-meter (4-foot) cross sections. The first module had survived the British Columbia winter, and to this day is still afloat. The other two, however, cracked and broke up in a series of spring storms. It seemed that, during assembly, they had been stored outdoors in the Canadian winter and the glue joints had failed to cure adequately.

Three new flotation modules were hurriedly assembled, this time welded out of 60-centimeter (2-foot) cross-section steel tubing, and a three-bag launch was tried in August of the same year. The problems were not over, however. On the occasion of the bag-raising, the divers experienced strong currents below a depth of 15 meters (50 feet). Consequently, they raised the 30-meter- (100-foot-) long bags only from a 15-meter (50-foot) depth, only half-filling them. The topping-off was completed by pumping water into them.

To the scientists' horror, the bags did not hang straight down, but started billowing out sideways close to the surface. They soon realized that the problem was one of salinity gradients. The deeper water of Saanich Inlet is more saline, or saltier, than that near the surface. The surface water has some freshwater from land mixed in with it, which makes it lighter and keeps it at the surface. The bags, though, did not have any of the more saline, heavier water in them, and so they floated on the top of this deeper layer. This was cured by pumping out some of the lighter water and replacing it with deeper, heavier, and more saline water. The bags then hung vertically again.

Although 1974 was a period of learning regarding the management of the full-scale bags, at the same time a complete season of experiments with the small bags had been successfully finished. Six bags had been routinely raised at a time in 30-day experiments, making a total of some 25 successful bags altogether.

In 1976, the experimental program went with few hitches. The big bags were raised

The bag hangs in the water, attached at the surface to its flotation module, which is counterbalanced by weighted shroud lines.

Reeve/Walter

Reeve/Walter

Workers prepare to raise the bags on three of the modules. It is a job requiring much muscle power.

twice during the season, each time the experiments lasting for 75 days, and each time fingerling salmon from local hatcheries introduced, to complete the food chain.

## ZOOPLANKTON MOST AFFECTED

The scientific data produced from these ongoing series of intensive experiments are both voluminous and far from fully analyzed yet, but preliminary conclusions can be summed up as follows. In general, the smaller the organism the more rapidly it is affected by any pollutant. Bacteria are most rapidly affected and fishes least rapidly affected.

Things are not as simple as they sound, however. Bacteria exist in thousands of different species and countless thousands of millions of individuals, and they can reproduce in an hour or two. Fishes, on the other

What a CEPEX bag looks like after it is hauled ashore. It has become discolored, much like the hull of a ship discolors.

Reeve/Walter

hand, are relatively few in species and numbers, and they often take several years to reach reproductive age. There are always a few species of bacteria that are resistant, and they can build up their numbers in a matter of two or three days once the rest are no longer competing with them. The phytoplankton—minute, floating aquatic plants—are less numerous, but still one or two species will survive, and they can double their numbers daily. The zooplankton—floating, often microscopic, aquatic animals—species are numbered in tens, and need at least three weeks to a year to reproduce. In 30- to 75-day experiments, they are most severely impacted.

Levels of pollutants that cause the quick death of small fishes have not been used. These fishes are continuously absorbing toxic materials in their food, however, and if they die, it will take years for resistant species to develop, if ever.

## UPSETTING ENTIRE ECOSYSTEM

This is not the end of the complexity, because it is one thing to say that there will eventually be enough phytoplankton replacing those killed to maintain the food chain, but what if they are not the right kind of phytoplankton?

The large chain diatoms common in Saanich Inlet were replaced by tiny forms, and it is difficult to imagine that these are equally suitable as food. Most creatures are adapted to the kind of food they eat. If the basic protein source of man were to change from cattle and sheep, for example, to insects in a matter of days, a dramatic upset in man's ecology could be predicted. Not only which creatures die but also how shifts in species affect the "structure" of the ecosystem as a whole must be determined. This can only be seen in experiments which run for months, and perhaps, in the future, for years□

📖 SELECTED READINGS

"Living Sea" by A. Fisher. *International Wildlife,* May 1977.

"Microorganisms and marine ecology" by R. S. Oremland. *Sea Frontiers,* September 1976.

*Pollution Effects on Marine Organisms* by C. S. Gram. Lexington, 1977.

River running has increased dramatically in the last few years. Here we see people rafting down the Youghiogheny River in Pennsylvania. Will this river and other wild rivers like it be able to withstand the onslaught of boats, onshore campsites, and people, people, people?

# WILDERNESS PERMITS

by

## Richard Saltonstall, Jr.

HISTORICALLY it no longer exists, but there is still a frontier in the United States. Except in Alaska, it has dissipated into microcosms, or small pockets, of the real thing. It has been reduced to unspoiled wilderness areas—high mountain valleys, northern forest lakes, southern bayous, southwestern desert ranges—but it is big in psychic terms. There is still a "frontier" to be confronted on its terms, not yours.

The question is how long U.S. wilderness areas can withstand, not the varying types of deliberate exploitation, but the increasing pressures of public recreation, how long it can resist being overwhelmed by those who love backcountry the most. I'm referring to public domain—parks, forests, primitive areas, and wild rivers protected by state or federal authority, not the unspoiled areas being scarred by indiscriminate second-home development. That's another story.

## MORE AND MORE PEOPLE

Two trends show up. Unlimited and unrestricted recreation leads to eroded mountainsides, contaminated lakes and rivers, and littered trails and shorelines. That's one picture. The other is the dominance of wild country by commercial franchises, resort operators, package-tour outfitters, or big-business guide services that take over the lion's share of the use-allocations imposed on public lands where such quotas are needed to protect fragile environments.

Of course, it does not seem right to have to go to a franchise holder in order to hike in Yosemite, ski tour in New Hampshire, or run an Idaho river. Neither situation—unchecked despoliation of the wilds or programmed tours—satisfies the basic needs of a mushrooming number of people who want to

People enjoy wilderness areas and national parks through observation and participation. Here a crowd observes Old Faithful geyser in Yellowstone National Park.

participate in an annual "adventure" or stint of self-renewal in the Great Outdoors.

The National Park Service's 286 parks are overrun with visitors and beset with management problems. Nearly 3,000,000 people will visit Rocky Mountain National Park in 1978. Its 105,000 hectares (about 260,000 acres) of high country will be littered, befouled, and dreadfully vandalized. Campers at Oregon's Crater Lake complain of severe gastrointestinal sickness attributable to contaminated water. Roughly five hundred citations are now issued annually in the White Mountain National Forest, where in 1974 vandalism cost the government $68,330. Campers scatter trash and food wastes, light fires without permits, harass other campers, and even threaten forest officers. Everywhere, the number of park visitors doubles by the decade.

## WILD RIVERS SUFFER

People problems are magnified enormously on wild rivers, where the action is confined to a corridor barely wider than the river itself. In some rock-gorges, campsites are thin sand shelves vulnerable to the slightest impact. Yet the river business is booming. On a warm weekend, more than 500 canoeists will run a section of the famed upper Current River in the Ozarks, and more than 15,000 will run the Grand Canyon in 1978. Except where access has been limited, river runners have multiplied fivefold in the past decade.

The Grand Canyon has become a flash point. Its beach campsites are becoming middens of people-debris and people-sewage. Charcoal deposits layer up from open fires, which are illegal, or from firepans emptied upstream. Sand strips are pocked with sewage, deposited, as required, from portable toilets. Biologists find increasing hazards to hygiene in the Grand Canyon.

## AMUSEMENT-PARK RIVERS

Roderick F. Nash, professor of history and environmental studies at the University of California at Santa Barbara and an accomplished whitewater guide, foresees a system of "amusement-park" rivers to accommodate the "whitewater freak" and "rapidomaniac" who is attracted to fast rivers like a downhill skier to steep mountain chutes. "Find enough water to float your boat and you could run bumper to bumper," Nash wrote in early 1977. "In such a scenario, upstream tows, similar to ski lifts, have a place."

Opposite the whitewater person is the river runner who seeks a wilderness experience with a group of friends. The rapids are only one of the many elements in the trip and, like the Indian and the first white canoeists—trappers and voyageurs—he or she will look for the safest passage through heavy water. Some rivers can serve all sorts of whitewater people and, Nash says, may eventually be restricted to different kinds of use by the week or month.

Scenes such as this at a wilderness area campsite have led some to suggest that access to such areas be limited to those with permits.

## QUOTA SYSTEMS

On the Colorado River in the Grand Canyon, the public as well as the environment is abused. The U.S. National Park Service (NPS) established a use-ceiling of 100,000 user-days in 1973, based on actual use in 1972. Ninety-two per cent of the quota is allocated to commercial outfitters and only 8 per cent to noncommercial parties. Yet since 1972, the number of qualified noncommercial applicants has grown fivefold, and four out of five are turned away. It appears likely that NPS will change the allocation, granting noncommercial applicants at least 35 to 40 per cent of the quota.

The Grand Canyon is not the only park where use-ceilings and restrictive quotas have become necessary. Western rivers under the jurisdiction of other federal agencies, such as the U.S. Forest Service and the Bureau of Land Management, Forest Service Primitive Areas, Federal Wilderness Areas, and a growing number of state and local parks have established reservation or quota-permit systems to protect fragile resources and to prevent crowding.

## TO LOOK OR TO PARTICIPATE

In 1872, Congress created the first National Park in Yellowstone as a "pleasuring ground for the benefit and enjoyment of the people." Not until 1916 was the National Park Service established "to conserve the scenery and the natural and historic objects and the wild life therein and to provide for the enjoyment of the same in such manner and by such means as will leave them unimpaired for the enjoyment of future generations." Congress also stipulated that "No natural curiosities, wonders or objects of interest shall be leased, rented or granted to anyone on such terms as to interfere with free access to them by the public. . . ."

It became obvious that certain concessions were needed within park confines, such as lodgings, stores, and outfitter/guides. Yet under a law passed in 1965 to clarify the scope of concessions, the so-called Concessioners Act, it was stated that commercial franchises should "be limited to those that are necessary and appropriate for public use and enjoyment of the national park area in which they are located and that are consistent to the highest practicable degree with the preservation and conservation of the areas."

In 1972, the centennial of Yellowstone, the Conservation Foundation of Washington published a seminal report, *National Parks for the Future,* that was based to a large extent on a major symposium of administrators and conservation professionals. The report emphasized that park administrators must do less toward offering the public a "spectator experience" and far more toward helping the public "to participate." The report criticized the growing reliance on concessioner services. Recreation, it was said, "means to re-create the individual, by exposing him to direct participatory experiences of the natural environment which depend upon activities indigenous to the environment rather than reliance on man-caused changes in that environment."

## ALONE OR AS A GROUP

Yet the trend is the other way, as shown by the system in the Grand Canyon where the overwhelming majority of river passengers are herded downriver on big rafts (most of them motorized). Fewer and fewer frontiers—real or imagined—remain open for

Cleanup operations in camping areas, wilderness and wild river spots, and national parks too frequently seem to be a losing battle, but the battle must be continued if future generations are to know any unspoiled wilderness areas at all.

those who want to take such places on biotic, not man-imposed, terms. Author and sometime ranger Edward Abbey strikes a telling note in his collection of essays, *Desert Solitaire.* "A venturesome minority will always be eager to set off on their own, and no obstacles should be placed in their path; let them take risks, for God's sake, let them get lost, sunburnt, stranded, drowned, eaten by bears, buried alive by avalanches—that is the right and privilege of any free American."

For the many people who do not feel secure on their own, Abbey recommends that rangers be trained to provide "practical guide service" and be naturalists as well. They're supposed to be, already. The funds for rangers and interpretive staff would come from big savings: cut out the road building and myriad other out-of-place facilities that currently burn up taxpayer dollars in parks, says Abbey.

While Abbey is right in his advocacy for the venturesome, in my opinion there has to be an entry permit and an entry fee—a single restriction that ultimately will provide more freedom for backcountry travel and will protect the public against commercialization and crowding.

## NEED FOR PERMITS

I have for some time advocated the issuance of licenses or permits for backcountry camping and other kinds of park use. You would pay, say $25 a year, for such a license and be entitled to go on your own, assuming all the risks, into primitive areas—up mountains, over tundra, through forests, and down rivers. At one time, I proposed that all users of public lands would pay for such a permit and be furnished with mandatory checklists for different degrees of usage. These checklists would, for example, list the needed equipment, clothing, and other gear for backcountry camping, day-touring, and family picnicking from the car or camper. Considering what many already pay for recreational trappings, such as campers and backpacks, a $25 annual fee would not be

National Park Service

burdensome. Besides, it would provide revenues for bigger and better field staffs on public lands.

I propose now, for starters, that a wilderness license be issued to those persons—the venturesome ones—who seek the primitive, backcountry experience, whether it be on Maine's St. John River or in the remote valleys in the High Sierras. Such a license would not exempt persons from applying for a use permit in restricted areas. But it should give them a priority in restricted backcountry preserves.

## ZONE THE PRESERVES

There is nothing new about having a backcountry or wilderness zone. For administrative purposes, NPS already categorizes areas as natural, recreational, or historical. In keeping with this policy, NPS ought to be able to formulate a code of behavior and the prerequisites of experience for the wilderness zone. These zoning guidelines ought to be standardized for all primitive lands in public jurisdiction.

Perhaps those who apply for licenses should also be required to give proof of their competence in the outdoors, just as motorists must demonstrate their ability in order to obtain a license to travel on public highways. Such proof of competence might at first be provided in an affidavit accompanying the application forms. Some day it may be necessary even to take a written test, an examination on the basics of natural science and woodcraft.

Only individuals with wilderness licenses would be able to go into "Backcountry" or on "Wild Rivers" on their own. Anyone else wanting to savor the solitude and raw beauty of such places would have to go with a commercial outfitter. The concessioners would, however, have to demonstrate that they were providing an essential service (as required under the 1965 law) and would be restricted so that campers would be well dispersed (two may be a crowd) in permit areas. Quotas would be allocated equitably. Those persons who qualify for wilderness licenses would be able to say in their applications how many commercial trips they had made in backcountry, or how often they had camped in various parks in a less primitive, more recreation-suited zone.

## NON-COMMERCIAL GUIDES

It is questionable whether publicly supported lands ought to be exploitable on a commercial, profit-making scale at all, if the taxpayers can provide revenues for alternatives. As Ed Abbey suggests, why not have the guides operating within the park system rather than being paid by outfitting businesses that charge high rates to make a profit from a resource in which they own no interest?

Such a system would keep the traditional guides, the seasoned woodsmen who really know their habitats and history, happily well off, and the novice would benefit from the guides' long association with the backcountry and its folklore.

## PEOPLE VS. NATURE

In the spring of 1976, more than a hundred persons—students, rangers, administrators, conservationists, and people like Abbey and Nash met on Mount Hood in Oregon to reach some consensus on the subject of wilderness and individual freedom. Everybody surely agreed with the stated conclusions of the conference that "one of the primary justifications for wilderness lies in the laws of nature, the inherent right of natural processes to continue," and that "one of these rights is the pursuit of individual freedom." But discord and disharmony were rampant on how to arrive at such a conclusion—how to manage backcountry so as to keep both the spirit of man and the diversity of nature intact.

In a real way, fear was the catalyst for this Oregon conference—as expressed by one of the participants, "fear that we were being moved out of those experiences that we enjoy so much." Another conferee reminisced about his forays into the Sierra nearly forty years ago, camping and climbing where he pleased and eating sumptuous meals in a throng. "The freedom to travel in so large a group, congenial though it was to most of us, is gone, or to camp freely, or to take splendidly weathered wood home by the bundle, or to make bough beds, or to improvise field-expedient furniture, or hack away with a scout axe, or to be alone more than an hour or so . . . even to drink water from a sparkling wilderness stream that coliform bacteria didn't get to first."

That is sadly true in too many places. But there is no reason why—with equitable allocations in restricted areas, with privileges like a license granted to those who are able and willing to take backcountry as it comes, and with management policies that promote perception and participation instead of the joy ride—there is no reason, to repeat, why one should not be able to find a few frontiers open when they are most needed □

 SELECTED READINGS

"Preserving our wild and scenic rivers" (collection of articles). *National Geographic,* July 1977.

"Prescription for a beatup wilderness" by B. Scott. *National Wildlife,* April 1977.

"Whither wilderness?" by F. Church. *American Forest,* July 1977.

"Wilderness—keep out. Does this mean us?" by C. A. Schoenfeld. *Outdoor Life,* October 1976.

For the first time in history, man is close to wiping out completely a naturally occurring disease—smallpox. The worst form of the disease has already been eradicated. A minor form of the disease is being eradicated from small pockets of infection in Ethiopia. In the photo above a World Health Organization worker questions Ethiopian villagers about the disease.

# HEALTH AND DISEASE

## contents

# HEALTH AND DISEASE
## review of the year

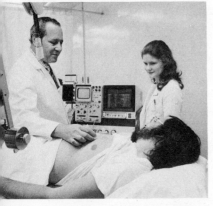

The use of ultrasonography as a diagnostic aid is spreading into cardiology. Above: ultrasound being used to determine heart-valve function. Below: sonogram showing normal mitral-valve function. Bottom: sonogram showing stenosis, or narrowing, of the mitral valve.

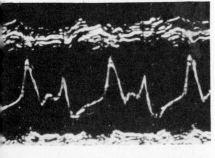

**Ultrasonography.** The use of ultrasound for medical diagnosis became increasingly common during 1977. Physicians have been able for some time to diagnose a variety of problems by using techniques that involve taking X rays after needles, tubes, and chemicals have been injected into the heart, abdomen, or other parts of the body to be studied. These techniques are called invasive because they involve piercing the skin and other tissues to get information necessary for diagnosis. Use of invasive techniques involves potentially fatal risks, such as bleeding, infection, and allergic reactions to chemicals. Ultrasound provides a noninvasive method to get information.

In ultrasound techniques high frequency sound waves are transmitted to the object to be studied and the returning echoes are recorded to produce a televisionlike image. There is no radiation and no known hazards. The technique was developed early in the twentieth century to locate submarines and other submerged objects. Its adaptation to medicine resulted in part from an obstetricians's noticing a resemblance between a submarine in the ocean and a fetus in the uterus. Improvements in techniques have led to its use now in virtually every field of medicine. In the newest advance in ultrasonography, two dimensional motion studies are now possible.

Obstetricians claim that the use of ultrasound has revolutionized their specialty. It can help determine if the fetus is dead or alive, can help diagnose many developmental defects before birth, and on a research basis is used to study the swallowing, respiration, and motion of the fetus in the uterus.

In cardiology ultrasound is used to help detect heart valve damage, congenital heart defects, heart tumors and other heart and circulatory problems. In ophthalmology it is used to help detect retinal detachments, tumors, and the presence of foreign bodies in the eye. ■ In other branches of medical science, ultrasound is used to help detect brain tumors and to help diagnose head injuries, to help detect gallstones and kidney, liver, and spleen abnormalities, and to help trace the spread of cancer in the body.

**Endoscopy.** Advances in one of the invasive techniques of diagnosis—endoscopy—continued during 1977. Endoscopy involves the insertion of miniaturized fiberoptic tubes called endoscopes into parts of the body like the bronchial tubes in the lungs and the duodenum, esophagus, and bile duct in the digestive system to permit direct viewing of the organ. The technique makes possible early diagnosis of some abnormalities hard to diagnose in other ways. Some physicians are also researching the use of the ultrathin endoscopes to treat some disorders. Endoscopes are usually named for the part of the body being examined. A bronchoscope is used for bronchial tubes, for example.

**Two new vaccines.** Two new vaccines were reported effective during 1977. One—called Pneumovax—offers protection against some forms of potentially fatal bacterial pneumonia. There are 83 known types of pneumococcal bacteria. The vaccine is derived from the 14 types that cause about 80 per cent of the estimated 500,000 cases that occur each year in the United States alone. The vaccine was developed by Merck Sharpe and Dohme and was approved by the U.S. Food and Drug Administration (FDA) after extensive tests proved it to be effective. The vaccine is intended for use primarily among older people, those with chronic illnesses, and very young children. The development of the vaccine was particularly timely since some forms of pneumococcal bacteria are believed to have recently become resistant to penicillin and other antibiotics used against them.

The other new vaccine is one against infections caused by the meningococcus bacterium that causes one form of epidemic bacterial meningitis. Scientists of the U.S. National Institute of Health reported that the vaccine had proved effective in preventing infection in all age groups. The American-developed vaccine had earlier proved effective in drastically lowering the incidence of infection among military personnel, but it was not until field tests among children in Finland during a late 1974 epidemic that its effectiveness and safety for all ages were established. The development moved researchers a small but important step closer to their goal of developing one vaccine to protect against a group of bacteria that cause the most common forms of bacterial meningitis. That development is, however, thought to be many years away.

**Lag in immunizations.** The Carter Administration has launched an "immunization initiative" to boost protection among Americans against common, preventable diseases like poliomyelitis, measles, rubella, whooping cough, tetanus, and diphtheria. In recent years adequate protection levels have sagged to potentially dangerous levels. In 1977 there was a 50 per cent increase in measles cases, a 75 per cent increase in rubella cases, and outbreaks of whooping cough in several states, and public health officials warn about the possible recurrence of epidemics of "conquered diseases." The new immunization drive aims to raise immunization levels for the young above 90 per cent by the fall of 1979.

**Progress against smallpox.** The worst form of smallpox, the kind that kills, blinds, and maims, has been eradicated. The last known case involved a three-year-old girl in Bangladesh in October 1975. Since then tens of thousands of United Nations World Health Organization (WHO) workers have searched—in vain—for additional cases of this form of the disease caused by the virus *variola major*. ■ A much milder form of smallpox, caused by the *variola minor* virus, remains in Somalia on the horn of Africa, but WHO officials believe that they are on the verge of wiping out this form also. When that occurs, it will mark the first time that mankind has wiped out any naturally occurring disease.

**Legionnaire's Disease.** During 1977 Legionnaire's disease proved to be a health problem with a wider dimension than originally apparent when it caused an epidemic that killed 29 and sickened 151 others during an American Legion convention in Philadelphia in 1976. Scientists at the U.S. Center for Disease Control in Atlanta, Georgia, discovered the cause of the disease—a hitherto unknown rod-shaped bacterium. They also found that the same bacteria had been responsible for two earlier unexplained outbreaks—one in St. Elizabeth's Hospital in Washington,

Merck Sharp & Dohme

Pneumovax, a new vaccine that offers protection against some forms of bacterial pneumonia, is purified in many steps, including an ultrafiltration process shown here.

Scientists discovered the cause of Legionnaire's Disease during 1977—a rod-shaped bacterium, shown below magnified 119,500 times.

Center for Disease Control

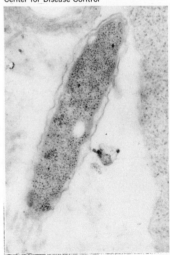

The care of severely burned persons has improved greatly in the last few years. Special centers with the most advanced facilities provide the careful and long-term care these patients need. Below a nurse prepares an immersion tub for a burn victim's twice-daily cleansing.

New York Hospital-Cornell
Medical Center Burn Center

D.C., in 1965 and one in Pontiac, Michigan, in 1968. Other cases of Legionnaire's disease have now been found scattered across the United States and in Europe, and during 1977 small outbreaks occurred in Ohio and in Vermont. Although the cause of Legionnaire's Disease is now known, much remains to be learned. Scientists do not, for example, know where the organism lives in nature, how it is spread, or why it seems to produce sporadic outbreaks.

**Brain makes its own pain killers.** Scientists discovered a surprising similarity between substances produced by the human brain and by the opium poppy. The finding has opened up a new dimension of body chemistry, offering insights into the nature of pain, pleasure, the emotions, and possibly some disorders like epilepsy and mental illness. The key discovery was that the brain and the pituitary gland make their own natural substances that apparently act like morphine, the pain-killing drug derived from opium. The spur for the discovery came from studies that showed that some animal brain cells had special sites to which opiate drugs such as morphine would fit in a seemingly perfect lock-and-key fashion. After identifying the receptors, scientists found that the body makes its own chemicals to fit these receptors. The discovery of these substances led to the recognition of a whole new family of chemicals called endorphines. (At first they were sometimes called enkephalins.)

It is considered likely that these brain chemicals are involved in the body's natural mechanisms for dealing with pain and that they may play an important role in explaining why some people are more susceptible to drug addiction than others. The discoveries have led to new hypotheses concerning pain, epilepsy, alcoholism, insomnia, and schizophrenia and other mental illnesses. Some of the endorphines have been used to treat severe pain, narcotic withdrawal, and schizophrenia with promising results, but much remains to be learned. Nevertheless, scientists feel that they have made an important step toward unlocking the mysteries of the brain.

**Lung cancer and smoking.** Deaths from lung cancer are increasing worldwide, and are unlikely to drop in the near future, according to a recent World Health Organization study. The sharpest increase is among women. The trend for lung cancer deaths is in sharp contrast to the statistics for all other types of cancer. The study attributed the rise in lung cancer deaths to cigarette smoking. It rejected the contention that air pollution was a major contributing factor. However, in blaming cigarette smoking for the rise in lung cancer deaths, the WHO study did not discount a link between air pollution and lung cancer. It said, "To remove air pollution would reduce lung cancer but would not reduce the excess lung mortality associated with cigarette smoking." The trend toward increasing lung cancer deaths among women was also attributed to their smoking "at work as well as at play."

The WHO report came at a time when, in the United States, Connecticut cancer experts recorded for the first time in that state's history more lung cancer among women than men aged 35 to 44 years. The 35-to-44 age group is the youngest in which cigarette smoking effects are clearly apparent. The statistics are a reflection of the increasing number of women who have taken up cigarette smoking in recent decades, a situation that is in sharp contrast to 1930 when only two per cent of women 18 years and older were smokers and when nearly 30 times as many men had the habit.

In 1978 102,000 people in the United States will develop lung cancer—79,000 men and 23,000 women. It takes decades for lung cancer to develop. Therefore current statistics reflect habits and life styles that began several decades ago. Now, although more young women are smoking at an earlier age and more heavily than previously, it is too early for the national statistics to reflect this potential time bomb. Nevertheless, the trend is clear. The ratio of male to female lung cancer is now 3:2 in the 35-to-44 age group, compared to 7:1 about 20 years ago and 4:1 about 10 years ago, according to reports of the U.S. National Cancer Institute.

**Heart attacks and cigarette smoking.** Cigarette smoking has also been associated with an increased risk of heart attack, but scientists have long been unable to learn how precisely cigarettes damage the body biologically—to produce cancer or circulatory problems. Now, two researchers at Cornell University Medical School in New York have opened what may be a new avenue of research into how cigarette smoking might initiate biologically damaging processes. They identified a substance in cigarette smoke that activates the blood clotting system. The substance, called rutin, is a protein that is present in both tobacco leaves and cigarette smoke as well as in many vegetables. Rutin was found to activate Factor XII, a blood substance that plays an important role in initiating the blood clotting process. This finding could help explain the link between cigarette smoking and an increased risk of heart attacks.

**New drug for heart attack victims.** In early 1978 doctors expressed cautious optimism about an international study that found that a drug, Anturane, had more than halved the incidence of sudden deaths from heart attacks among people who had previously had at least one heart attack. The surprising results offered a potential new use for an old drug, one that is marketed by Ciba-Geigy for the treatment of gout. At least 15,000 lives in the United States alone could be saved each year if people who have suffered a heart attack take the drug every day, according to the U.S. and Canadian researchers who did the Ciba-Geigy-funded study involving 1,475 heart attack patients at 26 medical centers. Each volunteer began taking the drug or a placebo on the first visit to his physician, from 25 to 35 days after suffering a heart attack. When the preliminary results were analyzed after an average of 8.4 months of treatment, the annual death rate from heart conditions was 9.5 per cent in the placebo group and 4.9 per cent in the Anturane group, a 48.5 per cent difference. The annual death rate for sudden heart deaths was 6.3 per cent for the placebo group and 2.7 per cent for the Anturane group, a 57.2 per cent difference. Except for gastrointestinal symptoms such as belching and mild abdominal discomfort, Anturane patients were not found to suffer any more side effects than those taking the placebo.

The FDA is studying an application from Ciba-Geigy for the new use of the drug Anturane, although there is criticism from some doctors that the study period of 8 months was too short to provide reliable results. The FDA takes the position that once it licenses a drug for a specific use, doctors should prescribe that drug only for approved use, but the agency has no control over the practice of medicine, and doctors can prescribe an already marketed drug for an unapproved use if they choose to do so within the usual bounds of the patient-doctor relationship.

Lawrence K. Altman M.D.

WHO

Cigarette smoking has increased considerably among women in the last few decades, with many, such as this teenage girl, starting to smoke at a very young age.

Take-your-own-blood-pressure machines are now found in many stores. These machines may have some value in alerting people to possible health problems. However, fears that they may not provide accurate readings and that they may lead some people to postpone seeking proper medical attention are causing many to question the wisdom of their use.

UPI

# THE STIGMA OF CANCER

## by Richard Severo

CANCER isn't just a disease. It is a stigma few want to discuss, remaining a study in ignorance, irrationality, and fear.

People who have cancer sometimes speak of themselves as the new lepers; of being rejected, overprotected, and misunderstood, all at the same time and by the very people they look to for support. And among those who want to help cancer patients, there is a sense of guilt they cannot define, a foreboding that they cannot understand.

• A wife in Texas will not kiss the man to whom she has been married for 27 years because she is afraid of catching his cancer, although doctors have assured her it is not possible.

• A sister in New York decided she could no longer share dishes and eating utensils with her brother, although they had lived together for 70 years. She was afraid of somehow contracting the lung cancer he got after smoking three packs of cigarettes a day for most of his life.

• A man in Oklahoma thinks cancer is the work of the devil, and a woman in Pennsylvania is sure that if you pray to God and are not "cured," it is a sign of retribution from the almighty.

• A mother in California told her children not to play with the child of a neighbor because one of his parents had cancer and the child might be a "carrier."

• A well-educated young woman first lavished sympathy and love on a younger cousin stricken with leukemia, then shut her out emotionally, despite remission and a hopeful prognosis. Finally she confessed to her: "I was frightened by the idea that I was getting closer to you and you were just going to die on me."

Cancer. For too many people, the very word evokes an almost medieval fear of the unknown, a false equation that cancer equals death. In an effort to learn more about the problems associated with cancer, medical reporters for *The New York Times* interviewed 38 cancer patients from various parts of the United States as well as medical researchers, psychiatrists, and surgeons who had studied the disease and the problems associated with it.

### COMMON—YET VIEWED AS EXOTIC

The reporters also spoke to members of families and friends and business associates of people suffering from cancer. What emerged was an unlikely case of mental gymnastics: a common disease that about 25 per cent of all people living in the United States may get in their lifetimes has come to be regarded as exotic, remote. The fears, expressed more frequently by people who did not have cancer than those who did, ignored positive indications suggesting more and more that cancer patients need not view the advent of their disease as marking the end of useful lives.

Medical researchers say that if all kinds of cancer are included, the disease has about a 47 per cent "curability rate." Fifty per cent of all stroke victims are dead within a year of the stroke and 35 per cent of all coronary victims are dead within a month of the heart attack.

Heart disease kills more people than cancer does, but cancer remains more awesome. It is an awe shared by the victim, the physician, and the family and friends who want to be supportive of the patient.

### UNLIKE OTHER DISEASES

Dr. Rene C. Mastrovito, a psychiatrist at the Memorial Sloan-Kettering Cancer Institute in New York, said that among patients with cancer, the question was repeatedly asked, "Why me?" They share, he said, "an inner revulsion, a concept of feeling themselves unclean."

It would appear that the revulsion felt by the victim was frequently mirrored by and magnified in those about him, with the result that his emotional adjustment was made even more difficult. The disease takes on proportions that are simply not seen in other illnesses, including those that rival cancer in its power to disable.

"There is no other illness with this mystique," said Dr. Mastrovito, "no other with less social value. Attitudes are changing, but traditionally, a man who had a heart attack had something socially redeeming about him . . . he was considered a hard worker.

"Even influenza could suggest you worked too hard. People with ulcers are regarded as worriers in a culture where worrying has an honorable connotation. With cancer, you get none of that feeling."

The feelings of people who do not have cancer, but who are trying to deal with it in friends or relatives, emerge frequently as brittle and ugly. Initial feelings and expressions of sympathy may give way to guilt, anger, and resentment that go unrecognized for what they are in the person experiencing the emotions. Much of the problem, said Dr. Mastrovito, lies in cancer's image as a killer.

## WAITING FOR DEATH

"When people believe that an illness is going to be terminal, they are literally waiting for the victim to die and so there is an unspoken anger and guilt that follows," he said. "The friend or relative of a cancer patient has to keep telling himself that he shouldn't be weary at all the visiting and traveling he has to do, shouldn't be angry at all the fuss he's going to."

"The anger and guilt emerges in the chronicity of the disease and it is exacerbated by the belief that cancer will waste the body and do terrible things—even if it doesn't—and an inability to know what to say to a patient under those circumstances."

Moreover, because of the notion that cancer always kills, people feel as if they are dealing "with someone scheduled to be executed," Dr. Mastrovito said. He added that friends and relatives felt the loss before it occurred. Because they were sure that death was approaching, they might try to withdraw from the patient before he or she died—so that when death came, perhaps the loss would not be felt so much. This self-defensive mechanism does not always help, however, and may leave the survivor feeling guilt for having withdrawn.

Keith Meyers/NYT Pictures

His leg lost to cancer, a young boy tries to return to normal life and deliver newspapers. His success may depend on the reactions of others to him.

## SOCIAL STIGMA

The social problems associated with cancer appear to be of considerable magnitude, although there are as yet relatively few data. It remains a problem somewhat neglected by medical researchers, who have understandably devoted most of their energies to studying the disease itself.

Many cancer patients and their families and friends have few or no adjustment problems because of the disease. In a sense, surveys probably give a somewhat distorted view since the people who are willing to talk about problems are those who have experienced them. Those without problems are sometimes surprised to learn that such problems exist.

But Orville Kelly, a former newspaperman who got cancer, then formed a national organization for cancer patients called Make Today Count, says he has heard thousands of stories that give credence to the notion that the shunning of cancer patients is widespread.

William E. Sauro/NYT Pictures

Dr. Rene Mastrovito about to begin rounds at Memorial Sloan-Kettering Cancer Institute in New York where he provides psychological counseling for cancer patients.

"Every time I give a workshop I hear the same stories," he said. "People keeping separate eating utensils, bed clothes, wives not kissing husbands, husbands not kissing wives. There is no stigma like cancer. How many times do you read in a newspaper that someone you know who died of cancer 'died after a prolonged illness?'" Cancer, he noted, is something families don't want to talk about or even admit to.

One patient at Sloan-Kettering, Joyce Weisberg, is in the unenviable position of being able to compare the reactions of those around her to her cancer of the breast with the way they responded a few years ago when she got multiple sclerosis.

"When I had multiple sclerosis, there was fear, but my friends did not equate it with their own death as they did when I got cancer," said Mrs. Weisberg, who recently had a mastectomy.

Robert Fasano, a sophomore at Sarah Lawrence College in New York, had similar perceptions about reactions to his cancer.

"I became a symbol for their own mortality and they didn't want to think about it," he said of some relatives and friends. Mr. Fasano discovered on New Year's Day, 1974, that he had Hodgkin's disease. Hodgkin's disease is cancer of the lymph glands, a form that often manifests itself among young people. He recalled that people would come to see him in the hospital and become so upset that "I would have to take care of *them.*"

Mr. Fasano isn't bitter: "I was scared; why shouldn't they be?" He also spoke of strain he sensed with one of his doctors.

"When I was really sick, I felt he was kind of gruff with me. Now I'm getting better and he wants to be pals with me. He deals with sick people and terminal people all the time and I guess he didn't know whether I would be a winner or a loser."

FEAR OF CONTAGION

The impressions of cancer patients interviewed by *The New York Times* were consistent with the findings contained in a study done for the California Division of the American Cancer Society by Professor Frances Lomas Feldman of the School of Social Work at the University of Southern California. The study dealt primarily with the experiences of cancer patients in work situations.

"More than half of the people we talked to had social or emotional problems related to cancer diagnosis," said Professor Feldman, who conducted her study in the Los Angeles area.

Professor Feldman told of one woman whose employer was glad to see her return to work but whose coworkers "moved their desks away from her and do not join her in coffee breaks as they had before."

Another woman who had a breast removed because of cancer was asked by a co-worker, "How does it feel to be only partly a woman?" Her social isolation became even more terrifying when her 15-year-old child lost her best friend because the other child's parents were afraid her child might be a carrier of cancer.

At Sloan-Kettering, one of the foremost cancer-research facilities in the world, no medical expert has found evidence to support the notion that cancer may be contagious. "The idea is nonsense," said Dr. Lewis Thomas, the institute's president.

Dr. Edward S. Beattie, Jr., general director and chief medical officer at Sloan-Kettering, points out that pathologists there devote almost all their working time to examining tumors "and there is no evidence that they have higher incidences of cancer themselves."

But with cancer, what is known does not comfort those who fear the unknown, a fear that is shared not only by lay people but also by physicians who are not involved in cancer research. Some interns and residents in New York hospitals acknowledge they have tried to avoid shaking hands with cancer patients. And a gynecologist told Helen Fisher that if she continued to have sexual relations with her husband, Robert, who has leukemia, she ran the risk of contracting the disease.

With courage and determination, Max Rogge learned esophageal speech after his voicebox was removed because of cancer and went on to lead a normal life—with a wife, child, and job as a truck driver.

American Cancer Society

William E. Sauro/NYT Pictures

Robert Fisher says "It isn't so bad to have cancer." His illness has, however, contributed to marital and employment problems he has encountered.

Mrs. Fisher did not heed the advice but acknowledged in a recent interview that the admonition had created additional stress in an already strained marital situation. The Fishers have since separated and although both agree cancer was not the cause, it placed a further emotional burden on them as they were trying to solve their problems.

Mr. Fisher also feels that his cancer has, at the very least, contributed to the problems he has encountered at his family's business.

Before learning of his cancer, Mr. Fisher earned more than $700 a week as sales manager and did extensive contact work with prospective clients. He says that his cousins, who are the principal executives in the operation, have more recently offered him an inside job paying around $200 a week.

Herbert Fisher, president of the company, confirmed that the organization had decided that "Robert was best suited for a job that did not entail meeting the public," but he declined to discuss the issue further, explaining that the company's relations with Robert were "a complicated situation." Negotiations are under way to purchase Robert's share of the company.

Robert Fisher was told three years ago that he had three to eight years more to live. "I haven't been dying those years, I've been living them," he said recently. "I now have a life without fear. I'm healthier now in a real sense."

Last summer, he took a 800-kilometer (500-mile) bicycle trip to Vermont. He studies pottery-making in Greenwich Village in New York City once a week and, despite his marital and employment problems, credits cancer with giving him values he wished he had a long time ago.

"It isn't so bad to have cancer," Mr. Fisher said. "I think that having hay fever is worse."

Robert Fisher's wry sense of humor has seen him through a difficult time in his life. The mechanism for Clare Lambert is a forceful candor that quickly emerges when anyone asks her about her experience with cancer.

## MODERN-DAY LEPERS

"It is the most important thing in my life," said Miss Lambert, a Ph.D. candidate at the New School for Social Research in New York City. "I tell people up front that I have cancer. I'm still bitter—bitter because of the suffering, because of other people, because of their perceptions of me."

Miss Lambert, who got Hodgkin's disease, tends to regard herself as cured. There has been no sign of it for five years. But she makes it clear that the emotional stresses that accompanied the disease are very much with her.

She recalled that in one hospital where she was a patient, some nurses stopped talking to her after the disease was diagnosed because they "were about my age and they related to me and it made them feel uncomfortable that such a young person got cancer."

Her isolation from young nurses was so apparent, she recalls, that one night an older nurse stopped by her room to apologize for the others.

Miss Lambert also remembered vividly the day she told one of her professors that she had cancer and he said, "Oh, my God, Jesus Christ," and ran from the room, leaving her alone and with the distinct impression that she would have to do much of her coping alone.

"Cancer is the modern-day leprosy . . . people have the idea that if you use the same telephone you're going to get it," she said.

Miss Lambert's view of the situation is by no means unique. A cancer patient in Los Angeles told Professor Feldman:

"The employment interviewer asked me to exchange the pen, with which I was filling in an application, for a pencil; pencils are cheaper to discard . . ."

## SOME EXCEPTIONS

To be sure, not all cancer patients report such bleak experiences. Janet Goldberg, a young stockbroker in New York City who had a mastectomy, reports she has had no problems because of it.

"Nobody was afraid to look me in the eye," she said. The night before the operation there was a party in her room, attended by many of her coworkers and friends. Moreover, she has not been rejected by men, she said.

"The male population of this city is surprisingly together," she said. "The people who accept me have that much more character."

If *The Times*'s survey is any indication, Janet Goldberg is something of an exception. She has a personality that is quite strong and positive.

There were only a few others who had her outlook and her experiences. Fred Velepec, a business executive who had cancer in his jawbone, recalled that once a drunk came up to him in a bar and with the abrasive admixture of honesty and belligerence drunks sometimes have, demanded to know, "What's wrong with your face?"

Mr. Velepec took it in stride and said, "Oh, I just had a little cancer, buddy." The drunk wandered off, less drunk than he was before he asked the question.

Mr. Velepec maintains that ugly incidents like that have been few and far between. And like Janet Goldberg, he is strong enough to deal with them. Others show strength, too, but the way they are treated

His leukemia controlled, Mike Finamore tries to bury any emotional scars of his illness and looks forward to a long and happy marriage.

speaks ill of a society that prides itself on its social awareness and its rejection of the kinds of inhumanity more commonly associated with the plots of Dickens' novels.

Timothy Nevin, an eighth-grader from Cherry Hill, New Jersey, talks convincingly of his friends and their support after he lost a leg from bone cancer. But at the same time, he can recall a middle-aged woman who came up to him in a bus station, gawked at his body, demanded to know what happened and when told it was cancer, retorted: "He didn't have no cancer. Doctors just like to cut people up."

Last winter, the children of one neighbor never tired of calling him "gimpy" and "peg leg" and once, when he dropped a glove, they quickly threw it down the sewer. His mother, Patricia Nevin, has not talked to the parents of the children involved because she feels that, in this particular case, "it just wouldn't do any good."

Despite the problems, Timmy remains vigorous, optimistic and doesn't regard himself as crippled in any sense of the word.

And in Yonkers, New York, 17-year-old Joseph Nicolino, another bone-cancer patient, can remember when five of his closest friends shaved their heads when he lost his hair from chemotherapy treatments, so that people wouldn't stare at him so much. Joseph said that most of the staring was done by "babies and adults."

## EMOTIONAL BLOWS THE WORST

A young woman who learned of her leukemia just as she was embarking on a career in law isn't stared at because her cancer cannot be seen. But from her friends and relatives she got a sense of urgency and lack of sympathy.

In her opinion, they resented her because they felt that with a cancer patient around, they shouldn't acknowledge their own needs. Then they began to chide her for not taking her illness seriously enough. Some old ties with relatives and friends have broken down and may never be renewed.

"Going through this illness is nothing compared to taking the emotional blows," she said. "Dealing with a physical problem is much easier. Nobody can mend a broken heart" □

 SELECTED READINGS

*Cancer: The Behavioral Dimension,* edited by Joseph Cullen and others. Raven, 1976.

*Living With Cancer* by Ernest H. Rosenbaum. Praeger, 1975.

*Needs of the Cancer Patient* by Joanne Parsons. Contemporary Books, 1975.

*Not Alone With Cancer: A Guide for Those Who Care; What To Do; What To Expect.* C. C. Thomas, 1976.

U.S. Customs

George Bakacs, APF

# LAETRILE

Laetrile is the chemical amygdalin, which is found in the kernels of apricots and some other fruits.

## by Joan Arehart-Treichel

LAETRILE has been the subject of heated controversy for several years. It is called a cancer cure by some, a complete hoax by others. What is the science behind the controversy?

Laetrile—the chemical amygdalin—is found in the kernels of many fruits, notably apricots, peaches, plums, and bitter almonds. It is also found in cassava, lima beans, and numerous other plants in a slightly different chemical form.

The notion of using Laetrile as a cancer drug received its first major impetus in the United States in 1920 when Ernst T. Krebs, Sr., a California physician, tried apricot pits as a cancer treatment. Laetrile became more popular in 1952 when Ernst T. Krebs, Jr., a biochemist, developed a purified form of Laetrile for injection. Yet only in recent years have thousands of people in the United States been clamoring for Laetrile, largely through the promotion of organizations such as the Committee for Freedom of Choice in Cancer Therapy and the National Health Foundation.

Some Laetrile proponents have been pushing the U.S. Food and Drug Administration to approve it. The FDA has resisted on the grounds that Laetrile is worthless against cancer. Other Laetrile supporters have tried to get around FDA prohibition of interstate commerce of Laetrile by smuggling it into the United States from Mexico or by legalizing its manufacture and use on a state-by-state basis. So far they have made headway, particularly in the latter direction. Fourteen states have approved Laetrile use.

The Laetrile controversy seems to keep growing. Should Americans be allowed to use the drug or not? Some scientists, however, believe that not enough attention has been devoted to the science behind Laetrile. What evidence is there for the safety of Laetrile and for its effectiveness against cancer? Is the evidence sufficient to pass judgment on Laetrile as a cancer drug?

### IS IT SAFE?

The first and somewhat easier question is that of Laetrile's safety. Extensive animal experiments on the safety and effectiveness of Laetrile were conducted by a team of researchers at the Memorial Sloan-Kettering Cancer Center in New York City and at the Catholic Medical Center in Woodhaven, N.Y., from 1972 to 1976. These experiments showed no harmful effects of Laetrile in mice except when very large doses were used. Nor when Laetrile was given along with accepted cancer drugs did it alter their benefits or toxicity.

Exactly how much Laetrile is safe for humans, however, has not been determined. Certainly it can be harmful if taken in sufficient doses. For instance, two cancer patients were treated for serious adverse reactions to Laetrile in one month at the Georgetown University Medical Center in Washington, D.C. One of the patients developed fever, rash, and gastrointestinal symptoms that promptly disappeared after discontinuation of Laetrile, only to recur after she resumed taking the compound. The other patient experienced a weakening of the eye muscles and eyelids. Within 48 hours of being taken off Laetrile, his condition improved dramatically and resolved itself completely within six days.

In another case, a Buffalo, N.Y., infant died from accidental ingestion of an unknown number of Lactrile pills her father was taking. Laetrile ultimately breaks down in the body into the poison cyanide. Several Californians who ate apricot pits as a health food suffered cyanide poisoning from them. A three-year-old girl who ate 15 apricot kernels experienced cyanide poisoning as well. Both acute and chronic cyanide poisoning have been reported among Nigerians, Jamaicans, and Malaysians who ate a lot of cassava.

## IS IT EFFECTIVE?

As for Laetrile's effectiveness, or lack of effectiveness, the evidence is more extensive and complex. First the test-tube evidence:

Unlike many cancer remedies of questionable value, Laetrile is a well-known and identifiable chemical substance, amygdalin. Amygdalin is broken down in the body by enzymes known as beta-glucosidases to yield dextrose and mandelonitrile, which is benzyaldehyde plus a molecule of hydrogen cyanide. Laetrile proponents offer several different arguments for how Laetrile's pharmacological actions can kill cancer tissues in the body.

One of their arguments, initiated by Ernst Krebs, Jr., is that cancer tissues are selectively killed by Laetrile because they contain more of the beta-glucosidase enzymes than healthy tissues do. Is there any scientific basis to this claim? Apparently not. According to Joseph R. DiPalma, professor of pharmacology at Hahnemann Medical College in Philadelphia, "Cancer cells which have been analyzed many, many times have very little content of this type of enzymes." Thomas H. Jukes, a nutrition scientist at the University of California at Berkeley, agrees, stating: "There are only traces of beta-glucosidase in animal tissues and even less in experimental tumors."

Another Laetrilist claim is that rhodanese, an enzyme that converts toxic hydrogen cyanide to nontoxic thiocyanate, is present in tumors in lower amounts than it is present in normal tissues, and hence tumors cannot protect themselves against hydrogen cyanide. Any basis to this argument? It doesn't look like it. According to Daniel S. Martin, a cancer-therapy scientist at the Catholic Medical Center and one of the investigators in the recent Laetrile studies at that center, assays of this enzyme have shown no such differences between cancerous and healthy tissues.

## A VITAMIN?

Still a third assertion by Laetrile proponents is that Laetrile is a vitamin—vitamin $B_{17}$—and thus a nutritional substance rather than a drug. Is there any evidence to support this claim? Dean Burk, a former National Cancer Institute scientist, believes that there might be. He asserts that it is "almost impossible . . . ever to declare scientifically that a given compound is not a vitamin" and that "meats, milk, cheese, eggs and other proteins may similarly produce cyanide when decomposed by suitable enzymes or catalysts." In contrast, Jukes declares that Laetrile has "not the slightest resemblance to a vitamin. The crucial property of a vitamin is that its absence from the diet produces a specific deficiency disease in vertebrate animals. The cyanogenetic glycosides do not have this property."

While Laetrile has really not been adequately tested to determine whether it is a vitamin or not, even if it were found to be a vitamin, its vitamin properties would not demonstrate that it is also effective against tumors. Only one other vitamin has shown any anticancer properties to date, and that is vitamin A.

Taking all of the above test-tube evidence into consideration, then, the conclusion is that none of it supports the ability of Laetrile to kill tumors.

## ANIMAL TESTS

Do animal experiments with Laetrile indicate any effectiveness against cancer? Take those conducted at the National Cancer Institute (NCI) or under NCI contract at other institutions. The first was conducted at the Warf Institute in Madison, Wisconsin, under NCI contract, in 1957. Laetrile was given to mice that had had tumors transplanted onto them—a common system for screening compounds for anticancer activity. Although the results of this experiment were not published, they showed that Laetrile produced no significant inhibition of tumor growth nor a significant increase in lifespan in the mice that had been given cancer.

In 1960, a second experiment was run, under NCI contract, at Microbiological Associates, Inc. This time Laetrile from a different source was tested against the same mouse tumors. Again no antitumor activity was found. The results were not published.

Then in 1969, a third Laetrile test was conducted at Microbiological Associates. This time Laetrile was tested alone or in combination with the enzyme that helps break it down in the body, beta-glucosidase, against leukemia in mice. The results, which were not published, showed that Laetrile was ineffective against cancer, either alone or in combination with the enzyme.

A fourth Laetrile experiment was carried out in 1973, under NCI contract, by Isidore Wodinsky and Joseph K. Swinarski of Arthur D. Little, Inc., of Cambridge, Massachusetts. Laetrile, in daily injections of 3,200 milligrams per kilogram of body weight down to 6.25 milligrams per kilogram, was tested alone or in combination with beta-glucosidase against four kinds of tumors in rodents. It was found ineffective alone or in combination with the enzyme. These results were published in the September/October 1975 *Cancer Chemotherapy Reports*.

A fifth experiment was conducted, under NCI contract, by W. R. Laster, Jr., and F. M. Schabel, Jr., of the Southern Research Institute in Birmingham, Alabama. Laetrile, in injections of 500 milligrams per kilogram of body weight down to 23 milligrams per kilogram was tested alone or in combination with beta-glucosidase against three transplanted mouse tumors. No antitumor activity was found. These results were also published in the September/October 1975 *Cancer Chemotherapy Reports*.

Finally a sixth experiment was completed, under NCI contract, at the Battelle Memorial Institute in Columbus, Ohio, by David P. Houchens and Artemio A. Ovejera. In one phase, mice with breast cancer or colon cancer were injected every four days with three doses of 400, 800, or 1,600 milligrams per kilogram of body weight of Laetrile. In another phase, mice with colon cancer were divided into separate groups and treated for nine days with either Laetrile alone; beta-glucosidase, the enzyme that breaks Laetrile down in the body into cyanide; or Laetrile and beta-glucosidase. The scientists report that they found no difference in the growth of the tumors that they followed for 42 days in the mice that did and did not receive Laetrile.

Thus NCI or NCI-sponsored Laetrile animal experiments concur with the test-tube evidence to date that Laetrile has no anticancer activity.

## SOME INITIAL PROMISING RESULTS

The most extensive animal tests ever conducted on the substance in the United States were done at Sloan-Kettering and the Catholic Medical Center.

Eleven series of experiments, 23 experiments all told, were conducted to determine whether Laetrile has any ability to counter spontaneous breast cancer or leukemia in mice. The $CD_8F_1$ strain of mice was used in most of the breast-cancer research, the Swiss Webster albino mouse strain for one breast-cancer study, and AKR strain mice for the leukemia studies. Nineteen of the studies were performed with Laetrile obtained from Mexico, the other four with Laetrile from Germany. The doses of Laetrile used in all but two of the experiments varied from 1,000 to 3,000 milligrams per kilogram of body weight, considerably more than Laetrile patients usually take. In one experiment, 40 milligrams per kilogram of Laetrile was used, which more closely approximated the 3 grams a day taken by many Laetrile patients. In the other experiment, doses as high as 4,000 and 5,000 milligrams per kilogram were used. Results from all the studies suggested that neither the source of Laetrile nor the dose level used produces any great differences in outcome. However, there were some discrepancies among the study results, apparently due to another cause.

In the initial set of six experiments, for instance, one of the investigators—Kanematsu Sugiura of Sloan-Kettering—gave Laetrile to 60 mice and saline injections to 60 control mice. He found that while 90 per cent of the control mice experienced lung metastases due to spreading breast tumors, only 21 per cent of the treated mice did. The investigators at Sloan-Kettering and the Catholic Medical Center conducted subsequent experiments to see whether they could confirm these initial promising results and perhaps even expand them.

Partial confirmation was achieved in a joint experiment conducted by Suguira and associate Franz A. Schmid. Whereas Suguira noted lung metastases among 100 per cent of control mice, he noted only 38 per cent among treated mice. Whereas Schmid identified 80 per cent of control mice with metastases, he identified only 44 per cent of treated mice with them. In fact, Suguira confirmed his initial results with two other experiments he conducted alone. In one, 91 per cent of control mice showed metastases, versus 22 per cent of the treated mice. In the other, 81 per cent of controls showed metastases, versus only 17 per cent of treated mice.

## NO CONFIRMATION

However, in the numerous other experiments conducted with or without Suguira, the investigators were not able to approach these promising results and in several instances even came up with better results for controls than for treated animals. For example, in an experiment on mice with spontane-ous breast cancer that he conducted alone, Schmid found lung metastases among 70 per cent of treated mice versus only 58 per cent for controls. In a joint experiment on mice with spontaneous breast tumors, Suguira and three other investigators found lung metastases in 42 per cent of the treated mice versus 21 per cent of the controls.

## EVALUATING RESULTS

Why such a discrepancy in results? Apparently it is because not all of the experiments were evaluated by the same method. Results favorable to Laetrile nearly all resulted from macrovision or microscopic examination and mostly from Suguira's visual observation. The results most unfavorable to Laetrile came from bioassay, where lungs from the test animals were shredded and injected into other mice. If the injections made tumors form, then one could conclude that the lungs had contained metastases.

A prime example of how these two methods of evaluation produced different results came from a blind experiment on spontaneous breast cancers in mice conducted by Suguira. In this arrangement, he did not know which of the mice had received Laetrile and which had not. Suguira's visual evaluation showed that 54 per cent of the treated mice experienced lung metastases compared with 63 per cent of control mice. Bioassay, in contrast, demonstrated that 85 per cent of the treated mice, compared with 83 per cent of control mice, were positive for them. In still another blind experiment conducted by Suguira, visual evaluation produced somewhat favorable results for Laetrile; bioassay did not.

Which type of evaluation is the one to believe? The bioassay results must be considered the stronger of the two since they are totally objective. There is no need to rely on an observer's eyesight or unintentional visual bias, which is the case with macrovision or microscopic examination. In other words, Suguira's positive results for Laetrile, dependent entirely on visual observation, could be pitted against the less favorable visual results obtained by the other investigators, but they simply cannot stand up against the negative results procured by bioassay.

These numerous booklets and pamphlets reflect the widespread public interest in laetrile as a possible cancer cure—a claim that repeated scientific tests have been unable to substantiate.

Science News

When all these results are taken together, then, they, like the NCI animal tests and test-tube research, rule out anticancer activity for Laetrile. What's more, the Sloan-Kettering investigators tested Laetrile against various kinds of transplanted tumors in mice. These results were totally negative.

## CLINICAL EVIDENCE

Finally, how about clinical evidence for Laetrile's effectiveness against tumors? Some 50,000 people in the United States have so far taken Laetrile for cancer. A number of them have not been helped by it or even have died. Yet others attest to Laetrile's curative powers or at least to its palliative effects—pain relief or feeling better. Do such testimonials constitute clinical evidence for Laetrile's efficacy?

No, most cancer scientists reply. For instance, in many cases where patients have claimed that Laetrile has brought about a cancer remission, pathology reports have not been available to document the before and after effects or even that a patient had cancer in the first place. As for Laetrile's palliative effects, scientists tend to point out that they are probably psychologically induced and that such a placebo effect could be achieved with any drug in which a patient believes. Yet, even if Laetrile's pain-relieving impact

were physiologically rather than psychologically induced, it would not be the same as antitumor activity.

## POLITICAL PRESSURE

Should a scientifically controlled clinical trial be conducted to test Laetrile's effectiveness against cancer? From a scientific viewpoint, no. All of the 40 anticancer drugs on the U.S. market were shown to be active against tumors in animals before they were shown effective against human cancers. In contrast, animal studies to date do not demonstrate antitumor activity for Laetrile. So it is highly unlikely that Laetrile would show any anticancer efficacy in a clinical trial. However, because of strong political pressure the NCI may break precedent and conduct such tests.

Whether even a well-conducted clinical study would quell the Laetrile controversy is questionable. But then medical science would at least have done all that it could in order to arrive at a fair conclusion □

 SELECTED READINGS

"Cancer researcher looks at Laetrile" by B. H. Morrison. *Chemistry*, July 1977.
*The Truth About Laetrile*, edited by Henry Harton. Public Affairs Publ. 1977.

# MIGRAINE

## by Vita West-Muir

This engraving by George Cruikshank, a 19th century English humorist and illustrator, depicts the torments of severe headaches, such as migraines.

IN Jefferson City, Tennessee, an archeologist named Cleve Smith recently discovered a skull with a half-inch hole bored in the right temple. The skull, he believes, belonged to a hapless Woodland Indian, perhaps as long as 4000 years ago. In a practice not uncommon among ancient men—excavations in places as far flung as Portugal and Peru have unearthed hundreds of similar skulls—the hole had been cut to release demons credited with causing the Indian's madness or, perhaps, his migraine headache.

The brutal process, called trephining, has, happily, been long since abandoned. Over the years, it has been supplanted by some equally bizarre, but less deadly, treatments for headache pain. The Romans put a live electric torpedo fish to the headache victim's temple. Some Mexicans still stroke the forehead with a toad. Sumerians "discovered" opium and its pain-numbing effect, and many a proper Victorian relieved his headache with the "joy plant."

Today there are safer drugs and treatments of many kinds, but still there is no real cure for the migraine headache. Nor do we know precisely what a migraine is. The word

migraine derives from the Greek word *hemicrania,* meaning half skull. Pain involving one side of the head is typical of migraine.

### WHAT IS MIGRAINE?

Most researchers agree that migraine is a bloodvessel disturbance. In response to any of a number of factors, blood vessels that supply the head and brain become dilated, or expanded in diameter. The walls of these vessels contain nerve nets that are very sensitive to stretch. Pain comes when the vessels expand and the nerves stretch. Blood coursing through the swollen vessels causes throbbing pain with each beat of the heart.

At the biochemical level, the arteries are painful when dilated because they are sensitized by chemicals, particularly serotonin and bradykinin. Serotonin levels drop sharply at the onset of a migraine attack, and this drop is believed to reduce pain tolerance.

Bradykinin, found in the body wherever there is inflammation, has been detected around the scalp arteries during migraine attack. Histamine, prostaglandins, angiotensin, acetylcholine, renin—at least a dozen chemicals in all—may be involved.

HEALTH AND DISEASE **241**

In those who experience classic migraine, blood vessels shrink before they swell. This causes a shortage of blood to the brain and is responsible for the aura, or sensation of lights flashing before the eyes, reported by many victims. When the vessels expand, the pain begins, usually in one temple or around the eye. It generally remains on one side of the head throughout the attack.

## WHO ARE MIGRAINE'S VICTIMS?

Migraine strikes selectively. Two thirds of its estimated 10,000,000 to 24,000,000 American victims are women. But one especially virulent brand of migraine, cluster headache, strikes ten times as often among men.

With a family history of the problem, you stand a greater chance of having it yourself. Over half of all migraine sufferers have a positive family history. The "disease" itself is not inherited. What seems to be passed from parent to child is instability of the blood vessels of the brain and scalp whose swelling is responsible for migraine pain.

Children are not immune. Migraine often makes its first appearance around puberty. Some 5 per cent of pubescent children are afflicted. It is harder to diagnose in younger children, who may be unable to report their symptoms accurately, but it strikes here too. Recurrent motion sickness, abdominal pain, headache, and aching limbs signal the problem. In a reversal of the adult pattern, boys are afflicted twice as often as girls.

Migraine generally diminishes and often disappears entirely in middle life. Why this is the case is not altogether clear. It may be related to loss of elasticity of the blood vessels—the first signs of "hardening of the arteries"—which is a normal concomitant of aging. If the vessels no longer stretch readily, the pain that results from this process never gets started. But not all migraine sufferers are so lucky. Some continue to have attacks well into old age. Pregnancy also seems to send the migraine demon scurrying in eight out of ten women.

## A MIGRAINE ATTACK

Migraine attacks on schedule—once a week, once a month, several times a year. The pattern varies with the individual. Pain may last for hours or days. The victim typically has no appetite, feels nauseated, and vomits. He may experience a host of other symptoms, including blind spots, speech difficulty, one-sided weakness, confusion, soreness of the scalp, swelling of the hands and feet, pallor, and chills.

The attacks are disabling, and the victim often waits them out in quiet agony. If he is lucky, and sleep comes, he may wake without a headache. But, the very act of lying down to get to sleep may make the pain worse. When the pain finally ends, the migraineur usually feels exhausted. Sometimes however, he feels oddly energized, but this may just reflect the relief felt when the long siege of pain is over.

## MIGRAINE COMES IN MANY SHAPES AND SIZES

Scientists generally recognize five types of migraine: Classic, common, ophthalmoplegic, hemiplegic, and cluster.

Classic migraine and common migraine are similar in most respects, but the aura, or visual illusions phase, is absent in the common variety. Lewis Carroll, a victim of classic migraine, is said to have patterned his fanciful *Alice in Wonderland* characters on hallucinations he saw during a migraine.

Ophthalmoplegic and hemiplegic migraine are considered the most severe forms, from a medical standpoint. These are distinguished by an alarming paralysis which accompanies the head pain. In the ophthalmoplegic type, the muscles around one eye (opposite the headache) show signs of paralysis, and the victim squints. In the hemiplegic type, all or part of the body on the side opposite the head pain may become numb or paralyzed.

Anyone who experiences paralysis or speech difficulty along with migraine should consult a physician immediately. This is especially critical for any woman using birth-control pills. Ophthalmoplegic and hemiplegic migraine have been known to cause permanent impairment in birth-control pill users. In such cases, the pills should be discontinued immediately and a doctor contacted at once.

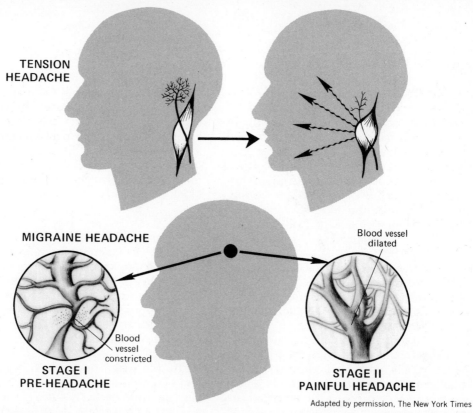

TENSION HEADACHE

MIGRAINE HEADACHE

Blood vessel dilated

Blood vessel constricted

STAGE I
PRE-HEADACHE

STAGE II
PAINFUL HEADACHE

In a tension headache, muscles of the head and neck contract. This causes pain. In stage I of a migraine, the artery constricts; this is the painless stage. In stage II, the artery dilates, causing pain.

Cluster headache is an exquisitely painful type of migraine. Its victims are primarily middle aged men, although women and people as young as 20 years of age may be affected. The headaches come in blindingly painful bunches over a period of hours, days, or weeks, and then vanish for months or even years before recurring. Occasionally, a cluster appears once and never recurs. The pain usually wakes the victim from his sleep and is so severe it may cause wild behavior.

Research on cluster headache has produced some interesting but as yet, inexplicable findings. The headaches seem to appear just after periods of intensive dreaming. One researcher has observed an odd physical characteristic—lion-like facial features—common among his cluster patients. And, in contrast to the stereotypical migraineur who is often a compulsive, perfectionist, overachiever type, the cluster victim is more often a burly, outdoorsy person.

The cause of cluster headache pain is not altogether clear since it is tricky to catch an attack in progress to study it. In only one reported case, so far, have doctors been able to monitor an attack. The arteriogram made in this instance revealed a swelling of the carotid artery, which then narrowed at the point of entry to the skull from the neck. The arterial swelling was accompanied by a release of histamine, a substance known to lower the pain threshold.

## WHAT CAUSES MIGRAINE?

Migraine sufferers inherit, along with a tendency of the blood vessels to swell, a marked sensitivity to substances which trigger the swelling and pain. The villain of the piece is tyramine (a chemical found in freshly baked bread, pork, aged cheeses, herring, yogurt, navy and lima beans, most citrus fruits, red vinegar, onions, and nuts). Many migraine sufferers also respond negatively to chocolate, which contains phenylethylamine, and, oddly enough, to large doses of ordinary table salt.

Alcohol can set off migraine attacks. Alcohol is itself a vasodilator, and anything that changes the size or shape of the blood vessels can trigger headache. In addition, it contains two dilator chemicals, tyramine and histamine. Since alcohol spells treble trouble for the migraine sufferer, doctors ask those who cannot give it up entirely to opt for drinks lowest in tyramine and histamine, and to restrict intake to two drinks. Haute Sauternes and Riesling wines, some Scotches, and all vodkas are tolerable. Alcohol-sensitive people should also beware raisins, grapes, and grape juice.

Monsodium glutamate (MSG) is another potent vasodilator to be avoided by migraine sufferers. It is a common ingredient in Chinese food and is responsible for "The Chinese-Restaurant Syndrome"—a complex of symptoms, including pressure and tightness in the face, a burning sensation over the trunk, pressing pain on the chest, and, for those sensitive to it, migraine headache.

Some migraine sufferers react badly to uncooked milk, probably because it contains tyramine, and many respond poorly to hot dogs and luncheon meats. Cured meats are heavy in nitrites and salt, which trigger or aggravate headache. Drinking coffee can give you a headache if you are caffeine sensitive, and so can not drinking it. Caffeine-withdrawal-migraine is familiar to many who change their coffee consumption pattern on weekends.

Foods are not the only rotten apples in the migraine barrel. Stress can start the paroxysms of pain—often after the stressful period has passed and the person begins to relax. High estrogen levels sometimes found in women taking birth-control pills or postmenopausal preparations, can trigger migraine; so can low levels, occurring at the onset of menstrual periods.

Many other things are known to precipitate attacks. Strenuous lovemaking can start up a migraine, as can other forms of vigorous exercise. The overexertion involved increases bloodflow, and small vessels may not expand quickly enough to accommodate the increased flow. Paradoxically, vigorous exercise at the first sign of cluster headache seems to blunt the painful force of this type of migraine in some. Marijuana smoking may increase the frequency of migraine in susceptible individuals. Changes in barometric pressure, skipping meals (presumably the drop in blood sugar is the pain stimulus),

sleeping later than usual (for the same reason), bright lights, menthol cigarettes, smoke-filled rooms, perfumes, dust, automobile fumes can all produce migraine attacks. The list is a long and highly idiosyncratic one. But the underlying factor is this: anything that can change the size and shape of blood vessels can cause a migraine headache.

## DIAGNOSIS

Prompt, accurate diagnosis of severe headache is important to rule out serious medical conditions, such as meningitis and brain tumor. Once these conditions are eliminated from consideration, a positive diagnosis of migraine can be made, and the headaches can be treated. Contrary to common belief, migraine headache *is* treatable. One need no longer endure the pain stoically. Moreover, doctors are beginning to find that you do yourself no good and you may do some harm by suffering in silence. Researchers have demonstrated that years of recurrent attacks can lead to permanent shrinkage of brain tissue.

Diagnosis of migraine rests heavily on careful history taking, including family history; dietary habits of the individual as they relate to his headache attacks; neurological evaluations; and physical examination. More sophisticated neuro-diagnostic techniques are also used. Some of these—computer axial tomography and liquid crystal thermography, for example—enable physicians to study bloodflow changes accompanying migraine. Electroencephalograms, radioisotope brain scans, and cerebral arteriograms help to rule out tumors and blood clots.

## PREVENTION AND TREATMENT

The best treatment for migraine headache is prevention of the attacks. If the attack can be shortcircuited in the early phase, it may be stoppable. Often, headaches can be avoided entirely by identifying what sets off the pain. Each person must discover for himself what triggers his migraines, and avoid these things. This may mean forgoing alcohol or chocolate or some favorite foods. It may mean changing a stressful way of life. But, freedom from pain should more than compensate for the deprivation.

## DRUGS

"When his brow pains a man and he vomits and is sick, his eyes being inflamed, it is the hand of a ghost; then reduce to ashes human bones and bray them; annoint him with them in cedar oil and he will recover." This is an ancient prescription for migraine. Luckily we know a bit more about the care and feeding of the migraineur nowadays. A number of drugs can reduce the frequency of migraine attacks, when taken regularly in a preventive program. The choice of medication is made by the physician on the facts of each case. For instance, since migraine can sometimes accompany depression, an antidepressant may be prescribed. For patients whose attacks are consistently signalled by anxiety, tranquilizers may be indicated.

Drugs that block the constrictive action of serotonin (cyproheptadine and methylsevgide, for example) are effective in some people. These drugs may create some disagreeable side effects, including nausea and diarrhea and should be used conservatively since their long term effects are still unknown. Most migraines are immune to the effects of aspirin once the attack has begun. However, researchers have found that as little as a single daily dose of two five-grain tablets has a preventive effect in some patients.

Once the headache has taken hold, drugs with a vasoconstrictive effect—those which shrink the swollen blood vessels—may be effective if taken immediately. Most commonly used is ergotamine tartrate, a rye-bread fungus derivative. But dosage is tricky. Just the right amount must be taken so as not to produce nausea as a side effect. For those who cannot take oral medications during an attack, suppositories and inhalers are available.

Cluster sufferers find some relief in ergot drugs, steroids, and lithium carbonate—the last, a drug best know for its use in treating of manic depression. Histamine desensitization is being tried with some success. This treatment involves injecting the patient with decreasing doses of histamine to get him "used to" this substance to which, it is believed, he is especially sensitive.

Drugs can be a godsend for the migraine sufferer in the short term. But there is a catch. Chronic use of vasoconstrictive drugs leaves the vessels in a shrunken state, and stopping their use causes the vessels to swell and pain. Add to this the known and unknown side effects which plague the drug user, and most experts agree that conservative use of drugs and heavier reliance on non-chemical solutions is a better route for the migraine victim to follow.

## NON-CHEMICAL APPROACHES

Learning to relax is the key for some. Easier said than done? Not with the help of a biofeedback machine. These electronic devices give the user information about very small changes in muscle tension and enable him to control heart rate, blood pressure, blood flow, and many other physiological processes. At the Menninger Foundation, migraineurs are trained to raise their hand temperature (as much as 25 °F) and, with it, increase blood flow in their hands. This simultaneously reduces blood engorgement, it is reasoned, in the vessels of the head and scalp. Once autoregulatory control is mastered, many people achieve its benefits without biofeedback machines.

Accurate diagnosis and careful management of the migraine patient by his doctor and himself can make a great deal of difference to the frequency, duration, and severity of the pain experienced.

The National Migraine Foundation offers this advice:

Don't treat yourself without a diagnosis.
Do follow a treatment regimen and consult frequently with your doctor.
Don't traffic in quackery.
Learn to handle the headache episode quickly.
Carry your medication with you.
Avoid or modify situations which bring on a headache repeatedly.
Get away from home from time to time and learn to unwind.
Try to reestablish your sense of humor, if you have lost it.
Find a relaxing, non-competitive hobby which requires some physical work.

For the migraine sufferer who lives by these rules, the nightmare may become a sporadic bad dream, or it may disappear entirely □

# WORRYING ABOUT ULCERS

## by Gilbert Cant

A HOPEFUL revolution is taking place in the world of the millions who suffer from ulcers. Radical changes in medical thinking, prompted by the acquisition of fresh knowledge, and development of a new class of medication combine to give promise of hitherto unattainable relief for the pain-racked victims of ulcers, the commonest disease of the stomach and other parts of the upper digestive tract.

For generations, the traditional remedy for ulcers of the stomach and of the digestive chamber just below it, the duodenum, has involved gobbling or gulping antacids in tablet or liquid form. It was believed that neutralizing the digestive acids in this way would not only relieve pain but promote the healing of ulcers and discourage the formation of new ones. This was almost certainly a half myth and may have been totally mythical.

Next came the prescribing of bland, tasteless, and unsatisfying diets, backed by a similar rationale—also a myth, it is now clear. More sophisticated were the prescription antispasmodic medicines. Their effectiveness is also now relegated by many authorities to the realm of mythology.

One of the hardiest myths has been the assumption or flat assertion that ulcers were part of the price paid by the upper-echelon executive or high-powered businessman driving hard for success or money. So ulcers came to be known as "the merit badge of Madison Avenue," although Wall Street or La Salle or Montgomery Streets would have been just as appropriate. Now it appears that this, too, was wrong: the blue-collar worker in an auto assembly plant is just as likely to develop ulcers as the president of his company.

Finally, there are disputes as to whether ulcers are increasing or decreasing in incidence or prevalence. In epidemiologists' jargon, incidence means the attack rate, or number of new cases each year, while preva-

Bruce Davidson, Magnum Photos

Ulcers were long thought to be the price paid by high-powered businessmen, but this and other ulcer myths have now been debunked.

lence means the total number of victims suffering from the disease at any one time.

The U.S. National Center for Health Statistics maintains that both incidence and prevalence increased, during a period under study from 1968 through 1975, by which time there were more than 4,000,000 victims in the United States. Other estimates today range from 10,000,000 to 20,000,000. However, other epidemiologists insist that the incidence of duodenal ulcers, at least, is declining. In this case, it is impossible to say that one side or the other is propagating a myth. Social changes, notably the more widespread availability of improved medical attention and general care, may explain the seeming paradox. This question, like many others, will be answered by the enthusiastic researchers now attacking all the unresolved problems of ulcer causation, treatment and—they hope—cure.

Meanwhile, the various medical signposts that seem to point to a decline in ulcer disease have prompted Dr. Morton I. Grossman, director of the Center for Ulcer Research and Education (CURE) in Los Angeles, to remark: "The medical profession has to hurry up and solve all the questions about ulcers so that we can take credit for the decline." Dr. Grossman was jesting, but it would not be the first time the profession claimed credit for a similar kind of event.

The most conspicuous ferment in the ulcer revolution has come from the School of Medicine of the University of California at Los Angeles and its cooperating hospitals and research centers. In April 1976, six leading investigators from this pool of physicians ran a symposium in which every tradition in ulcer treatment was discussed. Virtually all were debunked, causing Dr. Marvin H. Sleisenger of the University of California Hospitals in San Francisco to call the symposium "The Slaughter of the Sacred Cows."

## DO ANTACIDS HELP?

Antacids came first. Grandfather's standby, a teaspoonful of "soda bicarb" (baking soda from the kitchen cupboard) was instantly dismissed as too dangerous:

overdosage will cause kidney damage that may prove fatal. Dr. Arthur Schwabe, chief of gastroenterology at U.C.L.A., estimated that more than $100,000,000 is spent annually in the United States for countless antacids in tablet and liquid forms.

Dr. Schwabe did not urge that all antacids be swept summarily from the pharmacists' display counters. Rather, he advocated tailoring the prescribed doses of the safer antacids to what are judged to be the patient's individual needs. Few doctors now take the time to do that. For example, some patients, notably those with high blood pressure, should be steered away from medications with a high sodium content. And all should avoid any containing calcium. On an empty stomach, Dr. Schwabe said, the neutralizing effect of a supposedly appropriate antacid dose lasts only about half an hour, but, after a meal, from three to four hours. He rated the liquid form far more effective than the popular tablets.

In a carefully planned and controlled study conducted at three cooperating centers—Wadsworth Veterans Administration hospital, the Kaiser (Sunset) Hospital in Los Angeles, and the University of Texas Southwestern Medical School in Dallas—patients

UCLA School of Medicine

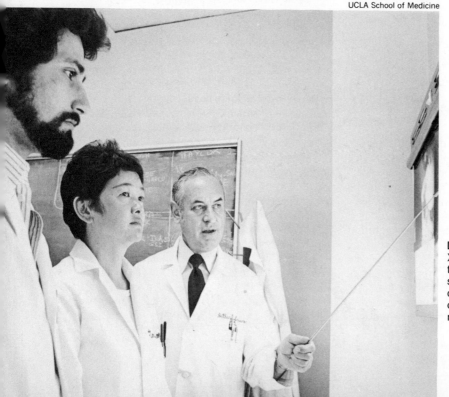

Dr. Arnold Schwabe examines X rays of the gastrointestinal tract with other medical personnel. He and other physicians now question the value of many traditional ulcer remedies.

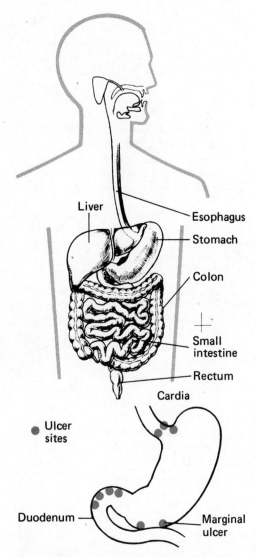

Top: Illustration of the digestive tract. Bottom: most common sites of peptic ulcer.

Labels on image:
Liver
Esophagus
Stomach
Colon
Small intestine
Rectum
Cardia
Ulcer sites
Duodenum
Marginal ulcer

ity of ulcer victims, the pain they feel is more important than medical proof of the healing of an invisible, internal wound. And the study shows the discrepancy between healing and symptoms.

## ANTISPASMODICS AND RESTRICTED DIETS DEBUNKED

Antispasmodic drugs, the prescription items on which $65,000,000 a year is spent in the United States alone, took a drubbing at the Los Angeles symposium. The experts agreed that all these medications have undesirable side effects, ranging from mere dryness of the mouth to blurred vision, constipation, and urinary retention. They cannot be used by patients with glaucoma, prostate disease, or chronic lung disease, or by the aged, or in hot climates.

Restrictive diets, long the bane of ulcer patients, were also found not helpful. This is not surprising. What is surprising is that their use has persisted so long after they were shown to be valueless. More than 20 years ago, Dr. Stewart Wolf, now at Temple University, pointed out that the lining of the stomach and duodenum can tolerate more irritation, whether chemical or mechanical, than the skin. Therefore any food that does not abrade or burn the skin will not hurt the digestive organs. What hurts them is what the organs themselves manufacture—acid and enzymes—and not what is put into them.

Despite evidence showing the valuelessness of restricted diet in ulcer care, many physicians continued prescribing purées and virtually unseasoned foods, hourly gulps of milk or half-and-half cream and milk, frequent small feedings, and a bedtime snack. So the Los Angeles symposiasts had to try, yet again, to eliminate the bland diet. Not only does it fail to achieve its purpose, said Dr. Schwabe, but it actually increases the acid load that is already excessive. "Patients," he said, "should be encouraged to eat three nutritious, enjoyable meals of their own choosing every day."

Dr. Sleisenger agreed on the basis of biochemical findings, but his psychological observations led him to make a reservation. "Frequent feedings of baby-type food, or milk, or milk and cream, seem to work magic

with duodenal ulcers took an antacid medication or a placebo, seven times a day for a month. At the end of the month, 78 per cent of patients receiving active medication had their ulcers healed. So did a surprising 45 per cent of those who had taken only placebos. The difference in healing rates was significant. But perhaps the most surprising finding was that the patients whose ulcers had healed did not feel any better than those with unhealed craters remaining. The two groups complained with equal vehemence of continuing, painful symptoms. To the great major-in many patients," he said. "Is it really psychotherapy? The patient in this situation seems to be reduced to early childhood or even infancy, to be cared for by being offered something to eat frequently, and to be ingesting only those foods most obviously identified with infancy. Perhaps 'mothering' is better treatment than acid neutralization!" But, of course, there's more than that to be said about the psychosomatics of ulcer patients.

Next to be struck out at the U.C.L.A. meeting was hospitalization. Not that it is bad for the ulcer, but because it makes an ulcerous crater in the bank balance.

## LESS SURGERY

One of the most damning diagnoses for an ulcer victim is "intractability." But just what is that? Dr. Oliver Goldsmith of the Southern California Permanente Medical Group in Los Angeles says that if an ulcer patient appears twice, within an interval of no more than two weeks, at some medical centers he is promptly labeled "intractable" and scheduled for an operation. At more conservative centers, operations for alleged intractability are rare. Yet, as Dr. Grossman points out, more than half of the patients who have elective (meaning nonemergency) surgery for duodenal ulcer have intractability listed as the primary reason.

Dr. Grossman would like to see severity substituted for intractability as an indication for surgery, and would define severity in terms of the frequency and duration of pain and the amount of time lost from work.

On one point, all the antitraditional thinkers at U.C.L.A. and elsewhere agree: there has been a marked decline in the number of operations for ulcer, explainable only in part by growing conservatism among surgeons, and the number should continue to decrease, perhaps at an accelerated rate.

There are two mandatory and urgent situations that call for immediate surgery: if the ulcer bleeds into the intestine, or, more dramatically, if it perforates—that is, if the acid burns a hole through the stomach or duodenal wall into the abdominal cavity.

Although there are innumerable variations, the basic operation for ulcer in either

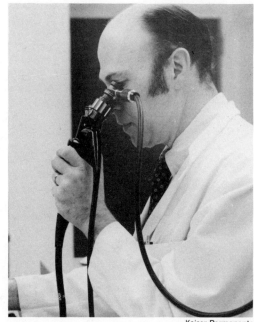

Kaiser Permanente

Physicians are now able to examine parts of the digestive tract, looking for ulcers or other disorders, using special fiber optic tubes known as endoscopes.

the stomach or the duodenum is to cut out the lower part of the stomach—the part where most of the digestive acid is secreted. At its simplest and best this is still a mutilative operation. Most medical centers combine this so-called "subtotal gastrectomy" with a severing—just outside the stomach—of all or selected parts of the vagus nerve, through which the brain transmits orders to make acid. Europeans doctors normally perform only the vagus-severing operation, which Dr. Grossman says is a better procedure because it avoids cutting into and further upsetting the stomach itself.

Long proclaimed as the definitive treatment or even "cure" for ulcer, surgery would deserve such a reputation better if it were more often successful. But from 10 to 20 per cent of patients suffer relapses, and nearly all the rest complain of assorted miseries: they have to consume antacids in such quantities that they look as though they were foaming at the mouth, and may also suffer from diarrhea and nausea—and are still on a restricted diet with little or no alcohol permitted.

Roger Malloch, Magnum Photos

The incidence of duodenal ulcers in women has risen sharply in the last 50 years. Are stress and women's changing role in society factors in this increase?

## NOW—A NEW DRUG

Since traditional medical treatments and surgery have proved so generally unsatisfactory, it is great news for an estimated 2,000,000 plus ulcer victims that the U.S. Food and Drug Administration has now approved a radically new medication that operates through entirely different biochemical channels from those of its predecessors. It involves an antihistamine, but an antihistamine unlike any other.

Histamine is a substance produced naturally by the body. Scientists have discovered that histamine produces two dissimilar sets of effects by acting upon two distinct types of receptor cells in the body. These are known as H1 and H2 cells. The H1 type includes cells in the nasal passages and other parts of the respiratory tract that are subject to dust and pollen allergies, notably ragweed, and still others responsible for a variety of food allergies. The H2 cells are in the lower stomach wall and when these are stimulated by histamine they provoke the secretion of excess acid. So Professor James W. Black of London's University College reasoned that what was needed was a medication that would block the uptake of histamine by the H2 receptors. He set out on the long and te-

dious task of producing what are awkwardly called "H2-receptor blockers." Working with Smith Kline & French laboratories in a London suburb, he synthesized hundreds of compounds over several years before he found one that worked for animals but was too toxic for humans. A second almost made the grade, but just failed to pass the toxicity test. Then came cimetidine, which is undoubtedly effective against several forms of upper-gastrointestinal disease, and so far appears to have relatively few side effects. British authorities approved cimetidine (trade-named Tagamet by Smith Kline) for virtually the whole spectrum of ulcers and ulcer-related diseases. Canada followed suit, and the United States approved its use in August 1977.

The F.D.A.'s approval was somewhat grudging, limited to the prescribing of Tagamet for up to eight-week treatments of duodenal ulcers and possibly longer periods for treatments of one of a complex of diseases known collectively by the forbidding name of Zollinger-Ellison syndrome. One form of this is gastrinoma, a disease in which multiple ulcers result from excess production of digestive juices in tumors of the pancreas. While some specialists remain skeptical of the value of cimetidine in the treatment of other ulcer diseases, they are virtually unanimous in acclaiming it for gastrinoma.

## WHO DEVELOPS ULCERS

One of the most perplexing puzzles in the ulcer maze is the question of why some people develop ulcers and others do not. At the genetic level, Dr. Richard Sturdevant of U.C.L.A. notes that the most widespread predisposing factor is having blood of Type O rather than A, B, or the rare AB. But still, only a fraction of Type O people develop ulcers. Inherited differences in patterns of secreting and utilizing complex enzymes and hormones may explain why first-degree relatives of gastric-ulcer patients are three times as likely as the rest of us to have that disease. The same threefold increase in risk holds true for the close kin of duodenal-ulcer victims.

Cigarette smoking may be a precipitating factor, possibly because smoking reduces the output of alkaline bicarbonate by the pancreas. Aspirin is almost universally recognized as a cause of ulcers, but there is some question as to whether heavy dosage (14 or more 5-grain tablets daily) will induce only the gastric form or the duodenal as well. Large doses of cortisone-type medicines also stimulate the formation of ulcers. But there are many more heavy smokers than ulcer victims. And distressingly large numbers of sufferers from arthritis, for example, take massive doses of aspirin and cortisone variants without developing ulcers. So what's left by way of explanation?

"Stress," say many authorities. This is too simplistic, others contend: it is the reaction or patterns of reaction to stress that count. But psychologists cannot agree as to whether the typical ulcer victim has a dependent personality and craves support, or is a wolf in human's clothing who wants to devour his enemies—but since that is impossible, devours part of himself instead. In fact, there almost certainly is no single, typical ulcer personality. Dr. Goldsmith says: "The disease spares nobody—no class of people and no age group. We see patients aged 9 to 90."

The physiologists go back to genetics. A predisposition to ulcer disease runs in families, but in no clear pattern. This apparently results from an inherited weakness in one of the several layers of the stomach wall. Since most digestive acid is produced by cells in this wall, it would seem logical to expect that a majority of ulcers would be gastric rather than duodenal. The reverse is explained by two facts. First, the normal stomach has a tougher, thicker, and stronger lining than the duodenum. Second, the stomach has the nasty habit of flushing out not only food but excess acid as fast as possible into the more vulnerable duodenum.

This also explains why the great majority of duodenal ulcers are in the first two to five centimeters (one or two inches) of the duodenum. Beyond that point the stomach's throw-away acid is neutralized by bile and by alkaline secretions from the pancreas. Although alcohol may exacerbate existing ulcers in some patients, it has not been convicted as a cause of ulcers.

Rohn Engh, Photo Researchers

Smoking is often a precipitating factor in the development of ulcers. It decreases the output of an alkaline substance by the pancreas, thus increasing the acidity of the gastrointestinal tract.

## PSYCHOLOGICAL HUNGER

Practically the only factors left to be considered are temperament and life style. So we come back to stress, what one regards as stress, and patterns of reaction to it. A situation that some people find intolerably stressful will be perceived by those of a different personality type simply as a challenge, which stimulates the adrenals rather than acid secretion. Dr. Goldsmith contends that the picture of the driven executive as the most ulcer-prone type has always been a fantasy. He believes that the muscular person heaving the garbage into a truck is as likely to develop ulcers as the head of the city sanitation department or the president of the corporation.

Dr. Meyer Friedman of Mt. Zion Medical Center in San Francisco, coauthor of the hypothesis that susceptibility to coronary disease and heart attacks is associated with a driving, striving personality that he classifies as "Type A," believes that the great majority of ulcer patients represent another subdivision of Type A. This seems surprising at first,

Researchers continue to try to develop drugs that will be effective against ulcers and other gastrointestinal disorders.

because the two groups are outwardly dissimilar. The coronary-prone individuals are, in many cases, visibly hostile. They typically do not seek to ingratiate themselves with other people but try to override them, and they usually have only two interests, the chosen career and one hobby. Ulcer patients, Dr. Friedman finds, openly seek affection, attention, and care from others. They are deeply interested in people as people and keenly observant of details about them. But in their quiet, inconspicuous way they are no less driven and driving than the supercharged man or woman on the executive ladder, and they become just as timebound by taking up many hobbies and striving for perfection in all.

The craving for attention that Dr. Friedman sees is in harmony with Dr. Sleisenger's theory of a need for mothering. The psychoanalyst Franz Alexander suggested 30 years ago that the ulcer patient suffers from a psychological hunger matching the physical hunger in his stomach—and one that is infinitely more difficult to appease. Dr. Sturdevant concludes that after all the theories have been examined "the first causes of ulcers remain unknown."

## MORE WOMEN NOW AFFECTED

Changes in the epidemiology of the disease are no less mysterious. Early in the nineteenth century, the commonest ulcer reported in Britain was the gastric ulcer that ended fatally. The great majority of the victims were young women living sheltered lives in rural quiet, "far from the madding crowd's ignoble strife." About midcentury, the pattern changed. The duodenal ulcer appeared more frequently, raced ahead of the gastric in incidence, and chose men, mostly in the 25-to-45 age range, as its preferred victims. Now, once again, the pattern has changed. Whereas the male victims of duodenal ulcers outnumbered women by about 20 to 1 a mere 50 years ago, the ratio is now closer to 4 to 1.

But fortunately, understanding of basic causes and changes in prevalence is not a prerequisite for improvements in treatment. Granting that so mysterious a disease as ulcer may yet outwit the best medical scientists, Dr. Sleisenger concludes optimistically: "We await the brave new era of treatment with powerful drugs which will abolish acid and reduce the need for any surgery" □

## SELECTED READINGS

*Living With Your Ulcer* by Theodore Berland and Mitchell Spellberg. St. Martin's Press, 1974.

"Peptic ulcer: latest on how to detect, treat—and prevent" by H. P. Roth. *U.S. News & World Report*, May 9, 1977.

"Relief for ulcer? cimetidine" by M. Clark and D. Shapiro. *Newsweek*, December 13, 1976.

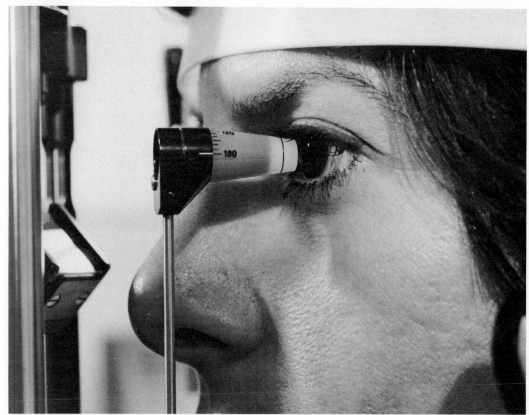

# GLAUCOMA

A tonometer is often used to detect glaucoma. The instrument measures intraocular pressure.

## by Richard Martin

SUZY Q was a slow, cantankerous two-year-old who often hid in her darkened bedroom, sobbing for hours at a time and occasionally pounding her head with her fists. Several doctors said she was mentally retarded and emotionally disturbed. But an ophthalmologist diagnosed her problem as glaucoma, a puzzling disease that is the second leading cause of blindness in the United States.

Today, two years after surgery corrected the condition that was causing her excruciating headaches and destroying her sight, Suzy (not her real name) "is one of the sweetest girls you've ever seen, and very smart," says Pei-Fei Lee, the Albany, New York, ophthalmologist who correctly diagnosed her problem. She's doing well in preschool classes, he adds, even though the vision left in her best eye is only 20/300, or about one-tenth of normal.

Many young victims of glaucoma, like Suzy, had been diagnosed incorrectly as mentally disturbed or retarded by pediatricians and other physicians unfamiliar with the disease.

Glaucoma mostly affects people who are past 40. But it can strike at any age, and doctors increasingly are coming to realize that it occurs earlier far more often than is generally supposed. Dr. John G. Bellows, a Chicago ophthalmologist who has 2,000 glaucoma patients, sees a pattern he calls "the phenomenon of genetic anticipation—if the mother has it at age 60, her daughter may have it at 30 or 40," he says.

Most estimates are that about 5,000,000 to 8,000,000 people in the United States have glaucoma. Dr. Bellows, who is director of the International Glaucoma Congress, a group of specialists, puts the figure closer to 10,000,-000. "I'd say there are two million to three million people walking the streets who have it and don't know it," because of the difficulty of detecting the disease, Dr. Bellows says. Research to Prevent Blindness Inc., a nonprofit organization in New York, estimates as many as half of those who have glaucoma don't know it.

## BUILDUP OF FLUID

Glaucoma is caused by a buildup in the fluids that normally circulate within the eye. The buildup creates pressure that gradually destroys the optic disk at the back of the eye, where images are formed.

Researchers are pushing to unlock the many mysteries of glaucoma. The mechanism by which increased pressure in the eye causes destruction of the tissues at the back of the eye isn't fully understood. Neither is the regulating mechanism that keeps the flow of incoming and outgoing fluids balanced in normal eyes. Better insights into these functions could lead to more effective drugs, improved surgical remedies, and perhaps ways of accurately predicting and preventing damage.

But part of the problem is that glaucoma isn't a textbook type of disease. "It's perhaps several dozen diseases lumped together," says Dr. Douglas B. Anderson of the University of Miami School of Medicine. "The different types all have their own causes and peculiarities, and their own treatments."

## NARROW-ANGLE TYPE

Of the three most common types, narrow-angle or closed-angle glaucoma is the most devastating. It often occurs without warning because of a structural peculiarity at the front of the eye that tends to block off the tiny drainage channels when the pupil dilates. Fluid continues to flow in, causing the pressure within the eyeball to double or triple quickly and painfully. Without prompt medication, an attack often causes total blindness within 24 hours. Besides pain, the most noticeable symptoms are blurred vision and fuzzy "halos" around bright lights.

Anything that dilates the pupil can trigger an attack—a darkened movie theater or candlelight dinner, adrenalin produced by stress, anger, or excitement, and some tran-quilizers, amphetamines, appetite suppressants, and other medications.

"I think every ophthalmologist sometime in his career probably precipitates an attack or two of narrow-angle glaucoma right in his office" when he dilates a patient's pupil during an examination, says Dr. Robert K. Abraham of the University of Southern California School of Medicine in Los Angeles. An unsuspecting victim couldn't pick a better place for an attack, he adds. "With rare exceptions, an ophthalmologist can bring the pressure down very quickly with drugs he has right at hand."

Eyedrops that constrict the pupil often can be used to control closed-angle glaucoma. An alternative is a relatively simple operation called an iridectomy, in which a small chunk of the iris, or colored part of the eye, is cut out to allow fluid to flow through even when the pupil is fully dilated. Dr. Abraham and others have reported good results with a newer variation of the iridectomy. By using a laser to burn the hole in the iris, they are treating some patients in offices and outpatient clinics without hospitalization.

## CHRONIC, OPEN-ANGLE, GLAUCOMA

Open-angle, or chronic, glaucoma is the most common type. It's insidious. Usually the fluid blockage occurs undetected, and the rise in pressure is painless and so gradual that the optic disk deteriorates imperceptibly. Over a period of months or years, vision gradually dims and disappears at the outer fringers of the visual field, slowly causing "tunnel vision" and eventually total blindness if it isn't caught.

The symptoms include foggy vision, halos around lights, and difficulty adjusting to darkened rooms. These signs have a way of disappearing for periods of time. Some doctors are convinced that adrenalin and stress play a role in chronic glaucoma as well as in the narrow-angle variety, but the evidence is less clear-cut.

Victims usually discover chronic glaucoma only after it is so far advanced that much of their peripheral vision is gone. Once detected, continued damage usually can be prevented by eyedrops or surgery to improve the fluid drainage and reduce pressure, but the vision already lost can't be restored.

## CONGENITAL AND OTHER TYPES

Congenital glaucoma, like young Suzy's, is often swiftly ruinous. It's difficult to accurately measure eye pressure of squirming babies and small children, and destruction that would take years in an adult's eye can occur in weeks in a tot's. The younger the child, the harder it is to recognize the symptoms. Pain is a common one. "Often it's manifested in very nasty dispositions—crying, biting and scratching themselves, or beating their heads against something," says Dr. Lee. Tired and watery eyes, aching eyebrows, and reading difficulties can be warning signs in toddlers and teen-agers alike, but they are often missed. "By the time we see most children, they've already lost their useful vision," Dr. Lee says.

Besides the three primary types of glaucoma, which occur by themselves, there are dozens of secondary types, caused by diabetes, tumors, vascular disorders, and other maladies.

"It seems like every year a new one of these subcategories is discovered," says Dr. Anderson of Miami. One kind, pigmentary glaucoma, occurs when tiny bits of pigment shake loose from the iris and clog the drainage channels. Brown-eyed men seem most prone to it, and some doctors suspect head-jolting activities such as boxing, jogging, or horseback riding aggravate the condition.

## DIFFICULTIES OF DIAGNOSIS

Damage usually can be avoided or minimized if glaucoma is found early enough. The surest way to spot it is to put an instrument called a tonometer on the eye to measure the pressure inside. But a single reading, or even a series of readings, can be misleading, because eye pressures fluctuate widely. They're generally higher in winter than in summer; usually highest around 5 a.m., lowest about noon. Moreover, while some eyes succumb to damage at small increases in pressure, others withstand relatively high pressures without harm.

"Perhaps the biggest breakthrough in glaucoma recently is the discovery that not everyone has their eyes damaged by intraocular pressure," says Dr. Anderson. It has brought a major change in philosophy among ophthalmologists. Many are disinclined now to start medical treatment for glaucoma solely on the basis of abnormal pressure.

"We have to find ways to predict which individuals are susceptible to the pressure and which aren't," Dr. Anderson says. "For all we know, 95% of those with high pressure won't have damage. But so far there's no real firm thing we can point to that says this person is in the 5% group and has a high risk or this person looks safe for now."

The search is on to find something firm, however, Hans Goldmann, a retired professor at Bern University in Switzerland, has

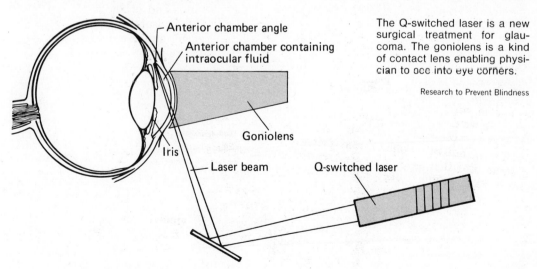

Anterior chamber angle
Anterior chamber containing intraocular fluid
Goniolens
Iris
Laser beam
Q-switched laser

The Q-switched laser is a new surgical treatment for glaucoma. The goniolens is a kind of contact lens enabling physician to see into eye corners.

Research to Prevent Blindness

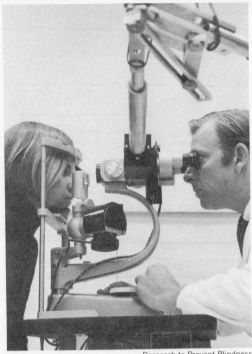
Research to Prevent Blindness

A laser beam, safely harnessed for treatment, is directed into a patient's eye. Multi-line spectrum laser permits the physician to selectively alter minute layers of eye tissue.

tracked the flow of fluorescein dye through the eye's circulatory system, seeking patterns that precede deterioration of the optic disk. Some U.S. doctors think his work might provide a mathematical basis for predicting which patients will develop visual losses at any given intraocular pressure.

### EARLY DETECTION

Detecting minute early losses in peripheral vision is critical to effective control of glaucoma because once deterioration of the disk begins it is sometimes difficult to stop it, even by lowering ocular pressure. At present, detecting those earliest losses is mostly guesswork, or "judgment calls" by a patient taking vision tests and a doctor examining the disk.

But more precise tools may be on the way for diagnosing and monitoring subtle changes in visual fields. Among them are two new instruments, one using laser scanning of the optic disk, the other taking infrared meaurements of blood circulation in the retina of the eye.

Another breakthrough could turn out to be an important link between glaucoma and high myopia, or extreme nearsightedness,

which itself is a leading cause of blindness. Myopia is caused by elongation of the eye. The longer the eye gets, the more nearsighted it is. Dr. Brian J. Curtin's studies at Manhattan Eye, Ear and Throat Hospital and Cornell University Medical College in New York show the progression of high myopia in children is related to ocular pressure.

By age 65, slightly over half of patients with high myopia are blind because of effects of stretching of the wall of the eye. Dr. Curtin's studies indicate that relieving elevated pressure in nearsighted children could prevent further elongation and severe myopia. His studies also raise the possibility that more careful screening of very nearsighted people could spot more cases of glaucoma before optic-disk damage occurs.

A surprisingly high incidence of glaucoma after successful cataract removal in nearsighted patients has recently piqued the interest of researchers. It is thought to be linked to the use of cortisone, a natural hormone, along with certain compounds used in postoperative medication for cataract patients. The substances apparently can produce glaucoma. "We don't understand the mechanism for this effect, but we do think it has something to do with why people develop primary open-angle glaucoma in the first place," Dr. Anderson says.

Prostaglandins, fatty acid substances in the body that have been implicated in a variety of diseases, recently were found to elevate ocular pressure. Researchers are looking into the possibility of prostaglandin inhibitors as new therapeutic agents for treating glaucoma.

### NON-SURGICAL TREATMENT

Eyedrops that speed outflow of ocular fluids currently are the most commonly used therapy for glaucoma. Most patients use them several times a day for a lifetime. But drops often sting, blur vision for hours, and cause headaches and other side effects. Pilocarpine, the most popular eyedrop, now comes in a pliable, plastic wafer that is worn behind the upper eyelid for a week at a time and gradually releases even dosages that prevent blurring and eliminate getting up in the middle of the night to put in drops. But pilocarpine severely reduces night vision in many patients.

Epinephrine, another leading drug, tends to cause red, itchy eyes and to leave black pigment deposits that eventually must be scraped off the inside of the eyelid. Epinephrine can also cause hypertension and can even lead to strokes in people predisposed to them. Some stronger types of eyedrops, which are being used less, seem to accelerate development of cataracts.

Some patients for whom drops are ineffective take pills that slow down the production of eye fluid. But the pills have side effects too, often "a tingling in the fingers, or some patients lose appetite and get depressed or just feel lousy," Dr. Anderson says. "In rare instances they can precipitate kidney stones, and in very rare cases people have died."

Better drugs to control glaucoma are being sought. Instances have been reported of dramatically reduced glaucoma effects through marijuana smoking. Several research efforts are aimed at creating compounds that produce effects similar to marijuana on eye pressure without affecting the mind. In one, Keith Green of the Medical College of Georgia in Augusta is testing certain ingredients of marijuana on laboratory animals and getting reductions of up to 25 to 30 per cent in ocular pressure for four to five hours at a time. "They work in the rabbit. They seem to work in the monkey," says Prof. Green. But the mind-affecting properties of the compounds haven't yet been eliminated.

What researchers find especially intriguing about Professor Green's studies is that a drop in one eye reduces pressure in both eyes. This indicates the eyes are under some kind of central control mechanism that doctors have never been able to pin down, and somehow marijuana derivatives are triggering that mechanism to simultaneously reduce the production of fluid and increase the outflow.

Surgeons have found that experimental severing of certain nerve pathways to the eye can lower pressure, but it is an exceedingly difficult operation. However, Dr. Monte G. Holland, at Tulane University School of Medicine in New Orleans, Louisiana, has found that those same nerves can be temporarily deactivated for months at a time by injecting a powerful drug, 6-Hydroxydopamine, into the eyeball. The injections, plus epinephrine drops, have succeeded in lowering ocular pressures of 92 patients whose glaucoma previously couldn't be controlled by either drugs or surgery.

## SURGICAL TREATMENT

Doctors at the University of Florida have reported some patients maintaining reduced, near-normal ocular pressures for a year or more after experimental laser surgery to burn new openings in obstructed outflow channels inside the front of the eye. But most pressures tend to go back up after four to six months, and experiments with monkeys have raised questions of whether repeated use of the laser might cause scarring that could ultimately cause pressures to rise higher than they were before treatment began.

Doctors are using some surgical procedures to freeze the ciliary body that produces the fluid, thereby reducing the fluid output. But the operation often has to be repeated over and over, and it is so uncomfortable and aggravating that few doctors use it.

An old standby, the filtering operation, remains the preferred surgery for pressure that can't be reduced by drugs. It involves cutting a shunt in the white of the eye to allow fluid to leak through. It can be used on practically any kind of glaucoma. In perhaps one out of five instances, however, the hole eventually seals over, requiring another operation. Another problem is too much leakage. In rare instances, the eye collapses temporarily from lack of fluid, often pushing the lens against the cornea and damaging it, causing a cataract. More often, too much leakage causes a cataract because circulation of ocular fluid is insufficient to adequately nourish the lens, and it hardens and turns opaque.

A newer variation of the filtering operation, a trabeculectomy, filters fluid out from beneath a flap of tissue that acts like a trap door. Not all ophthalmologists agree a trabeculectomy works better than filtering operations, but most consider it safer □

As part of a self-care learning program, people learn how to examine the ear and what signs to look for in their examinations.

© 1977 Henri Dauman

# THE SELF-CARE SURGE

## by Robert C. Yeager

SELF-CARE, the idea that consumers can and should assume more responsibility for their own health, just may be medicine's fastest rolling new bandwagon. Almost no one agrees on its limits. Some criticize its rhetoric, and a few harbor genuine fears over its safety. But the self-care movement comes at a time when increasing numbers of patients are celebrating the Emersonian virtues of medical self-reliance.

Whatever their doctors' qualms, ordinary people are learning to handle stethoscopes and blood pressure cuffs, and administer breast self-exams and Pap smears. As much as anything, self-care practitioners are learning to heed the messages of their own bodies—and to appreciate the importance of exercise, proper nutrition, relaxation, and habit control in leading healthier lives.

"One of the most exciting things that's going to happen in the next ten years," predicts Dr. B. Leslie Huffman, Jr., president of the American Academy of Family Physicians (AAFP), "will be the increasing involvement of patients in their own health care."

### ALREADY MOVING FAST

Much suggests this is already happening. In 1977, residents of Maine's doctorless Chebeague Island opted for self-care training rather than the part-time nurse-practitioner recommended by state health officials. "They wanted to know how to use the system as well as do for themselves," says Dr. J. Michael Taylor, community medicine director at the Maine Medical Center in Portland.

The health care organization Kaiser Permanente has been a trailbreaker in patient education since the mid-1960s. In the fall of 1977 it started offering comprehensive self-care instruction at its Oakland, California, Medical Center. Pediatricians in suburban Maryland and in Denver, Colorado, are teaching middle-class mothers to take their children's throat cultures. Patients in Lyndonville, Vermont, learn "instant pediatrics," including use of the otoscope in evaluating simple ear inflammations, as part of a new self-care course being offered by two young family doctors. Foot care, dental hygiene, diet, and stress control are only some of the self-care topics taught at 25 community centers by health professional teams from the University of California at San Francisco. And medical training for U.S. Skylab astronauts is spelled out in a little-known but extensive National Aeronautics and Space Administration self-care manual that tells, for example, how to immobilize a fractured clavicle, or collarbone, treat external ear infections, and examine the prostate.

## HEALTH ACTIVATION PROGRAM

Self-care's classic agenda is perhaps best outlined in the "health activation" program developed by Dr. Keith W. Sehnert, Vir-

ginia-based family practitioner and self-care pioneer in the early 1970s. The main elements of his program, typically taught during 16 two-hour sessions, are:

*Communication/consumerism.* Role-playing and other techniques teach the student how to recognize symptoms and report them in a meaningful way, what side effects to expect from drugs and which ones don't mix, and how and when to challenge the doctor.

*Self-help.* "Hands on" instruction includes how to measure blood pressure, how to use stethoscopes, how to use otoscopes (for mothers to determine whether their youngsters' eardrums are red and inflamed or normal looking), and, optionally, how—in lab sessions—to test stool samples for blood. Training in cardiopulmonary resuscitation and other emergency techniques includes, for example, how to tell whether a fellow partygoer's chest pains or other symptoms are a heart attack and how to help if someone is choking.

*Coping.* This includes learning yoga to relax, the importance of nutrition and exercise, and the dangers of stress, smoking, alcoholism, and overmedication.

George Bakacs, APF

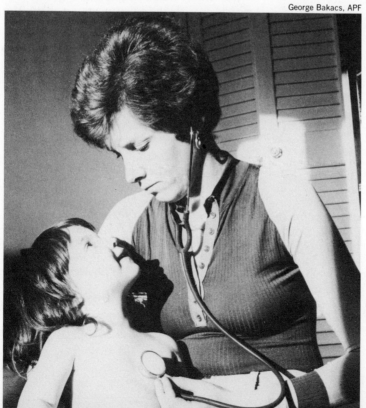

In some self-care programs, mothers are being taught how to use a stethoscope and other medical instruments to examine and sometimes treat their children.

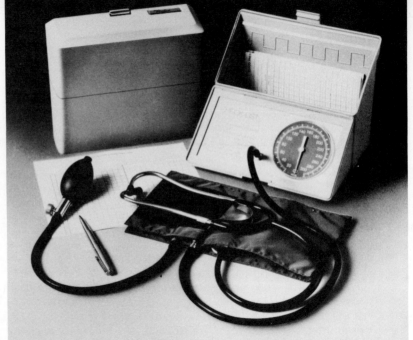

Hypertension is a common medical problem, and many people now use a sphygmomanometer to measure their blood pressure between visits to a physician.

## VALUE OF A HEALTHY LIFESTYLE

Self-care enthusiasts say a healthy lifestyle is the simplest way to reduce doctor-dependence. They point to interpretations of mortality data in a state health department study of 7,000 California adults. The results suggest that 45-year-old men who practiced at least six of seven good health habits lived an average of more than 11 years longer than those who practiced only two or three. The seven good health habits were no smoking, moderate drinking, adequate sleep, regular meals, daily breakfast, normal weight, and exercise. In a recent Stanford University study, over-all risk of cardiovascular disease was significantly reduced by self-activated lifestyle changes (chiefly reduced smoking, improved diet, and exercise) in 500 northern California residents subjected to a pro-habit-control media campaign.

## PROBLEM OF SELF DIAGNOSIS

Still, the prospect of patients trying their hands at diagnosis and treatment appalls many doctors and raises a host of questions in any clinician's mind. How much training would patients need? How could self-care be limited to the patient and members of his or her immediate family? How would doctors' roles be altered? Most important, what risks would patients run of harming themselves or loved ones? Would self-care mean self-malpractice? Answers to most of those questions remain elusive.

"I've been in family practice for 22 years," says Dr. Holger Rasmussen, a Fremont, California, physician and a member of AAFP's board of directors. "Every so often I look in someone's ear and don't know what the hell I'm seeing. People with high blood pressure often don't exhibit early symptoms, and appendicitis can be the most difficult diagnosis in the world to make." Indeed, Dr. Rasmussen recently treated an appendicitis victim from Alaska who spent "a week or so" suffering with the misconception, based on incorrectly interpreting a first-aid manual, that he had gastroenteritis.

"The really tough question for self-care," says Dr. Rasmussen, "is whether you can teach people to be good diagnosticians. Frankly, I'm a bit skeptical."

"Much of the published information has been conflicting," complains Dr. Huffman, "particularly in terms of diet and exercise. People come in with one book that tells them to fast and another that says they shouldn't. One authority says it's good to jog and the next one disagrees." Dr. Huffman, who plans a major expansion of patient education (including self-care) in his Maumee, Ohio, practice, insists that "any self-care program should be carefully coordinated under the supervision of one's own physician."

## USE OF MEDICAL INSTRUMENTS

Even among doctors who champion self-care, disagreement is commonplace.

Maine's Dr. Taylor, for example, is convinced self-care instruction should stop well before the use of medical instruments. "I don't think you should teach a patient how to flick an ophthalmoscope or focus on the retina—nor would I ask a patient to distinguish between systolic and holosystolic heart murmurs with a stethoscope. I don't think you should give people half knowledge and half technical skills that could leave them with a false sense of what they can do."

On the other hand, in Lyndonville, Vermont, Dr. Lloyd L. Thompson holds few such reservations. "I'm willing to let self-care go as far as the doctor and patient feel comfortable with it," he says. Dr. John H. Renner, now chairman of the department of family medicine and practice at the University of Wisconsin Medical School, believes self-care should be closely monitored by each patient's own physician but would consider using that control to push the limits of self-care even further. "I've put together some nifty little surgical kits for patients," says Dr. Renner, "and I've had patients I taught sew up themselves and their relatives. Many things are possible if self-care is promoted by a trusted provider who respects the patients."

## REDUCING MEDICAL INTERVENTION

Self-care proponents argue that from one third to three quarters of visits to the doctor's office could be avoided if patients were better informed. Moreover, they contend that establishment medicine is stumbling toward an era of diminishing returns, that its scientific, cure-oriented approach to health often ignores those with chronic ills who now make up the bulk of the nation's disease burden. Other frequent targets of self-care advocates: unnecessary operations, over-medication, and disorders produced by medical treatment. Lowell S. Levin, a leading spokesman for self-care and an associate professor of public health at Yale University School of Medicine, estimates that as many as 25 per cent of hospital patients are discharged with additional medical problems, a figure he believes may be reduced only by less reliance on professional care.

The medical profession gets strong support from American Medical Association President John H. Budd and from Dr. Phillip R. Lee, professor of social medicine and director of the Health Policy Program at the University of California in San Francisco. And a new study sponsored by the California Medical Association and the California Hos-

At-home urinalysis kits are available. When a few drops of urine are placed on a special reagent strip, the strip changes color. Different colors indicate different things about the urine. One color indicates the presence of sugar in the urine, for example, while another color indicates the presence of blood.

both George Bakacs, APF

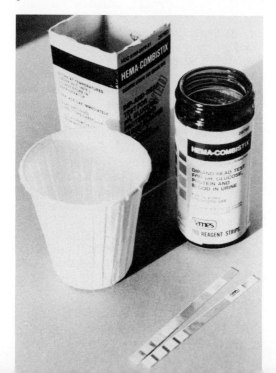

Self-care programs encourage better communication between health care professionals and lay people. Here a physician (second from right) discusses the delivery of health care with a group of concerned community members.

pital Association sharply disputed Levin's contentions. It pegged "potentially compensable" medically-induced injuries in that state's hospitals as less than 5 per cent. "The health of the American people," insists Dr. Budd, "is good and getting better."

Still, both physicians welcome self-care's promise of improved disease prevention. Indeed, Dr. Lee thinks some of those hopes have been fulfilled. "Diet has changed —there has been a dramatic increase in the popularity of healthier bran cereals and bread, for instance—and millions have stopped smoking. Exercise has changed, too; there are 30,000,000 people playing tennis now and millions are jogging. Those are important dimensions of self-care."

Figures released by the U.S. Census Bureau seem to bear him out. Markedly fewer heart-disease deaths in 1973 to 1975 have boosted life expectancy significantly, adding four years to average survival figures for women (to 81 years) and three years for men (to 71.8 years). Even doctors who worry about the potential dangers of wrong diagnosis find hidden advantages in continuity of treatment maintained by self-care patients who move to new geographic areas or are transients who frequent many different inner-city clinics.

Another important hope: that medically knowledgeable patients will be more inclined to follow their doctors' advice. "We all know that just telling patients about disease hasn't really improved compliance that much," says Dr. Frank F. Snyder, director of family practice residency programs at Toledo Hospital in Ohio. Nearly all doctors welcome the idea of greater self-responsibility among patients. "It simply is not fair," says California's Dr. Rasmussen, "for patients to put everything on their physicians, to say, 'You're God and I don't have to do anything about the problem myself.'"

## HEALTH ASSISTANTS

Self-care for general health consumers "makes sense," based on his experience with chronically ill patients at Harvard-affiliated Beth Israel Hospital in Boston, says Dr. Anthony L. Komaroff. Under his direction, high-school graduates with as little as two weeks' part-time instruction use computer-based protocols, or instruction programs, to care for people who have diabetes, hypertension, and cardiovascular disease.

Among an initial 381 diabetics seen by the "briefly trained" health assistants, monitoring physicians found no instances in which important clinical findings had been missed. They reported that "control of serum glucose levels in diabetic patients and blood pressure levels in diabetic patients with hypertension was as good in the protocol-treated group as in the physician-treated group." Over all, the protocol systems scored with better recognition of new abnormalities and were credited with helping achieve a 20 per cent saving in physician time. Finally, says Dr. Komaroff, the health assistants proved "remarkably good at providing psychosocial support important to their patients."

Mothers who learned to take and interpret throat cultures from their children agreed with professionals in determining which specimens were streptococcal-positive, or contained streptococcal bacteria, in 136 of 137 paired home versus clinic cases. The program was directed by Dr. Harvey P. Katz, chief of pediatrics at the Columbia, Maryland, Medical Care Plan. Indeed, the group in which parents did the throat cultures reported fractionally lower complication rates than those done by professionals. "Two thirds of families felt our home-culture approach improved medical care and stated it reduced anxiety, decreased contagion, and eliminated unnecessary visits for their children and siblings," Dr. Katz reports. Like Dr. Komaroff, he strongly urges close links and careful controls between doctors and self-care practitioners. But, he adds, "there is a tremendous untapped potential for participation by patients in their own care."

Children themselves have proved "remarkably rational" as health decision-makers in a five-year study project by the University of California at Los Angeles' Center for Health Services Research. Some 600 youngsters who have been involved give their teachers a "care card" whenever they want to see the nurse. Then they help in choosing their own course of treatment. "It may sound trivial to those who spend their time repairing severed arteries and broken limbs," says Dr. Charles E. Lewis, professor of medicine and chief of UCLA's division of general internal medicine and health services research. "But this is the first time most of these youngsters have had input into their own care."

Statistics at the Midpeninsula Health Service, Inc. (MHS), in Palo Alto, California—which is counting on self-care to reduce "professional interventions" and costs—

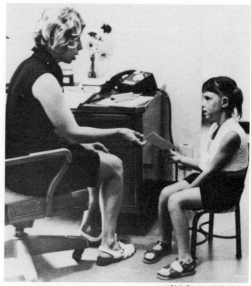

UCLA Dept. of Medicine

Even small children can be taught how to describe their symptoms and discuss how they feel with a physician or other medically trained person.

show that patients make an average of less than two visits per year, despite a membership in which one in three persons is over 60. "That's well below the national average," maintains Stanford professor of medicine Halsted R. Holman, a founder of the service and president of its board of directors.

New MHS members attend self-care seminars where role-playing teaches them how to use "decision tree" flowcharts in discussing their complaints with a health professional over the telephone. MHS nurse-practitioner Judith A. Staples recently guided a member, over the telephone, through a butterfly closure of a deep foot laceration, with excellent results. In another instance, a patient spotted an unusual upper-abdominal mass and surgeons removed a gastric carcinoma before it metastasized.

## SELF-CARE IS NOT NEW

In truth, of course, absolutely nothing about self-care is new. Thomas Jefferson started a self-care course at the University of Virginia because the plantation owner-fathers of most students were totally unskilled in medicine. Dr. Benjamin Rush, Continental Army surgeon general and signer of the Declaration of Independence, argued that lay citizens had a right to medical as well as religious freedom. Herbalists, eclectics, homeopaths, and water-curists rode the wave of Jacksonian populism that surged across the nineteenth century. Scores of writers attacked the medical profession, arguing in effect that anybody could be his or her own doctor.

A century-and-a-half later, self-care books are again pouring off publishers' presses. By one conservative estimate more than 600 titles have hit the market since 1973. Only a few—notably *Our Bodies, Ourselves,* the classic self-care manifesto of the Women's Movement—boil with the political fervor of the earlier time. Even so, booksellers' shelves burst with evidence that the nation's heritage of folk remedies—and susceptibility to quackery—maintains its vigor.

## REDUCED COST AND GREATER INDEPENDENCE

Clearly, cost reduction is part of self-care's allure. In many parts of the United States, for example, the average total expense of an initial visit to a physician has spiraled to well over $100 according to one study. But self-care also speaks to a deep hunger in many people for greater personal independence.

Last year physicians told Francis B. Dubois, chairman of a major California farm corporation, that he needed a coronary bypass operation. So ravaged by angina that he was unable to cross a street without severe pain, the 63-year-old Dubois turned instead to Dr. Travis' Wellness Resource Center and a southern California natural foods clinic. Through biofeedback and other techniques, Dubois learned to relax and express his inner feelings. Now he meditates at least 20 minutes each day, watches his diet, and jogs eight kilometers (five miles) every morning. Dubois reports a lower pulse rate and, with his doctors' concurrence, has discontinued all medication except propranolol. "I had thought of myself more as a victim than as contributor to my condition," he says. "Now I've taken responsibility for my own predicament—and my own welfare."

For others, self-care's chief attraction may be that it is the only kind around. Organizations like Mended Hearts (bypass patients) and Make Every Day Count (terminal cancer patients) deal with people who cannot expect a "cure" in the traditional sense. Typically, they are staffed by volunteer fellow sufferers and fill a craving for kinship.

So far, government has done little to encourage self-care. The U.S. National Center for Health Services Research launched a study to determine whether self-care training by one non-profit health education firm can reduce visiting rates among patients at a local family-practice clinic, but results won't be known for some time. The center has yet to release self-care research recommendations by a panel of experts assembled in early 1976. Congress still has not appropriated some $10,000,000 authorized under the Consumer Health Information and Health Promotion Act of 1976.

## NOT FOR EVERYONE

Self-care is not for everyone. Some patients, particularly the elderly, genuinely need and desire the comforting presence of an authority-figure doctor. Physicians, too, may feel unduly challenged by patients who boldly stride onto their professional turf. Self-care inherently demands complete candor between doctors and their patients—a requirement some professionals staunchly oppose.

Even so, the potent appeal of self-care seems certain to grow. Circulation of the self-care-leaning Harvard Medical School *Health Letter* has increased tremendously as have subscriptions to the fledgling *Medical Self-Care* magazine.

"For a long time the idea has gone around that ordinary people can't comprehend anything about medicine," says Dr. Glenn O. Turner, a Springfield, Missouri, cardiologist who developed a widely published self-warning system for heart attacks. "We're finding out that simply isn't true" □

 SELECTED READINGS

"Learning to be your own M.D." by Sandra Rosenzweig. *The New York Times Magazine,* April 2, 1978.

"New era in health care: medical devices you can use at home" by K. Anderson. *Popular Mechanics,* December 1977.

*Our Bodies, Ourselves* by the Boston Women's Health Book Collective. Simon and Schuster, 1971.

Paul Almasy/WHO

Many people in poor countries are in need of the basic services of life. Above, a notice in Colombia, South America, of a vaccination program.

# PEOPLES OF THE WORLD

## contents

# PEOPLES OF THE WORLD

## review of the year

Food production greatly exceeded the population growth rate in 1977 and there were near record harvests in many areas. The food supply was not, however, well distributed and certain areas of the world still suffered from severe food shortages. The photo above shows storage of surplus grain, while the photo below dramatically depicts the plight of many in areas where food shortages are common.

**Population and Food.** The world's population increased by just under two per cent during 1977. At the same time world grain production increased nearly ten per cent, to nearly 1,456,000,000 tons. Although the food production increase greatly exceeded the population growth rate, there were no significant improvements in diets for the 500,000,000 people that the United Nations says are malnourished or facing starvation. The near-record harvests were simply not well distributed and so brought about little overall change in the basic problem of feeding the world.

Long-term forecasts of food availability continue to be discouraging. Factors that affect food supply—land, water, energy, fertilizers, other inputs—are generally in tight supply; and weather is unpredictable, uncontrollable, and ultimately decisive. At the same time, population growth, together with rising affluence and demands in the industrialized nations and among the ruling groups in less developed nations, continues to press on available food supplies. The International Food Policy Research Institute predicts a shortfall of over 100,000,000 tons of grain for the poor countries by the year 1990.

The World Food Council, established by the 1974 UN World Food Conference in Rome, has been working steadily to stimulate and coordinate follow-up efforts of the conference and to help gather information that will ease the chronic food shortage problem. At its June 1977 meeting in Manila, the Philippines, the Council reiterated the world's concern for the hungry and stressed again that the major long-term solution to the problem of hunger must be to increase agricultural production where the hungry people are—on the small farms of the food-deficient countries. ■ The International Fund for Agricultural Development, called for by the Conference, was formally established with an initial capital of $1,000,-000,000. Its function—to lend money to spur agricultural development—will begin shortly. ■ Meanwhile, the Food and Agricultural Organization of the United Nations echoed warnings and the need for urgent action at its biennial conference in Rome in November 1977 and began planning a World Conference on Agrarian Reform and Rural Development for June 1979.

The United States, the largest producer, consumer, and trader of grain, remains the dominant power in the world food system. Just over one-half the grain traded worldwide starts in the United States. One of the many ironies of the current world food situation is the fact that the U.S. grain production was so high in 1976 and 1977 that Secretary of Agriculture Bergland found it necessary to announce a program in which farmers would be given incentives to set aside a certain percentage of land planned for wheat and corn. That this attempt to safeguard farmers' income was considered insufficient was attested to by a loosely organized, but vociferous, strike initiated by the newly formed American Agriculture Movement in December 1977. ■ In general the Carter administration showed sensitivity to the problem of hunger and malnutrition in food-deficient countries. It began a new program that includes better loan arrangements and domestic and eventually international grain reserves of up to 35,000,000 metric tons.

Martin McLaughlin

**Anthropology and Archaeology.** Asia, as well as Africa, may have been the birthplace of the human race. In early 1977 an international team of scientists headed by David Pilbeam of Yale University, reported that it had found 8,000,000-to-13,000,000-year-old fossils of "pre-man" in the arid badlands of Pakistan's Potwar plateau. Most of the specimens are upper or lower jaw fragments and have been classed as belonging to *Ramapithecus.* The find was called "extremely significant . . . because of its completeness in a well-dated context" by anthropologist Donald Carl Johanson of the Cleveland Museum of Natural History. The fossils are, according to Pilbeam, of a "diverse intermediate group"—not really apes and not really men; they give support to the idea that the split between apes and man occurred more than 13,000,000 years ago. It seems likely to Pilbeam and others that the same evolutionary process which in Africa led to the emergence of man (genus *Homo*) also occurred in Asia, and that 3,000,000-to-5,000,000-year-old "near men" may be found in Asia.

Yale University

David Pilbeam examines *Ramapithecus* fossils found in Pakistan and believed to be at least 8,000,000 years old.

In early 1978 Chinese scientists were able to push back the age assigned to the earliest fossil of true man found in Asia by more than 1,000,000 years. Chinese researchers studied teeth found in China's Yunnam province and using magnetic methods dated the teeth at 1,700,000 years old. They identified the specimens as belonging to *Homo erectus,* the stage in human evolution just before the appearance of *Homo sapiens,* or modern man. This discovery represents the oldest relic of true man known on mainland Asia.

Meanwhile anthropological work continued in Africa. In November 1977 Mary Leakey announced the possible finding of the oldest footprint of man's ancestor. (See "Oldest Footprints of Man's Ancestor?" on page 268.)

Mark Stevens

As part of an intensified search for the earliest remains of humans in North America, archaeologists work at "Dry Creek" dig in Alaska.

Meanwhile the search for the earliest Americans continues. The presence of humans in North America at least 40,000 years ago was reported by Dr. Rainer Berger of the University of California at Los Angeles. He reported finding on Santa Rosa Island, off Santa Barbara, California, stone tools and a charcoal-lined fire pit containing dwarf mammoth bones that cannot be dated by the usual radiocarbon method, which is limited to dating objects no older than 40,000 years. There are other clues hinting at the early appearance of man in North America, some dated at more than 70,000 years ago. Many of these finds and the ways of dating them are, however, controversial, and much remains to be learned about North American prehistory. ■ Central and South American prehistory also remains much of a mystery, but pieces of the puzzle are being put together. Excavations in 1977 confirmed earlier estimates of the existence of a Mayan settlement in Belize (formerly British Honduras) in 2,500 B.C. and suggested that other settlements may have occured there before 4,000 B.C.

National Geographic Society

This footprint, one of a trail of five, may have been left by man's oldest direct ancestor, 3,500,000 years ago.

# THE OLDEST FOOTPRINTS?

ANTHROPOLOGIST Mary Leakey is tracking footprints on an African plain left by creatures more than 3,000,000 years ago.

About 50 kilometers (30 miles) south of Olduvai Gorge, Dr. Leakey is studying lines of fossil footprints left in deposits of volcanic ash. It was in this northern Tanzanian site that she and her late husband, Louis Leakey, made their famous finds of ancient hominids, or manlike beings.

There, at a site called Laetolil, erosion has exposed the tracks of prehistoric antelopes, cats, mongooses, and what appears to be a deinotherium, an extinct elephantlike animal with downward-curving tusks protruding from its lower jaw.

"And there is a possibility that we might have found footprints of hominids at Laetolil," Dr. Leakey said. Many more careful anatomical measurements must be done to confirm the possibility.

"But if it's true, it is very, very important," said Dr. Leakey at her home outside Nairobi. Dinosaurs have left older prints, but the Laetolil tracks, at 3,500,000 to 3,750,000 years, would be by far the oldest known footprints of man's ancestors.

The oldest hominid prints on record data from 200,000-300,000 years ago, and belong to the makers of relatively sophisticated hand axes.

## COUSINS AND DIRECT ANCESTORS

It was an evolutionary stray which put Olduvai, and the Leakeys, on the map. One morning in 1959, Mrs. Leakey wandered out into the rocky gorge and unearthed the thick-browed skull of *Zinjanthropus* (*Australopithecus boisei*), the fossil for which the Leakeys are most famous.

"It changed the fortunes of Olduvai," said Dr. Leakey. The National Geographical Society has funded the work at the gorge since 1960 and now supports Laetolil as well.

Paleontologists and archaeologists disagree sharply about how the hominids relate to one another. But, most agree that Zinj, as they have nicknamed him, is a distant cousin of modern man rather than a direct ancestor.

The Australopithecans appear to have developed big teeth with which they ground a largely vegetarian diet. *Homo habilis*, probably a precursor of *Homo sapiens*, lived at Olduvai at about the same time as Zinj and was already using sharp pebble tools to scrape meat from hides and bones.

But Zinj, dated at 1,750,000 years ago was hardly an evolutionary failure. *Homo sapiens*, whose oldest known remains date from just over 100,000 years ago, must go far to better his record.

## TOURISTS CONSTANT

Olduvai became a shrine for people curious about their earliest origins. Tourists visiting the game-filled Serengeti Plains of Kenya could also make a stop at the gorge. Then in early 1977, the Tanzanian Government closed its border with Kenya, a political act which had a surprising scientific bonus.

"At last I can get some work done," said Dr. Leakey. During the dry seasons, she works from a tent camp at Laetolil, where discoveries suggest that the genus *Homo*—containing modern man, *Homo habilis,* and *Homo erectus*—may be more than 3,000,000 years old. During the rains she writes in the stone house at Olduvai.

UPI

The late Louis Leakey and Mary Leakey working at northern Tanzania site where they made their famous finds of manlike beings.

Tanzania allows Dr. Leakey and anyone connected with her work to cross the border freely. In September 1977 the International Louis Leakey Memorial Institute for African Prehistory, a modern, $1,000,000 conference and study center on the grounds of the National Museum opened. It is directed by paleontologist Richard Leakey, the son of Louis and Mary Leakey.

Noting that the institute has an underground, bomb-proof vault for the storage and study of the precious relics, Dr. Leakey remembered, "We used to carry the fossils around in shoe boxes."

## CONFERENCE HEATED

During the week-long conference of African prehistorians following the institute's opening, Dr. Leakey sat quietly while her colleagues argued heatedly over when and why the hominid genera—*Homo, Australopithecus,* and *Ramapithecus*—went their separate ways. Yet the debaters often paused to appeal to her on matters of fact: the date of a find, the date of a publication, or the official number of a fossil.

Asked which was most important to an archaeologist, the searching or the writing, publishing, and speaking, she replied: "Oh, one lives for one's field work. It is 90 per cent of one's life. The moments at conferences, presenting papers, are quite brief."

Thus, with the tourist flow slowed to a trickle, Dr. Leakey is able to settle down to her field work, on her knees in the eternal African dust beneath the blazing African season sun □

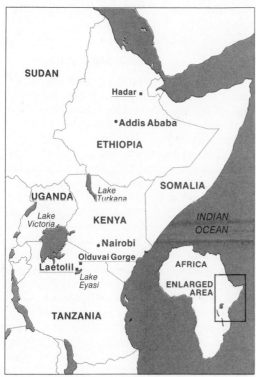

National Geographic Society

The seal of an elephant has been found on many relics of the Indus culture at the Mohenjo Daro site.

Jehangir Gazdar, Woodfin Camp

# RELICS OF THE INDUS CULTURE

## by George F. Dales

WITHOUT a key to our 20th-century languages, how will archaeologists of A.D. 6479 know what to make of a 1979 fire hydrant buried in 45 centuries of rubble? Or a birdbath? Or a yellow Rolls-Royce?

That is our problem today with the plethora of artifacts and art objects dug up recently at various sites in the Indus Valley. We have not deciphered the language of the people who lived 4,500 years ago in what is now Pakistan and western India. So we don't know what to make of such things as a conical piece of ceramic that looks like the hub of an airplane propeller, or a stone bird that looks like a penguin (penguins in Pakistan?). The objects are well-wrought and beautiful—but cryptic. Some were fashioned by city folk and some by country dwellers. The works of both, and the urban and rural environments in which they lived, are fascinating challenges.

Our vantage point for viewing ancient Asian civilization has been traditionally the city—the massive remains whose sheer bulk captivate the imagination of the searching archaeologist.

The city, by definition, can be expected to contain the most concentrated, uniform, sophisticated aspects of an ancient culture—monumental architecture; major works of arts and crafts; physical symbols of the social, economic, and intellectual lives of the inhabitants; and, very likely, archives, both official and private, of written documents. Small wonder the archaeologist's spade—like a cultural divining rod—has led expeditions to concentrate on urban sites.

But the view of a civilization from the city alone is incomplete and distorted. Thus excavations at smaller village or provincial sites often can provide valuable and fascinating new perspectives.

A striking example of this urban-rural contrast is seen in the greater Indus Valley of Pakistan and western India. There, in the 1920s, were discovered and excavated two impressive urban ruins of a previously unknown and unexpected ancient culture. Harappa, in northern Pakistan, and Mohenjo Daro, in the northern part of Sind in southern Pakistan, were heralded as twin capitals of a 4,500-year-old civilization that dominated the vast Indus plain from the foothills of the Himalayas to the Arabian Sea.

A single enigmatic, 18-centimeter (7-inch) fragment of a sculpture gave rise to the theory that this ancient empire was ruled by a priest-king. Equally mute architectural remains prompted interpretations of sacred baths, priests' colleges, and state granaries. One need only visit Mohenjo Daro, or look at its layout, to be impressed by the remarkable organization and planning that resulted in a 260-hectare (approximately one-square-mile) city with its main streets forming a general grid plan, and all the brick buildings oriented almost uniformly in north-south, east-west directions.

## UNKNOWN PEOPLE, UNKNOWN LANGUAGE

The nature of those early excavations, and the publicity they received, was such that the ancient Indus—or Harappan—civilization was rigidly stereotyped as a model of the world's first monolithic priest-king-dominated state, characterized by a technological and artistic uniformity enduring virtually unchanged for a thousand years. A grim, monotonous, uninviting human societal experiment indeed, if it was really true. And our attempts at a better interpretation are made more difficult by the fact that the Indus script, of which we have thousands of short examples on stone seals, metal objects, and pottery, never has been deciphered.

Herein lies the real challenge for the handful of present-day archaeologists who have the opportunity to conduct fresh excavations at sites of this most ancient of South Asia's fully developed urban civilizations.

View of Mohenjo Daro, which is thought to have been a capital of a 4,500-year-old civilization along the Indus River. It is now the site of extensive excavations for clues to early Indus culture.

George F. Dales

George F. Dales

Excavation site at Balakot, a coastal site whose ruins and artifacts are being studied and compared with those of the more crowded interior centers such as Mohenjo Daro.

But the pace of new research has been excruciatingly slow. In India only two Harappan towns have been excavated extensively—Kalibangan, in northern Rajasthan, and Lothal, a seaport in Gujarat. In Pakistan the principal sites of Harappa and Mohenjo Daro have been excavated intermittently since the 1930s, and a few other sites have been excavated through the years.

Starting in 1973, two American expeditions have had the opportunity to work at new sites in southern Pakistan. Dr. Walter A. Fairservis, Jr., of the American Museum of Natural History in New York has been excavating Allahdino, a unique small Harappan settlement a few kilometers east of Karachi. The University of California at Berkeley has completed four seasons of excavation at the coastal site of Balakot, some 90 kilometers (55 miles) northwest of Karachi. Both excavations are providing some fascinating comparisons between the highly organized, crowded cities and the remotely situated smaller settlements near the southern seacoast of Pakistan. This opportunity for excavating provincial sites has come during an otherwise discouraging lull in Indus civilization archaeology.

## SAVE MOHENJO DARO

Top priority is being given the crumbling remains of Mohenjo Daro. The hundreds of brick structures literally are disintegrating before our eyes. The culprit is salt, which permeates the brickwork, weakening and crumbling it. In another 20 to 30 years, the exposed walls may be in total collapse.

This naturally has been a matter of concern for decades, but it was only in the 1960s that steps were taken by the government of Pakistan to determine the causes of the problem and to implement corrective measures. A direct appeal was made to UNESCO to study the situation. As a result, a master plan for attacking the problem of salt-caused decay was presented, together with an elaborate scheme for restoration of the monuments and development of the site as a tourist attraction.

Basically, the master plan directs its attention to problems created by the waters—both underground and floodwaters from the Indus River—which constantly moisten the ground and the brickwork, facilitating the action said to be responsible for depositing the destructive salts in the brickwork. The present water table—artificially raised as the result of extensive canal and irrigation projects—is close to the ground, and about one third of the remains at Mohenjo Daro are buried not just in sand but in water.

The master plan calls for lowering the water table by installing, in stages, two concentric rings of tube wells around the site and for building a gigantic earthen barrier to divert the waters of the Indus away from the site. But the estimated costs for all this are very high.

Two other factors may complicate the Mohenjo Daro problem even further. Both concern the sources of the salts. Windblown sands and dust are major transporters and depositors of salts. Thus Mohenjo Daro may be experiencing daily downpours of windblown salts which will pursue their destructive course even if the ground and floodwaters are controlled.

Even more insidious, and virtually impossible to combat, are ancient salts incorporated in the bricks when they were manufactured 4,500 years ago.

Decisions will have to be made—and made soon—if anything enduring is to be salvaged from the rapidly deteriorating remains of Mohenjo Daro. If the entire site cannot be saved, at least selected areas could be dewatered, the salt leached from the walls, and restorations made and truly preserved for future generations.

## EXCAVATING A COASTAL VILLAGE

The University of California Balakot project originated through my long interest in the question of maritime activities of the Indus folk, especially as they might involve trade and cultural contacts with the Persian Gulf and the Sumerians and Babylonians of Mesopotamia.

The three-hectare (about seven-acre) site of Balakot, rising about 8 to 10 meters (25 to 30 feet) above the cultivated plain, is about 11 kilometers (7 miles) from the present sandy coastline of Sonmiani Bay. The rate of sedimentation and sand deposition in this region is astonishingly rapid, so the distance from the sea does not preclude the probability that the site in 2000 B.C. was very

adapted from UNESCO publication

Mohenjo Daro ruins are being destroyed by salt. Groundwater (A), the horizontal movement of water from partly excavated walls (B), and rain and dust storms (C) are all adding salts to the walls (D), causing them to crumble.

near the coast, and also near the mouth of the Windar River, which itself has shifted its bed to the east and south of the site. The western half of the site is a high, steep-sided mound dominating the lower half of the settlement.

The functions of the various structures on the high mound are unknown. In most instances, only the foundations of walls remain, so that we cannot uncover rooms intact with furniture in place. But floors are excellently preserved and we have excavated

George F. Dales

Closeup of a wall in Mohenjo Daro crumbling from salt accumulation. Unless such destruction can be halted, the pieces of an ancient and little known culture may be lost forever.

numerous rooms with perfectly preserved storage jars and stone and brick drains. It appears that the structures on the western high mound are not common domiciles. The walls, some almost one meter (3 feet) thick, and the formality of the layout bespeak public or perhaps administrative buildings.

## PIECING TOGETHER A CULTURE

Our lack of information on social and political organizations is amply compensated for at Balakot by other types of discoveries. Most plentiful of the finds is the pottery. Hundreds of complete or restorable vessels and hundreds of thousands of pottery shards have been excavated since 1973.

One large, well-preserved pottery kiln was discovered, associated with several smaller kilns in which were found clay figurines of bulls—the humped species common to much of South Asia today. Bull figurines (no cows) are found everywhere at Harappan sites, and Balakot has yielded a fine new collection which will provide interesting comparisons with the big-city varieties from Mohenjo Daro.

One of the major aims of the Balakot project, apart from the traditional search for architecture, ceramics, and artifacts, has been to collect floral and faunal remains that will help us reconstruct something of what the physical environment was like when Balakot flourished four to five thousand years ago. And the remains are plentiful indeed—more than 20,000 specimens of animal bones, teeth, and shells were collected just in one season of work.

Preliminary sorting in the field reveals that the Harappans were butchering cattle (zebu), water buffalo, goats, sheep, and, more rarely, gazelles and pigs. Fish bones and shells of gastropods and bivalves indicate another basic source of food for the Harappans.

One of the fascinating discoveries is the evidence of large-scale and intensive exploitation of marine resources by the Balakot Harappans. In addition to collecting for food, they also gathered huge quantities of shells—mostly of the species *Meretrix casta,* a clamlike bivalve, and less frequently a large conch shell. These two types of shells provided the raw material for what appears to have been a local industry.

Manufacturing areas complete with grinding stones, hammer stones, and shells in all stages of working have been found. The principal product was shell bangles for the personal adornment of the Balakot women and probably small girls, to judge from the sizes of the bracelets. The majority of these beautiful items of jewelry were manufactured from the *Meretrix* shell by a tedious process of alternate grinding and chipping.

Attention also has been directed toward recovering evidence of the plant life present at Balakot during the Harappan period. Seeds and endocarps (the innermost layers of seed covers), as well as casts and impressions of leaves, stems, and seeds in bricks, pottery, and other clay objects, provide the basic evidence for the ancient plant life.

Thus our observations and preliminary studies give a picture of a sophisticated, well-to-do, self-sufficient coastal village retaining rigid ties with the Indus cities, especially Mohenjo Daro. The specific reasons for sites such as Balakot (and the two other

Harappan sites on the coast) having been established in such isolated locations can only be inferred from the mute evidence. It is significant that these three Harappan coastal sites are approximately one day's sail from each other and that there are no known similar sites farther inland along the coast.

Physical proof of formal trade with the Middle East has not been forthcoming from our excavations, with the exception of a few examples of Persian Gulf-type painted pottery. But how else does one explain the location of these sites if not as outposts intentionally located to facilitate and protect coastal commerce? Sumerian and Babylonian cuneiform documents describe extensive long-distance seafaring ventures, presumably into the Arabian Sea, in this period.

## FAR-FLUNG HARAPPAN OUTPOSTS

Regrettably, the Harappans have not left us such convenient evidence. But we know from excavated raw materials that must have been imported from outside the Indus Valley, and from the far-flung distribution of Harappan sites, that the Harappans were very active in the exploitation of distant resources. Most astonishing in this regard is the recent discovery of a mature Harappan settlement up in northeastern Afghanistan, close to the border. The discovery and excavation of such frontier sites adds exciting dimensions to the picture of Harappan civilization that the major cities, such as Mohenjo Daro, cannot provide.

## AN EVEN EARLIER PEOPLE

Balakot has yielded other new insights—totally unexpected when we began work there in 1973—into a long period of human occupation going back centuries before the arrival of the Harappans. The lower and earlier portion of the mound of Balakot was built up from virgin soil by the successive dwellings of some obscure folk known to us only through the discovery of their exquisitely manufactured and colorfully painted pottery, their distinctive clay bull figurines, their flint tools and grinding stones, their stone beads, and their mudbrick houses. Radiocarbon dates, and the stratigraphy of Balakot itself, suggest that

George F. Dales

Hundreds of thousands of pottery shards have been found at the Balakot site. Analysis of these fragments will, it is hoped, yield information about the life at Balakot and how it differed from life at a big city like Mohenjo Daro.

these early Balakotians dwelt there around 3000 B.C. and that they, for reasons we do not know, abandoned the site long before the arrival of the Harappans.

No primitive people were those unnamed earlier folk. In addition to their remarkably developed ceramic industry, there is evidence that they were using copper. Furthermore, the architecture excavated displays a standardization of mud-brick sizes, construction techniques, and regularized orientation heretofore considered to have been introduced into South Asia by the Harappans. The study of these new finds it just beginning, but it already fires the imagination.

The mute potsherds, the brick walls, the butchered animal bones, and the mass of other cultural debris must be made to reveal what insight they can into the life and times of South Asia's earliest civilization□

 SELECTED READINGS

*Indus Civilizations* by Mortimer Wheeler. Cambridge University Press, 1968.

*Mohenjodaro and Indus Civilizations* by John Marshall. South Asia Books, 1973.

Primitive farming methods are still used by Andean farmers.

P. O. Stackman-Ostman

# THE LIVING LEGACY OF THE ANDES

## by Pablo Macera

THREE South American countries, Ecuador, Peru, and Bolivia, make up the heartland of the ancient civilization of the Andes. Other countries like Colombia and Chile also played some part in this civilization, whose influence can be felt even in the extreme north of the Republic of Argentina.

Over an area of almost 3,000,000 square kilometers (750,000,000 acres) millions of people live—often without realizing it—according to norms of conduct that evolved thousands of years ago.

In speaking of "the civilization of the Andes," we are not merely referring to the famous Inca emperors of Cuzco. The Incas were to Andean civilization what the Romans were to classical Mediterranean civilization or the Persians to Mesopotamia: an end rather than a beginning.

A simple date demonstrates this fact. The Incas began their conquests in the middle of the fifteenth century and their empire was only 80 years old when it was destroyed by the Spanish invaders. Andean civilization, on the other hand, had begun to take shape thousands of years before. The most ancient inhabitants of what is today Peru and Ecuador lived 20,000 years ago alongside the giant sloth and the sabre-toothed tiger.

Around 2000 or 3000 B.C., the population of the Andes began to domesticate numerous plants—Lima beans, kidney beans, cotton, potatoes, and maize—and such animals as the llama, the guinea pig, and the duck. The invention of pottery, which also dates from this period, allowed them to make more efficient use of fire and water.

Some 3,000 to 4,000 years elapsed between the formation of the first agrarian societies in the Andes and the Spanish conquest in the sixteenth century. Empires rose and fell during this time, and many highly complex and sophisticated cultures were implanted in various parts of the vast Andean region. Three of these cultures—Chavín, Tihuanaco, and Inca, dating from 1000 B.C., 800 A.D., and 1400 A.D. respectively—still constitute a unifying link between Peruvians, Ecuadorians, and Bolivians. We can say that geographically Chavín was an "Ecuadorian" culture, Tihuanaco a "Bolivian culture," and that of the Incas a "Peruvian" one, although this is an approximation since Peru, Bolivia, and Ecuador are very recent creations, barely 150 years old.

## BASICALLY AN ANDEAN CULTURE

How much of these ancient Andean civilizations disappeared when the Europeans arrived? How much still survives? Even in the Andean countries, no one knows for certain, and the question arouses vigorous controversy.

Those who hold conservative political views claim that they belong to a Western, Christian society. For them, Andean culture is only of marginal importance within the framework created by European colonialism. Moderates say that theirs is a mixed society—a mestizo culture—whereby they try to mask the conflicts that exist between Andean and European culture.

The truth is quite different. A provincial, Western-type culture does, of course, exist in these South American countries, but it is found primarily in certain urban areas, where its future is in question.

The mestizos, members of a group which is difficult to define from a scientific standpoint, have never managed to emerge as an entity independent of Andean or European culture.

But for most of the population, Andean culture is still the only frame of reference. This is true not only of the Amerindians belonging to different ethnic and linguistic groups, but also of all the other inhabitants of Ecuador, Peru, and Bolivia.

## ECONOMIC AND SOCIAL STRUCTURE

At least 90 per cent of the place names in these countries come from the Andean languages. But more important, Andean and

Alpha

In the rural areas of Peru, Ecuador, and Bolivia farmers still use the simple tools of their Andean forefathers and still grow the same crops as the early Amerindians did.

not European culture shapes economic and social structures in the rural areas of Ecuador, Peru, and Bolivia, and this is where the overwhelming majority of the people live.

South American farmers were of course subject to the feudal system of the *hacienda,* or ranch, and the Spaniards tried to introduce new crops and farming techniques. But 400 years later, the Amerindian ways still prevail.

The ancient crops—such as the potato, maize, and yucca—still form the basis of their diet, and the people of the Andes practice many of the earliest farming techniques used by their ancestors before the Spanish Conquest. Oxen, ploughs, wheels, and metals are practically unknown. Farmers still use wood and stone tools, without the help of animals.

## WAY OF THINKING

Andean civilization has not only survived at the economic and technological level. It also shapes the people's ways of thinking and their most sophisticated art and religious forms. The peoples of Peru, Ecuador, and Bolivia do not perceive, organize, or represent space or time like Westerners.

In the rural Andes, people still handweave objects whose patterns and vivid colors recall ancient Inca motifs—often geometric shapes and stylized representations of the human form.

Europeans think of time in terms of progress and are sure that the future is bound to be better than the past. In Andean civilization, time is cyclical, with an ascending and a descending phase leading to a great Universal Crisis (*Pachacutec*), which may bring about the end of the world.

This is a cosmic vision no doubt suited to ancient agrarian societies subject to seasonal cycles. It is also appropriate in an environment in which natural disasters—earthquakes, floods, and droughts—are so frequent.

## CRISIS, STRIFE, AND BALANCE

Nevertheless, Andean culture does not express an attitude of pessimism and resignation. Instead, it embodies the idea that the human mission is to reestablish a cosmic balance through such concepts as *Tinkuy* and *Paikiki*. *Tinkuy* denotes the idea of struggle, and also of union. *Paikiki* is the magic counterpart which compensates and counterbalances. The people of the Andes still think of their lives in terms of *Pachacutec* (crisis), *Tinkuy* (strife and union), and *Paikiki* (parity and equilibrium).

When they are confronted with desperate hardship and poverty which give the lie to the Western idea of progress, they do not lapse into pessimism. They know that their duty is to join with the positive forces in the universe to overcome *Pachacutec*. This cosmic vision is reflected in the way space is used and represented in poetic symbolism.

## MASSIVE HORIZONTAL ART

Like all despot-ruled agrarian societies that could tap large manpower reserves, the Andean societies erected buildings that required enormous masses of material. This practice survived into the Spanish colonial period because the Spaniards had the same abundance of workers as the Inca emperors and the Chavín priests.

Egyptian and Babylonian architecture also used enormous masses of material. All these edifices are designed according to a special order, or rule, which in the case of Andean civilization may be described as the horizontal principle. On the coasts and in the mountains, everything was built on the horizontal. Human creations were parallel to the landscape, so that the buildings seem designed to express the hidden potential of natural shapes.

We find this principle throughout the region: in a temple of the pre-ceramic period on the coast; in sanctuaries of the Chavín and Tihuanaco cultures; and in the ranch houses of the colonial and republican periods. It has also survived in mid-twentieth century buildings such as the Lima Civic Centre, where a young Peruvian architect made bold use of concrete to create large masses which, far from clashing with the urban surroundings, actually reflect them.

But this use of parallel and horizontal lines is nowhere more evident than in Cuzco, where all is sad and grandiose. Nothing is more Andean than Cuzco cathedral, built nevertheless by a Spanish architect. The massive cathedral stretches along one side of the square like an immense parapet defending the Sacsahuaman fortress, unlike the Jesuit church of La Compañia which rises vertically towards the sky.

## FOR APPEARANCES

It is important to remember, however, that the economic and social foundations of Andean civilization were profoundly altered by the European invasion of the sixteenth century. The conquerors demanded recognition as conquerors, and to survive, the conquered peoples had to disguise their true feelings.

Feigning appearances is the second principle of Andean civilization under Spanish and creole domination. For the last 400 years Andean civilization has worn camouflage.

In Ecuador, Peru, and Bolivia, "yes" can mean either "yes" or "no," but one can never be sure unless one knows the people and circumstances well. Language not only enshrines the legitimate and necessary hipocrisy of the underdog. It is also a tactical device for preserving what is one's own and triumphing over a dominant culture by taking over one of its power bases.

It also presupposes a generalized use of metaphor. Whites and creoles in South America today contemptuously describe the Indians as liars because they cannot understand that metaphors have become an underpinning of Andean culture—a structure reinforced by the colonial situation. Let us examine some results of this process in the vast area stretching from Quito, Ecuador, to the frontiers of Bolivia and Argentina.

## WHICH CULTURE WINS

Until the arrival of the Europeans, Andean women fastened their cloaks with a brooch shaped like a waxing moon whose masculine counterpart was the *Tumi* or sacrificial knife. This ambivalent sexual shape (moon-*Tumi*) did not disappear in colonial or republican days but tended to be replaced by the shape of the soup spoon introduced by the Spaniards.

In Andean civilization there were two basic ritual objects: the *Conopa*, a stone figure shaped like a llama, and the *Kero*, a

Monkmeyer

At festival time, the Andean blend of pre-Columbian, Spanish, and Catholic cultures becomes apparent as the people don costumes and perform dances and rituals.

**279**

The devils' masks worn during carnival time in the Andean nations display Catholic and Spanish influences but are also inspired by ancient Inca gods.

Monkmeyer

wooden receptacle with straight sides. The *Conopa*-llama symbol changed into a pottery bull, and in Ecuador the *Kero* was turned into a cup. The progression is suggestive: from moon to spoon; from reclining llama to bull; from *Kero* to cup. In each case the utilitarian shapes of the triumphant culture have been incorporated by the defeated culture, which apparently renounced its own sacred forms.

Among the Chinchero Indians of Peru and the Urochipayas of Bolivia, the *quipus,* a form of writing that uses knotted string, imitates a girl's tresses, since both words and hair come out of the head. No scribe was allowed to read the sacred letters without first donning a female wig. This special reading wig was kept in a foxskin bag, the fox being a female deity symbolizing cunning and cleverness.

An even more famous example appears in the Oruro carnival in Bolivia and the Puño fiesta in Peru. They are basically the same feast, which derives from ancient pre-Spanish rituals practiced between lakes Titi-caca and Poopo. The devils' masks in these rituals are doubtless influenced by Catholic iconography, but they are variations of religious images of much earlier date: the heads of the god of Chavín and that of the great deity Viracocha which has survived at Tihuanaco. The Andean gods worshipped more than 4,000 years ago are still dancing in the twentieth century.

A few months ago, while visiting the Callapa sanctuary in the Department of Oruro, Bolivia, I was struck by the naive mural paintings of Noah's Ark, and even more fascinated by the figure of St. James over the main altar. The St. James *Matamores* (the Moor-slayer) of the Spanish reconquest of Spain from the Moors had been transformed into St. James *Mataindios* (the Indian-slayer) of the Spanish conquest of Latin America. The Amerindians took over St. James and identified him with *Illapa,* the thunder-god of their own religion.

Indian depictions of St. James were decked out with all the trappings of the enemy. The oldest look like 16th-century Eu-

Peruvian Indians still play the rondador, or panpipe, a musical instrument played since ancient times.

Bruce Coleman

ropean soldiers. In the eighteenth century they were dressed like provincial governors, and in the nineteenth century they are shown wearing the military uniforms of creole generals.

The St. James of Callapa had moved even further into the future: stripped of the silks he wore a mere ten years ago, he was wearing green battle dress.

The Callapa St. James also reflects another historical experience: he has the wig and glasses which, according to the sacristan, were worn by the *guerrilleros*.

AND THE FUTURE?

What is the future of Andean culture? Many fear it will disappear in the process of industrialization which is under way in Latin America. For many, industrialization and modernization mean adopting Western cultural models.

This danger is compounded by the social structure of the Andean countries. A city-based white and mestizo minority dominates a great majority of poor, rural Indians and mestizos. To understand this phenomenon one must remember that the independence revolutions led by Washington in North America and by Bolívar in South America were basically elitist revolutions.

In countries like Peru and Bolivia, the creoles have been in power for 150 years, and think of themselves as Europeans who happened to be born in another continent.

The cultural uniformity which today's world is heading for is a danger for the whole human race. The survival and free development of cultures like that of the Andes broadens the scope of human heritage ☐

📖 SELECTED READINGS

*Changing Rural Society: A Study of Communities in Bolivia* by William J. McEwen. Oxford University Press, 1975.

*Ecuador* by J. J. Aviles. Gordon Press, 1977.

*Peru* by Victor Alba. Westview, 1977.

*Peru, Bolivia, and Ecuador: The Indian Andes* by Charles P. May. Nelson, 1969.

Each year, small starling-sized birds called dovekies fly into Greenland's Arctic by the tens of thousands, where many are snatched from the air into the nets of Polar Eskimos. For centuries dovekies have been a source of food and legend to the people of this region.

All photos: Fred Bruemmer

# GREENLAND'S HUNGRY ESKIMOS

## by Fred Bruemmer

IT started to snow shortly after Jes Qujaukit-sok and I left Qânâq, the main settlement of the Polar Eskimos in northwestern Greenland. It was early May and we were bound for the floe edge, the limit of landfast ice, some 72 kilometers (45 miles) to the south. Whirling snow enveloped us, so dense we could barely see the 11 huskies pulling our long sled. The snow was soft. The sled slid along smoothly, silently. We seemed to float through an infinite, encompassing world of white, suspended in time and space. With an uncanny sense of direction Jes guided his dogs through this vast and featureless void, and ten hours later we arrived at the floe edge, at the precise spot where he had planned to be.

We sat on the sled near the ice edge, waiting for seal and hoping for narwhal. The snow ceased, and the arctic night grew clear and cold and beautiful: the water a satin-smooth glossy black, the ice deep blue, the light honey-yellow on the far mountains.

A pod of beluga whales swam past, milky-white backs arching out of the dark water, and we could hear them trill and grunt. Flocks of eider ducks passed, plump, heavy-bodied birds, their wings whistling

through the stillness of the night. A pair of ivory gulls, long-winged and pure white, circled down to inspect us, their cries strident and ternlike.

### THE DOVEKIES COME

And then the dovekies came, thousands, tens of thousands, perhaps hundreds of thousands, dark, amorphous clouds of birds against the luminous blue-green of the sky, all headed northwest towards the immense breeding slopes of the Siorapaluk-Etah region, flying fast, urgently, to keep their date with destiny.

May, in the dialect of the Polar Eskimos, is called *agpaliarssuit tikiarfiat*—"The dovekies are coming." By tradition the dovekies (or little auks as they are called in Britain) are supposed to arrive on May 5 at their breeding cliffs near Savigsivik facing Melville Bay, southernmost of the six Polar Eskimo settlements, and three days later they are expected at Siorapaluk in the north, the northernmost village in the world, 1,600 kilometers (1,000 miles) above the Arctic Circle. Here, at the top of the world, I would live with an Eskimo couple for a month, marveling at the life-giving relationship between this bird and the people of Siorapaluk. Later, I would spend time with other Eskimos, as I was now with Jes Qujaukitsok, observing the "miracle" that came from the heavens.

Dovekies are starling-sized but chubbier, black on head and back, white on belly and chest. The beak is short and stout, the feet dark and webbed, and above each eye they have a tiny, coquettish spot of white feathers. The black-white plumage is elegant and practical. The cells of the white feathers contain air, which provides excellent insulation against the chill of arctic water. The cells of the dark feathers on the upper part are filled with melanin granules that absorb and conduct the sun's warmth.

They breed in the Arctic in colonies that number in the millions. In the Thule district of northwestern Greenland alone, home of the Polar Eskimos, their breeding population has been estimated at 30 million. Their total population may exceed 80 million. In flight, they look like fat, black-and-white cigars with wings. They love company and usually crowd together in immense flocks.

To the Polar Eskimos, the dovekies were once a vital food and are still important. A thousand years ago, small groups of Eskimos lived scattered over the farthest north of Canada and Greenland. In the 13th century the climate began to change. The "Little Ice Age" began. Winters became even colder and longer, summers shorter and chillier. Ice cover increased. The Eskimos of the Far North died out or left. Only one small group remained, the Polar Eskimos, living in an exceptionally game-rich region, a sort of arctic Eden. They lived in a world hemmed in by ice: the immense Humboldt Glacier to the north, the 160 kilometer (100-mile) wall of glaciers facing Melville Bay in the south. Beyond their narrow strip of coastal land rose *Sermerssuaq*, the giant glacier, the two-mile-thick icecap of Greenland.

Over the centuries, totally isolated, they forgot the existence of other people. They were, these 200-odd Polar Eskimos believed, the only people on earth living in a land bounded by ice. In fall, winter and spring, they hunted sea mammals. In summer, they lived nearly entirely on birds, on eider ducks and, primarily, on the numerous dovekies.

## WHAT ROSS DISCOVERED

In August, 1818, the explorer John Ross arrived in Melville Bay and saw "myriads . . . of that species of seafowl known by the name of little awk (sic) . . . together with vast numbers of whales and sea-unicornes (narwhal)." On August 8 he saw people on the shore ice. The Polar Eskimos had been discovered. Understandably, they were awed and horrified. Mistaking the sails for giant wings, the Eskimos assumed the ships had flown down from the moon.

Summer in the high Arctic, when Ross had first invaded this northern sanctuary, is short. Now, in the Thule region, the average temperature of only one month (July) is above the freezing point. But the sea is extremely rich in nutrients, and during this brief but intense summer, under constant daylight, the growth of phytoplankton is stupendous, and planktonic animals living on it swarm through the polar waters.

The small black and white birds are well-suited to the area. Their feathers insulate them from the cold arctic waters.

Lichen-covered rocks and crevices provide nesting places for the dovekies in June, where they mate and breed. There the birds are easy prey for other animals—and for humans, who overturn the stones to get at dovekie chicks and eggs.

In June I lived in Siorapaluk with Inuterssuaq, an old hunter of great skill and dignity, and his wife Naduq. He was a superb storyteller and nearly every evening after supper, which at this time of the year usually consisted of dovekies, he would lean back in his chair, his dark, deeply-lined face in reminiscent repose, and begin: "*Aglani, aglani* (long, long ago) . . ." and unfold for me the legend of his people, tales of hardship and hunger and sometimes of great happiness.

## A RELIABLE FOOD SOURCE

Dovekies figured prominently in his stories. For the Polar Eskimos, these little seabirds had always been the one reliable source of food. Seal hunting might fail, walruses might avoid their coasts one year, but the dovekies always came, punctual, predictable and in millions. And in their millions, they altered the landscape, profoundly influencing the existence of other animals of this region, and through them the Polar Eskimos.

When one travels along the coast of the Thule region in summer by boat, most of the narrow strip of land between sea and icecap appears drab and dun. Average soil accumulation is less than one-half centimeter (one-fourth inch) per century. But where the dovekies breed on talus slopes, some rising to a height of more than 300 meters (1,000 feet), the landscape changes dramatically. The rocks and boulders of the slopes are encrusted with bright orange lichen. Adjacent slopes and valleys, well fertilized by the myriad flying birds, are richly carpeted with grasses, flowers and mosses. Near the colonies, peat accumulation can be 4 to 5 meters (12 to 15 feet) thick. The rich plant growth provides food for arctic hares and ptarmigan. Both are of some importance to the Eskimos.

The arctic foxes of the region subsist primarily on dovekies. Their pelts—a rich, dark smoky blue-gray—are an important source of income for the Polar Eskimos and are also still extensively used for clothing. Children, and some women, wear parkas of fox fur, and all Polar Eskimo women wear delightful little fox fur pants, down-soft, coquettish and cozy.

Every day, weather permitting, we were up on the dovekie slopes near Siorapaluk where the annual take (adult birds, eggs and chicks) among Eskimos from all the polar villages is probably between 200,000 and 400,000. At first I accompanied Naduq, but I soon gave that up since it was devastating to my ego. Naduq, well into her sixties, rushed up the steep slopes, over loose, slippery, treacherous scree with catlike agility, while I panted behind. Since speed and stealth are of the essence, my bumbling presence was not appreciated in any case.

## THE NESTING GROUNDS

The dovekies had arrived at their nesting grounds in May but did not start to lay their eggs until the latter part of June. Their first visits were short and perfunctory. They spent the nights at sea, feeding, and arrived at the slopes early in the morning. For a while the immense swarms, probably several million birds, circled and wheeled high in the sky, clouds of birds that changed abruptly from brilliant, flashing white to black depending on whether their backs or bellies were turned toward the observer. Then, crying excitedly, they descended upon the slopes.

Now, in June, they spent more and more time on the immense talus slopes. They sat together in thousands upon the snowdrifts, so that the snow looked soot-speckled from afar. They crowded together on favorite rocks, or poked into clefts and crevices. Here and there, in the exuberance of spring and mating, dovekies soared suddenly into the air in peculiar, butterflylike display flights, warbling loudly, jubilantly. One dovekie is a very noisy little bird. It chirps and trills and cheeps. Occasionally it screams shrilly in fright or anger. Multiply that by millions, and the result blends into one great, enveloping, throbbing, pulsating noise.

They panic easily. When frightened by an enemy, a gyrfalcon, glaucous gull or raven flying overhead, the dovekies in mass alarm hurtle themselves into space, pour down the slopes at fantastic speed like an avian avalanche, wheel and usually swoop back and forth laterally across the mountainside. The predator, faced with so many fast-moving targets, finds it impossible to concentrate on any one victim and consequently often gets none.

Around the middle of June, the dovekies begin to claim their nesting places, and the harmony that seems to have reigned until now gives way to considerable squabbling.

Most of the dovekies are eaten fresh, either raw or boiled. The fat is chewed off the skin, then the lean meat is eaten.

You see a dovekie creep hopefully beneath a boulder. Moments later, a muffled row erupts below, and after a while the dovekie emerges, ruffled and upset, evicted by another occupant.

But the slopes are immense, covered with frost-shattered rock debris; the number of crevices, crannies and nooks is virtually unlimited and eventually all seem to find suitable spots. The dovekie does not build a nest. It lays its single, pale-blue egg on the ground. For such a small bird, the dovekie lays a very large egg, averaging 3¼ by 5 centimeters (1.3 inches by 2 inches).

After a 24-day incubation period, a dark-downed voracious chick emerges and keeps its parents busy for the next 20 days or so stuffing the little glutton with plankton. Toward the end of August the chicks are fledged. They are rather fat and globular. For a few days, they emerge briefly at night and test their wings. Then, a bit wobbly, their short wings whirring frantically, they fly with their parents out to sea. In fall and winter, the dovekies migrate south, keeping close to the ice edge by preference. Many come to the sea regions east and north of Newfoundland. "Bullbirds," Newfoundlanders call them.

A skillful Polar Eskimo can catch as many as 300 dovekies a day. The Eskimos' long-handled nets were once made from bone, ivory, driftwood, and sealskin, but now imported man-made materials such as nylon and bamboo are used.

For the Polar Eskimos, the dovekies have always been important as food and for other uses. In spring, when the sun is incredibly intense in this high Arctic region and its ultraviolet rays reflected from snow and ice scorch even the weather-hardened faces of the Eskimos, they rub themselves with dovekie skins. The subcutaneous fat is an excellent, soothing ointment. In the past, Polar Eskimo women made *artiggis,* inner parkas, from dovekie skins.

CATCHING DOVEKIES

The simplest method of catching dovekies was to haul them (and their eggs) out from underneath the stones. The Polar Eskimos used to set thousands of *negat,* snares made of braided narwhal sinew, to catch the birds. Some they simply killed by throwing stones, and in fall they rolled rocks aside to get at the chicks. But by far the most important method was to catch flying dovekies with long-handled nets. The net, called an *ipu,* consisted of a scarfed bone, an ivory or driftwood handle, a hoop of wood, or driftwood, or baleen, and a netting of sealskin thong or plaited sinew cord.

Nowadays, the news of the dovekies' arrival is sent by radio to all Polar Eskimo settlements. The net's handle is made of wood, often bamboo preferred for its lightness and strength, the hoop of split cane and the netting of nylon. Apart from these innovations, the annual dovekie hunt proceeds much as it has done for centuries. What makes their hunting technique possible and successful is the dovekies' habit of flying back and forth, occasionally singly, usually in flocks, and sometimes in immense swarms, low across the mountainside. The hunter hides behind rocks on the scree slopes, or behind low stone bulwarks. As the birds fly over, the net flicks up, and one or more dovekies are scooped out of the air, pulled in and killed nearly instantaneously by pressing in the chest. Some of the dead dovekies are propped up on nearby rocks as decoys.

I returned to Siorapaluk in September. The dovekies were gone. The great mountain slopes seemed still and forlorn without them. Light snow was falling and the land looked gray and triste. The foxes were yapping hoarsely on the slopes, moseying sadly among the rocks where the dovekies had sat all summer, so droll, delightful and delicious. Now they had left. The feast was over. The dovekies were far out at sea, their true realm. Nine months would pass before they would swarm again over these vast talus slopes of the high Arctic □

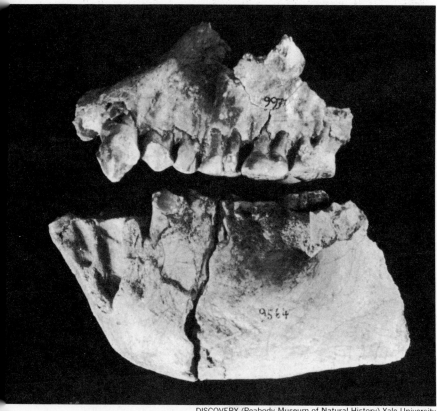

DISCOVERY (Peabody Museum of Natural History) Yale University

Associated upper and lower jaws of *Sivapithecus indicus*, the most complete specimen of its kind yet found.

# HUMAN EVOLUTION

## by Gina Bari Kolata

AS long as there have been fossils to study, investigators have devised scenarios to describe the history of the human lineage. This history has been pushed back further and further so that now many anthropologists are searching for traces of the human line among hominoids that lived as long as 14,000,000 years ago. The term "hominoid" is used for all members of the superfamily Hominoidea, which includes the great apes, humans, and fossils resembling them.

Recent fossil finds in Pakistan and eastern Europe are providing new evidence on which to base scenarios and are leading to new scenarios. These finds are also leading some investigators to question some previously accepted ideas about the diversity of species that existed at the time the human line evolved.

As they re-examine widely held anthropological theories in light of their most recent data, some anthropologists are concluding that they have let certain scenarios get the better of them—that they have developed casts of mind that impede their attempts to understand the past. They are now trying to free themselves of these preconceived ideas of how hominoid evolution occurred and are suggesting new interpretations of their data. Some anthropologists and geologists are concentrating on the influence of the environment on hominoid evolution. Another anthropologist suggests that birth-spacing patterns may have played a major role in this

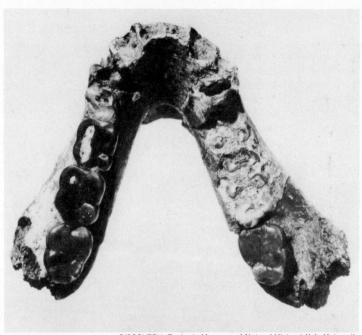

A *Ramapithecus* jaw found in four pieces by Wendy Barry and Martin Pickford.

DISCOVERY (Peabody Museum of Natural History) Yale University

evolution. Still others are using the most recent data to defend the classic view that tool use led to the distinction between human and ape ancestors.

## DIVERSE EARLY SPECIES

One result of the recent finds of hominoids dating from the Miocene epoch, which lasted approximately from 25,000,000 to 13,-000,000 years ago, is the growing realization among anthropologists that these species were far more diverse than was previously realized. For example, David Pilbeam of Yale University and his associates found three species of these hominoids living in the same area of Pakistan during the Middle Miocene, from 17,000,000 to 7,000,000 years ago. These species, known as *Sivapithecus, Ramapithecus,* and *Gigantopithecus,* are referred to by Pilbeam as the sivapithecids. He says that it is impossible to point to any one of these species as the human ancestor.

Pilbeam's analysis of his recent data from Pakistan contrasts with previous analyses of hominoid fossils. Previously, anthropologists tried to divide all extinct hominoids into two groups: those of human lineage and those of ape lineage. Many investigators further assumed that once the ape and human lineages arose from their common ancestor, these species gradually and continuously evolved toward their present-day forms.

The assumption that Miocene hominoids could be divided into two groups led anthropologists to the assumption that simple markers, such as thickness of tooth enamel, could be used to classify the species. Since present-day humans have thick enamel and present-day apes have thin enamel, hominoids with thin enamel were said to be of human lineage and those with thick enamel were said to be of ape lineage. These markers turned out to be not only uninformative but also misleading, Pilbeam says. The Miocene hominoids share features of both humans and apes and cannot be accommodated by the two-group classification scheme, according to Pilbeam.

## ROLE OF ENVIRONMENT

New clues to the lives and fates of the early hominoids are arising from attempts by geologists and anthropologists to reconstruct the environments of these animals. Their results lead them to propose that the sivapithecids appeared during the Miocene when some heavily forested areas gave way to mixed environments consisting of dense forest, savanna woodlands, and more open areas.

The sivapithecids differ substantially from an even earlier group of hominoids known as the dryopithecids. Dryopithecids lived both before and during the Miocene in heavily forested areas of Africa and Europe. It now seems likely that they never left these areas for more open environments. The sivapithecids, on the other hand, seem to have lived on the boundary between the forests and the open areas and to have exploited both.

Evidence that some of the Miocene hominoids lived in mixed environments is not extensive, but many anthropologists find it convincing. Sivapithecids were not present among assemblages of savanna-dwelling animal fossils found in China, Greece, and Iran. Nor were these hominoids found in the typical forested environments of Europe and Africa during the Miocene. The earliest well-dated *Ramapithecus* remains were found at Fort Ternan in Kenya, and they date to a time, about 14,000,000 years ago, when this area changed from forest to a mixed environment.

Peter Andrews of the British Museum of Natural History and Judith Harris Van Couvering of the University of Colorado found that during the Early Miocene, tropi-cal rain forests included Kenya, but that about 15,000,000 years ago volcanoes formed in Kenya, particularly at what is now Fort Ternan, and changed the landscape. The slopes remained forested, but a savanna developed at the base of the mountain on top of the lava.

Pat Shipman of New York University recently reported results of an extensive study of the environment and fossil remains of animals that lived at Fort Ternan. She found that the state of preservation of the animals reflects the environments in which they lived. She has divided the animals into four major environmental groups: a savanna group, including elephants and giraffes; an aquatic group, which presumably lived in a nearby stream; a forest group, including squirrels and the forest-dwelling apes of the dryopithecine group; and a group that seems to have lived in an area between the forest and the savanna. This group of animals from the mixed environment includes *Ramapithecus.*

Although no other fossil assemblage has been as extensively analyzed as that from

Anthropologists John Damuth and Kay Behrensmeyer collect and record bone fossils found on the surface of a plateau.

DISCOVERY (Peabody Museum of Natural History) Yale University

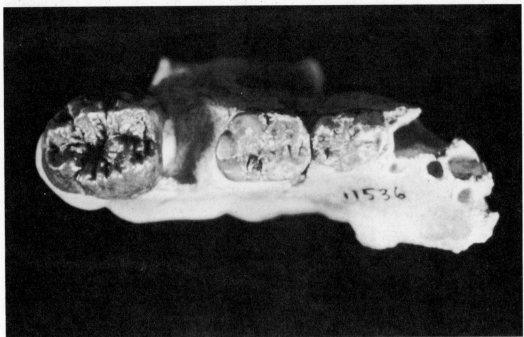

DISCOVERY (Peabody Museum of Natural History) Yale University

Infant jaw of *Sivapithecus indicus,* showing milk molars and second permanent molar.

Fort Ternan, there is evidence that *Ramapithecus* lived in a mixed environment in Pakistan (along with other sivapithecids) and possibly also in Turkey during the Middle Miocene.

Anthropologist Kay Behrensmeyer of the University of California at Santa Cruz found that sivapithecids lived in the Potwar Plateau in Pakistan about 9,000,000 years ago, when the area consisted of woodland and bush with patches of grassland but no dense forests. She found, for example, that forest animals such as arboreal primates and rodents are "conspicuously rare or absent from the fauna." In contrast, she found that the sivapithecids lived among small to medium-sized browsing and grazing ungulates that are typical of wooded and densely bushed areas, but not of forests.

An excellent *Ramapithecus* specimen from Turkey is a jawbone found by Ibrahim Tekkaya of the Mineral Research and Exploration Institute of Turkey in Ankara in 1973 and described in 1974. The area where it was found, about 65 kilometers (40 miles) northeast of Ankara, contains fossils of a mixed group of animals, Shipman says. Neither forest nor savanna animals dominate the collection, although both are present. These data, then, do not contradict the mixed-environment hypothesis. Although sivapithecids have also been found in Greece, Hungary, India, and possibly China (no one outside China has seen the specimens), the environments in which these animals lived have not been determined.

If it is true that sivapthecids appeared during the Miocene as forests gave way to mixed environments, what does this indicate about the course of evolution? Pilbeam, for one, believes that changes in feeding behavior, which are related to changes in habitat and ecological niche, may be a key to understanding the later stages of hominoid evolution.

## CLUE IN THE JAWS

Pilbeam stresses that none of the three species of Miocene hominoids found in Pakistan resembles either apes or humans living today. He points out that the sivapithecids all have jaws and cheek teeth similar to those of hominids that lived in East Africa about 4,000,000 years ago. Hominids include humans and their ancestors but not apes.

For example, the sivapithecids and the later hominids all have jaws and cheek teeth that are large in relation to their body sizes. In contrast, apes and forest monkeys have small cheek teeth and jaws. Moreover, the dryopithecids, which are believed by Pilbeam to include the ancestors of both the sivapithecids and the modern apes, had small cheek teeth and jaws. Anthropologists interpret these changes in teeth and jaws as evidence that the Miocene and later open-country hominids changed their diets as they moved out of the forests.

The change in environment from dense forests to mixtures of forests and more open country may have provided the necessary conditions for the existence of the sivapithecids. Stephen Jay Gould of Harvard University and Niles Eldridge of the American Museum of Natural History argue that new species arise "instantaneously" in geological time rather than evolve slowly from existing species. New species are most likely to arise from a small isolated population that lives at the periphery of the ancestral range, Gould says. The Miocene hominoids that lived in mixed environments could have evolved from isolated populations of the forest-dwelling dryopithecids in response to the changing environments in certain areas of Africa, eastern Europe, and Asia.

Movement of the Miocene hominoids into more open country may have affected their morphology and behavior, Pilbeam speculates. For example, the smaller species of this group may have become bipedal as a partial consequence of the change to feeding in the open. The adaptation of the sivapithecids to a mixed environment may be a key to their competitive success. Maximum opportunities are provided to species that live on the boundary between two environments and are able to exploit both.

## BUT TOOL USE?

This emphasis on changes in environment and feeding behavior contrasts with the traditional view of hominoid evolution. Proponents of the traditional view say that the use of tools by human ancestors is what distinguished them from all other animals and enabled them to compete successfully with other animals for resources. The view is still held by many anthropologists, among them Milford Wolpoff of the University of Michigan.

Wolpoff is bothered by the facts that there was more than one species of hominoid living during the Miocene, that all of the sivapithecid species had large cheek teeth and jaws, and all are now said to have lived in mixed environments. What, then, determined which species died out, and which (if any) was a human ancestor? The answer to this question is as yet impossible to determine, Wolpoff says, because there is a gap in the fossil record between the late Miocene, about 7,000,000 years ago, and the period when hominids are first detected in eastern Africa, about 4,000,000 years ago. Some of the later hominids in eastern Africa used tools, were bipedal, and are thought to be ancestors of humans. Anthropologists have no evidence that the Miocene hominoids used tools or were bipedal. Until more evidence is obtained indicating which Miocene hominoid was successful and why, Wolpoff sees no reason to discard the tool-use hypothesis.

## BIRTH SPACING

Another explanation of how the sivapithecids became differentiated from the dryopithecids is that time between offspring, or birth-spacing, may have been the crucial factor. Owen Lovejoy at Kent State University has devised a birth-spacing explanation of hominoid differentiation as well as the success of sivapithecids in competing with other species. By successful he means that they occupied more area and existed in greater numbers than other species. His hypothesis arose from observations of birth-spacing in living primate females, which, except for human females, only rarely become pregnant while they still have dependent offspring. Those whose offspring remain dependent for many years thus have long periods between births.

For example, chimpanzees of Gombe National Park in Tanzania are reported to

DISCOVERY (Peabody Museum of Natural History) Yale University

The Kenya Dig where 14,000,000 year-old *Ramapithecus* fossils were found. The site, Fort Ternan, was formerly a forest. It now has a mixed environment.

give birth on an average of once every 5.6 years. A consequence of this birth-spacing is that every female must live about 20 years in order to produce enough offspring for the population size to remain stable. Old World monkeys, on the other hand, have life-spans roughly equal to those of the apes but have much shorter periods of infant and childhood development. Their average birth-spacings are 2 to 3 years. Most of the world is populated by monkeys rather than apes, Lovejoy points out, "even though apes are more intelligent."

Lovejoy speculates that the early hominoids gained a competitive advantage over other primates because they overcame this birth-spacing problem and gave birth more frequently—even while they still had dependent offspring. He goes still further and says that this development may have affected not only hominoid population size but also some of their other behavior. It may, for example, have led the hominoids to become bipedal in order to carry and care for several dependent offspring. Hominoids with several dependent offspring may have banded together and developed a social organization for mutual support and protection.

## NEED FOR MORE EVIDENCE

As always, anthropologists are hindered by a paucity of data when they try to formulate and evaluate their theories of human evolution. But as more and more Miocene hominoids are discovered, anthropologists are convinced that devising scenarios to explain evolution will lead them to a fuller understanding of the human past. Now that they are increasingly aware of the problem of developing preconceptions about what to expect from new finds, they believe the scenarios will be more useful. According to Glynn Isaac of the University of California at Berkeley, "Most people think that what is important is to have a series of alternative models that can be tested." As anthropologists begin to focus on the Miocene, such a series of models is being developed □

 SELECTED READINGS

"Ecology of early man in south Africa" by R. G. Klein. *Science,* July 8, 1977.

"Pakistan fossils: new origins for man." *Science News,* April 16, 1977.

"Ramapithecus" by E. L. Simons. *Scientific American,* May 1977.

# IN MEMORIAM

SEVERAL people important in science and technology died during 1977. Among them were Lord Adrian, Nobel laureate in physiology and medicine; Louis Fieser, developer of vitamin K; Milton Helpern, an expert on forensic medicine; and Sergei V. Ilyushin, renowned aircraft designer.

## LORD ADRIAN

Edgar Douglas Adrian shared the 1932 Nobel Prize in Physiology or Medicine with Sir Charles Sherrington for his work on the function of the neuron, the basic unit of the nervous system.

Adrian was born on November 30, 1889, in London, England. He attended Westminster School and studied medicine at Trinity College, Cambridge, and at St. Bartholomew's Hospital in London. Except for World War I military service, he spent his entire career at Cambridge University. He became professor of physiology there in 1937 and also served in several administrative posts. He was master of Trinity College from 1951 to 1965 and chancellor of Cambridge University from 1967 to 1975.

Adrian discovered that the intensity of a stimulus does not affect the intensity or transmission rate of an impulse along a nerve fiber once threshold, or the minimum stimulus required to elicit a neural response, is reached. A nerve always conducts an impulse of the same size, regardless of the stimulus, and this impulse does not decrease as it is transmitted along the fiber. Adrian also showed that there is a certain delay before another impulse can be carried. These findings are now known as the "all-or-none" law of nerve transmission.

Adrian arrived at his conclusions after isolating single sensory nerve fibers and connecting them to sensitive electrical amplifier vacuum tubes and recording the intensity and rate of impulses. He was once described as "the man who has photographed thought and made the nerves audible."

Adrian also did pioneering work on human brain waves and gave support to

Lord Adrian

Bettmann Archive

Louis S. Fieser

Wide World

Milton Helpern

Wide World

Sergei Ilyushin

Wide World

early work on electroencephalography, the recording and interpretation of the different types of brain waves.

Adrian was made a baron in 1955—just one of the many honors he received during his long and illustrious career. He died in London, on August 4, 1977.

## LOUIS FIESER

Louis Fieser, the chemist who developed vitamin K, was born in Columbus, Ohio, on April 7, 1899. He attended Williams College and received his Ph.D in chemistry from Harvard University in 1919.

Known as the "grand old man of organic chemistry, Fieser made many other contributions to chemistry in addition to his work on vitamin K. In 1951 he was part of the research team that helped find the final link by which a common coal-tar derivative could be transformed into the drug cortisone. Cortisone and its derivatives are very widely used drugs that have brought relief to many who suffer from rheumatoid arthritis and numerous other inflammatory ailments.

Fieser was also known for his early work on cancer-causing chemicals and for his work on napalm, the gasoline component used in incendiary bombs.

Emeritus professor of chemistry at Harvard University, Fieser died in Cambridge, Massachusetts, on July 25, 1977.

## MILTON HELPERN

Milton Helpern, chief medical examiner for the city of New York for twenty years and internationally known leader in the field of forensic medicine, was born in East Harlem, New York City, on April 17, 1902. He received his B.S. from City College in 1922 and his M.D. from Cornell University Medical School in 1926. After serving his internship at New York City's Bellevue Hospital, he joined the staff of the medical examiner's office in 1931. Except for World War II duties as a civilian consultant to the U.S. Army Air Force in England, Helpern remained in the medical examiner's office for his entire career. He became chief examiner in 1954, retaining the post until his retirement on December 31, 1973.

Helpern was once described as "Sherlock Holmes with a microscope." His job was to explain the cause of any death in New York City that was sudden, unattended by a physician, violent, or suspicious. He frequently visited the scenes of such deaths and performed autopsies and highly sophisticated laboratory analyses to determine the exact cause of death.

His work alerted people to possible medical dangers—disease outbreaks and environmental dangers, for example. He was frequently called upon to testify in court about the cause of death and his testimony was often invaluable in criminal cases as well as in insurance and inheritance cases.

Helpern put part of his extensive knowledge and experience into a 1,350-page book, *Legal Medicine, Pathology, and Toxicology,* which he coauthored with Dr. Thomas A. Gonzales, Dr. B. Morgan Vance, and Dr. C. J. Umberger. It is the definitive work on forensic medicine.

After his retirement, Helpern was appointed distinguished visiting professor at the Center for Biomedical Education at City College. He also continued to attend conferences and to give lectures. He died in San Diego, California, on April 22, 1977.

## SERGEI ILYUSHIN

Sergei Vladimirovich Ilyushin, world renowned Soviet aircraft designer, was born on March 30, 1894 in the north Russian village of Dilyalevo, Vologda Province. After working as a laborer, he went to St. Petersburg, where he became interested in aviation. In the Czarist army, he worked his way from hangar sweeper to pilot. Then, after joining the Communist Party, he worked on airplane repair during the Revolution. His knowledge of planes increased and he was admitted to the Zhukovsky Air Force Engineering Academy, graduating in 1926.

Ilyushin subsequently held many design posts, becoming one of the Soviet Union's leading aviation experts. His first major success was the TsKB-26, which broke altitude and distance records in 1936, but he first came to world attention during World War II as the designer of the heavily armored IL-2 plane, widely known as the "flying tank."

He continued his design work and was responsible for many of the Soviet Union's most successful planes. Among his designs were the IL-14, which was the mainstay of Soviet commercial aviation for many years; the long-range turboprop IL-18 that was an international standard in the early 1960s; the Soviet's first jet bomber, the IL-28; the widely used 180-passenger IL-62 jet; and the new IL-86 Airbus with a 350-passenger capacity.

Little is known about Ilyushin's private life. His death date was not revealed but is believed to have been in early February 1977.

Lawrence Livermore Laboratory

The Shiva laser system at the Lawrence Livermore Laboratory, California, can provide 30 million watts of optical power.

# PHYSICAL SCIENCES

## contents

# PHYSICAL SCIENCES
## review
## of the year

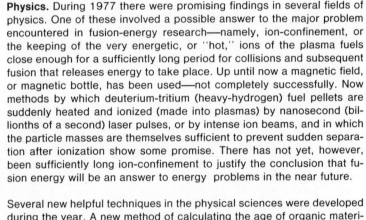

**Physics.** During 1977 there were promising findings in several fields of physics. One of these involved a possible answer to the major problem encountered in fusion-energy research—namely, ion-confinement, or the keeping of the very energetic, or "hot," ions of the plasma fuels close enough for a sufficiently long period for collisions and subsequent fusion that releases energy to take place. Up until now a magnetic field, or magnetic bottle, has been used—not completely successfully. Now methods by which deuterium-tritium (heavy-hydrogen) fuel pellets are suddenly heated and ionized (made into plasmas) by nanosecond (billionths of a second) laser pulses, or by intense ion beams, and in which the particle masses are themselves sufficient to prevent sudden separation after ionization show some promise. There has not yet, however, been sufficiently long ion-confinement to justify the conclusion that fusion energy will be an answer to energy problems in the near future.

Several new helpful techniques in the physical sciences were developed during the year. A new method of calculating the age of organic materials has been discovered. Determination of the carbon-14 fraction present in a material by radioactive decay measurements is one of the most widely accepted means of identifying the geologic age of organic materials, and times of the order of 20,000 years may be rather easily determined. Now, however, it appears that carbon-14 analysis by mass spectrographic methods is even better, allowing calculation of times up to the order of 70,000 years and perhaps with further development to 100,000 years. ■ A new method of separating uranium-235 and uranium-238 where the separation fraction seems to be greater than that of the gaseous diffusion process has also been devised. When rarefied vapor jets interact with uranium hexafluoride ($UF_6$) gas, the molecules of the lighter U-235 isotope diffuse more readily into the interaction region of the jet and $UF_6$ than do the heavier U-238 isotopes.

Georgia Pacific

Dust power—another new energy source? Combustible dust—in this case, flourlike wood particles from a plywood sanding factory—has been harnessed as an energy source by Georgia Pacific. This energy-from-dust installation not only provides energy but also eliminates what used to be a costly problem of disposing of the dust. The photo shows two-story tall carburetors that turn dust into heat.

Experimental and theoretical studies of the atom and its nucleus also continued during the year. A group of investigators at Fermilab reported discovery of a new particle (or group of particles)—named "upsilon"—with a mass some six times that of a proton or neutron, and an accompanying new quark, tentatively called "bottom." This finding brings the number of suggested quarks to six. Quarks are hypothetical but unobserved subnuclear particles having fractional electron charges among other characteristics. ■ A new set of heavy particles was added to the list of particles—electrons (positrons), muons, and associated neutrons—generally classified as leptons, or light particles. The new set of tau-leptons is much heavier than previously identified leptons.

In the medical field, increasing attention, including experimental work, was given the use of beams of heavy ions for both therapy and diagnosis as a replacement for some uses for X rays. For therapy in particular, it appears that proper manipulation of such beams results in the injection of energy into a highly localized region of concern with less injury to surrounding healthy tissues than is caused by corresponding X-ray use.

Among other important findings in physics during the year 1977 was the discovery that when energy in the form of short laser pulses at an individual frequency is applied to molecules made up of several atoms, the energy is shared, affecting all interatomic vibration modes and not just that near the input frequency. This result is essentially the same as that resulting from generalized energy input by heating.

Hugh F. Henry

**Chemistry.** About 350,000 new chemicals are discovered and added to the Chemical Abstract Service's registry of some 4,000,000 chemicals each year. Along with the increasing availability and consequent use of chemicals has come growing concern about their appearance in the environment and their effect on living organisms. In a survey of waters of the Great Lakes and of some industry-intensive main river basins, the U.S. Environmental Protection Agency (EPA) found traces of more than 200 chemicals not of natural origin. The compound appearing most frequently was chloroform, an agent suspected of causing cancer in humans. Other chemicals found frequently were alkyl phthalate esters that are widely used in making plastics and the industrial solvents benzene, acetone, and toluene. ■ The EPA also found that three chemicals used to prevent microorganisms from destroying wood are toxic and now requires that potential users of these compounds justify their use. The chemicals are pentachlorophenol (PCP), creosote, and arsenic compounds.

A new test to determine possible cancer-causing and other harmful effects of chemicals is being used more and more extensively. Developed by Bruce N. Ames of the University of California at Berkeley, the new test checks the ability of chemicals to change the genetic material of several strains of bacteria, notably Salmonella. Chemicals frequently affect all living cells in similar ways and indications that a certain chemical might cause genetic changes or produce cancer in bacteria cells can be a first indication of similar possible effects on plant and animal cells. An advantage of the Ames test is that it reveals results in days or weeks and not in the months and years needed with older methods that relied on extensive animals tests. Although quicker and cheaper than other methods, the Ames test is not, however, without serious flaws. For example, some chemicals might not cause genetic damage in bacteria but might do so in animal cells and some chemicals that produce no genetic change might still produce cancer in animal cells.

Chemists were able to further their knowledge of early organic matter during 1977 through a study of 21 meteorites found well protected on an icy mountain in Antarctica. Two of the meteorites are thought to represent the unchanged material from which the solar system formed and to provide evidence that organic matter existed before life on earth.

As development of the space shuttle proceeded, chemists began to think more and more seriously about the manufacture of certain materials in space—materials that could, for example, be more easily and more economically produced away from the earth's atmosphere and convection currents in liquids caused by heat and gravity. Among the advantages of space manufacturing they point to the ready availability of solar energy, the fact that materials could be suspended in space without interference by container walls, and the possibility that some dangerous processes could be isolated from life on earth.

Eugenia Keller

UPI

A laboratory assistant testing water samples for possible contamination. Many water supplies have been found to contain carcinogenic and other harmful contaminants.

In the Ames "spot test" for mutagenic activity, substances to be tested are applied to Petri dishes containing *Salmonella* bacteria and the effects of the substances on the growth and reproduction of the bacteria monitored.

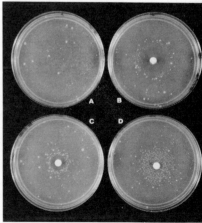

University of California, Berkeley

In the seventeenth century, Sir Isaac Newton discovered that the force of gravitation operates between all material bodies in the universe.

Bettmann Archive

# GRAVITY'S RAINBOW

## by P. C. W. Davis

GRAVITY is familiar as the force that keeps our feet on the ground. As discovered by Isaac Newton in the seventeenth century, it operates not only at the surface of the earth, but between all material bodies in the universe, with a force which diminishes steadily with distance. Without gravitation, the sun would explode, the planets would fly into interstellar space, and the galaxy would disintegrate like a spinning wheel.

Although found throughout the universe, gravity is incredibly weak compared with, say, electrical forces. The electric attraction between the parts of an atom is some forty powers of ten greater than the gravitational attraction. This feebleness makes theories of gravitation very hard to test in the laboratory. It is not at all easy to produce gravitational fields to order, as one can with electric or magnetic fields. Only in recent years, with rapid advances in technology, have we enjoyed the real prospect of detecting and measuring subtle gravitational effects. There are great hopes that within the next few years these advances will change the status of gravitational physics from being a remote branch of science relevant only to astronomers, to a full, laboratory-based, experimental subject.

### EINSTEIN'S THEORY

Only two mathematical theories of gravity have been widely accepted: Newton's and Albert Einstein's.

The sizes and shapes of the planetary orbits are described to high precision by Newton's theory, and as long ago as 1798, the English scientist Henry Cavendish succeeded in verifying Newton's law for the gravitation between two bodies in the laboratory. This was no mean feat if it is realized that even the force of gravitational attraction between two large bodies such as battleships is a mere hundred grams weight.

We now know that Newton's theory cannot be correct, however, because, among other things, it assumes that the gravitational force between two bodies acts instantaneously, whereas the theory of relativity forbids any action to operate faster than light.

The theory constructed by Einstein starts out from an entirely different conceptual base than Newton's. It does not treat gravitation as a force at all. Instead, it conceives of a massive body as distorting space and time, rather as though they are elastic. The effect of this spacetime warp, or distortion, is to disturb the motions of the other bodies in the vicinity. Thus gravitation is reduced to geometry. We may now say that the earth moves in a curved path around the sun not because it is forced away from uniform motion, but because it is continually negotiating an easy path through the bent space-time in the neighborhood of the sun.

### RADAR-RANGING

Bizarre though it may seem, the elasticity of space and time are real effects which have been measured. Unfortunately, even the immense gravitation of the sun produces only a tiny distortion. Experiments are now in progress to detect this minute effect on the space near the solar surface, in an attempt to verify Einstein's theory.

The technique is to send out from earth a radar signal which passes close to the sun, and then on to another planet, such as Venus, located on the remote side of the sun. The echo of the signal is then detected on earth, and the time for the signal's round trip measured very precisely. Because of space distortion near the surface of the sun, the radar rays are slightly bent, and their travel time is a fraction longer than it would be in the absence of curvature. As the planet—

Venus in this case—moves gradually closer to the line-of-sight between the earth and the sun, it is expected that the signal delay will increase by about thirty microseconds a day, an easily measurable change for an astronomer.

One of the problems with the radar-ranging experiment is that other, less exotic, effects than gravitation also disturb the radar waves. One difficulty is that a planet does not have a smooth surface, so that the pulses get somewhat fuzzy when they reflect from the uneven terrain. The difference in response time for radar waves bouncing from the top of a mountain or from a valley might be as great as a few dozen microseconds. Only by continuing the radar experiments over many months can these errors be reduced. At present, the results agree with Einstein's prediction to an accuracy of eight per cent, but after several more years of measurements this percentage should be narrowed.

Last year, the arrival of two U.S. Viking lander spacecraft on Mars provided a wonderful opportunity to improve on radar-ranging, because the spacecraft itself can be used to send back signals it receives from earth. Thus, instead of bouncing radar waves

Library of Congress

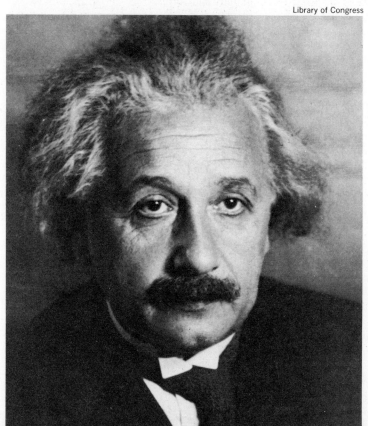

In the twentieth century, Albert Einstein presented a detailed mathematical theory of gravitation that is now widely accepted. Recent technological advances now permit experiments to be conducted to verify Einstein's theory.

**299**

randomly off the Martian surface, the signals are detected by Viking and transmitted back. In this way, only radio waves from a precise location on Mars are received, and the problems of the planet's varying surface features are avoided. The measurements made using the Viking craft have confirmed that space is indeed curved near the sun, by an amount in agreement with Einstein's theory to within one per cent accuracy.

## GRAVITY WAVE DETECTION

When Newton formulated his theory of gravitation, he thought of it as an instantaneous action at a distance across the empty space between bodies. Einstein showed that there was no meaning to the concept of instantaneous, and the structure of space and time require that any gravitational influences must propagate at the same speed as light. This means that were the sun, which is about eight light minutes distant from us, to break into two, we would not know it for about eight minutes. A light minute is a measure of distance used in astronomy. One light minute, or the distance light travels in a vacuum in one minute, is about 18,000,000 kilometers (11,000,000 miles).

Einstein's theory describes gravitation so that it is somewhat similar to electromagnetism, and many gravitational effects are analogous to more familiar phenomena in electrodynamics. In particular, we know that when electric charges are disturbed, electromagnetic waves are produced which spread out from the region of disturbance at the speed of light (light is an electromagnetic wave). In the same way, Einstein's theory predicts that if gravitating masses are disturbed, gravitational waves will be produced. These curious effects may be envisioned as ripples in the fabric of spacetime. They are thought to occur at all wavelengths and frequencies, just as do electromagnetic waves.

In recent years, efforts to detect gravity waves have been pursued with great determination, following the pioneering work of the U.S. astrophysicist Joseph Weber, working at the University of Maryland. Many astronomical events—supernova explosions, the collision of stars and black holes, the motion of double stars, for example—are expected to

University of Maryland

U.S. astrophysicist Joseph Weber pioneered in studies to detect gravity waves produced by astronomical events.

generate gravity waves. The problem is that, because of the weakness of gravity, only enormously energetic astronomical catastrophes can produce wave disturbances great enough to be detected with present technology.

The method of detection is simple enough. When gravitational waves pass through matter, they can set it ringing at the same frequency as the waves, so all the experimenter needs to do is to monitor the vibrations of a lump of matter. In practice this is exceedingly difficult to carry out properly because all sorts of other, more energetic, disturbances pollute the experiment. Some way has to be found to filter out the effects of all other disturbances, so that those caused only by gravity can be detected.

The most popular apparatus is a cylindrical metal bar one or two meters (30 or 60 inches) long, carefully balanced and isolated as much as possible from the ground. Cooling the bar to near absolute zero, which is about −273° Celsius, or −459° Fahrenheit, helps to reduce random thermal effects. This

This carefully balanced, cylindrical metal bar, isolated as much as possible from the effects of any earth-based vibrations, is used to try to monitor gravity waves coming from astronomical sources.

care is essential. Detecting a fractional length change of one part in a thousand million million requires a high level of technology and experimental expertise, and these experiments are still in the process of rapid development.

All detectors rely in some way on the phenomenon of resonance. Resonance is the increase in strength of the vibration of a mechanical system when it is driven by a force at its natural frequency of oscillation. It is the principle used for tuning a radio. We have no real certainty of the frequency of the gravitational waves likely to be most prolific in the terrestrial neighborhood, so detectors are built with natural frequencies in the 1,000 to 2,000 hertz (cycles per second) range as an estimate, and the hope is that they will be tuned to the presence of any incoming waves of this frequency that might be mixed up with many others. To eliminate random disturbances from terrestrial sources, several detectors are best operated in tandem, and coincidental responses searched for.

Great excitement greeted announcements by Weber in the early seventies that frequent coincidental events had been re-

corded on his two detectors at the University of Maryland and the Argonne National Laboratory near Chicago. The news sent the theorists scurrying to investigate astrophysical processes that could produce intense bursts of gravitational waves with such startling frequency. Since that time, other experimental groups have failed to confirm Weber's results, and it seems that we must wait a few years for the next generation of more sensitive detectors before an unambiguous confirmation of the existence of these fleeting waves.

## QUANTUM GRAVITY AND BLACK HOLES

The world of gravity physics was turned upside down in 1974 with a discovery by the British mathematician Stephen Hawking concerning black holes. Black holes are the enigmatic objects which remain when superdense matter implodes, or collapses inward, under the overwhelming power of its own gravity. Black holes have been studied for many years as theoretical playthings. So far no black hole has been positively identified, though the X-ray source Cygnus X-1 is thought by many astronomers to be one.

If radio telescopes, such as this one, could detect radio waves from an exploding black hole Einstein's theory of gravitation would be confirmed.

Finding one would be a very important confirmation of Einstein's theory. Hawking's discovery may make that prospect much less remote.

What he found is that when the laws of quantum physics—which describe the behavior of elementary particles—are applied to black holes, the theory requires that the holes are not actually completely black after all, but rather glow dully with a definite temperature. For a collapsed star, the temperature is exceedingly small and the effect would be utterly negligible. But there may exist in the universe microscopic black holes no larger than the nucleus of an atom, yet possessing a mass greater than Mount Everest. The temperature of these mini-holes would be intense: a million million degrees.

Moreover, as the holes radiate energy, they shrink in size—literally evaporating away. For a mini-hole of the size of the nucleus of an atom, this evaporation process is slow, taking thousands of millions of years to dissipate all the mass. However, as the hole shrinks, it heats up and radiates still faster. During the last fraction of a second it explodes violently with a force of many hydrogen bombs.

The Hawking phenomenon depends crucially upon the fact that the spacetime around a black hole is intensely curved. If we could detect the resulting explosions as the black hole disappears, it would confirm Einstein's theory of gravitation. One of the ways in which this might occur is by detecting the burst of gamma rays that would be produced by the explosion of a black hole.

Another possibility is to look for radio waves from the exploding hole. These might be generated as the hole disintegrates in a final energetic pulse of charged particles, if the hole is in a weak magnetic field. Such fields are known to permeate the interstellar spaces. This method of detection could be performed with existing radio telescopes. It seems to offer a more promising technique than gamma-ray astronomy, because radio waves can be detected at much lower energies.

Of all the experiments which are feasible in the near future, only this one offers the hope of testing our theories under conditions of intense gravitational fields. The gravity at the surface of a mini-hole is some thirty powers of ten greater than at the surface of the sun, and effects of spacetime curvature play a dominant role. So far, Einstein's theory has only been tested in the weak gravitation of the solar system.

## LABORATORY-CONTROLLED GRAVITY

In the experiments described so far the experimenter's role has been a passive one: to build sensitive equipment and rely on the earth or more remote astronomical objects to supply the gravitational effects. Much more information about the phenomenon of gravitation would be obtained if we also had control over the source.

The extreme weakness of gravitation implies that the creation and manipulation of gravitational forces in the laboratory would require still more sensitive equipment for its detection. As already mentioned, Cavendish was able to measure the ordinary Newtonian force between delicately-suspended heavy weights in the laboratory.

What is of interest to today's physicists is not this gross effect, but the subtle corrections to it that arise as a result of spacetime

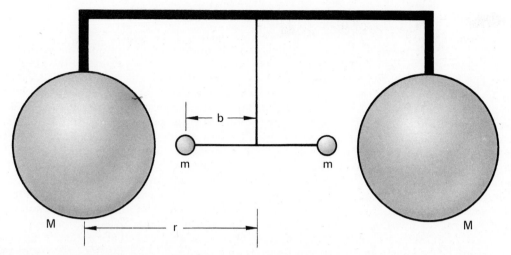

Schematic illustrating dumbbell experiment devised by Carlton Caves and his associates to determine if there exists a separate "magnetic-type" force of gravity between two rotating masses that is over and above the usual Newtonian gravity existing between any two objects.

curvature as predicted by Einstein's theory. Such is the advance of modern technology that we may be on the threshold of actually being able to measure these effects, some of which have never before been observed.

One of these concerns the effect of a rotating mass. According to Newton's theory, the gravitation outside a rotating body is the same as that outside a static one of the same shape and composition, but in Einstein's theory the effect of rotation of a body reaches out into the void beyond the surface and sets up, picturesquely speaking, an invisible vortex in space. This vortex can exert forces on other bodies, causing them to be "dragged" round with the rotating mass. In principle this effect should be detectable on earth-orbiting satellites, or even by sending electromagnetic signals simultaneously to either side of the rotating sun. In practice it may be easier and cheaper to detect it in the laboratory by setting up huge, rapidly spinning masses, and investigating the gravitational disturbances in their vicinity with delicate and highly sensitive equipment.

## SUPERCONDUCTIVITY EXPERIMENTS

One such experiment proposed by Carlton Caves of the California Institute of Technology uses a cavity waveguide with superconducting walls. The waveguide is a hollow tube bent in a circle to form a torus (donut), and the superconducting surface acts as a highly efficient reflector. Conse-

quently, it is possible to fill the tube with microwaves (electromagnetic radiation). These waves will reflect their way around the inside of the tube and set up a fixed wave pattern rather like a circular version of the standing waves on a plucked guitar string. The wave pattern will appear to be stationary in the laboratory, but if the ring is placed around a five-kilogram (2.3-pound) mass spinning at one kilometer (0.6 mile) per second, the dragging effect of the local gravitational field causes the pattern to rotate in the same direction. The effect is, however, almost inconceivably small. Even after two weeks, the pattern would only rotate 1/10,000,000,000,000 of one revolution. This is just about detectable by monitoring the microwave field strength through a small porthole.

The major problem is to develop superconducting technology to a point where a wave pattern can be sustained over such a long duration without being absorbed by the walls of the cavity. Another difficulty involves subtracting out any disturbances produced by earth vibrations.

## MAGNETIC FORCES

Whether or not a "magnetic-type" force of gravitation exists between two rotating masses, over and above the usual Newtonian force of gravitation between them, which is present even in the absence of rotation might be somewhat easier to detect. The theory that when the masses are counter-rotating, the "magnetic" gravitational force is actually repulsive may also be detectable.

The possibilities have been investigated by Caves in collaboration with Kip Thorne of the California Institute of Technology, and Vladimir Braginsky of Moscow State University. One experiment they suggest may be carried out in the following way: a dumbbell arrangement of two masses is suspended horizontally from its center so that it can twist back and forth under the action of a very small disturbance. One of the dumbbell masses is rapidly spun on its axis and lined up close to another, larger, spinning mass. The larger mass is first spun in one direction, to attract the dumbbell mass, then in the opposite direction to repel it. Very sophisticated techniques that filter out the effects of earth movement, as well as changes in the ordinary Newtonian gravitation between the component parts due to random jitter motions, may enable attractive and repulsive magnetic-type gravitation forces to be detected.

## IS GRAVITY GETTING WEAKER?

One of the most important features about Einstein's theory is that the strength of gravitation from a fixed source remains unchanging in time. On the other hand, a number of rival theories predict that gravitation should grow progressively weaker as the universe expands. If gravitation "ages" in this way, it would have profound implications for the structure of the galaxy, the sun, and even the earth, for over time scales of thousands of millions of years the gravitation of these systems would fall appreciably. Recently, some observations of the moon have been used to support the weakening-gravitation theory, but the complexities of lunar motion prevent a definite conclusion at this stage.

In principle it would be possible to detect a weakening of the earth's gravitation by examining the effect on a pendulum's period of oscillation, or time required for one complete swing. After a thousand years it would be found that a pendulum clock was losing about one second per year relative to, say, an atomic clock. In practice, it is much easier to use a horizontal pendulum that oscillates, not due to the earth's gravity (which is vertical), but due to a large, fixed mass in the laboratory. The period of this pendulum would be very long because of the smallness of the gravitational field involved, taking maybe an hour or two to swing backwards and forwards just once. After about a week, a change in the period of one part in a million million could be detected, which would be sufficient to confirm or refute most of the varying-gravity theories.

Very advanced technology is required to perform this experiment. Braginsky, Caves, and Thorne propose that the pendulum be a "dumbbell" torsion balance of the type described above and that the entire apparatus—pendulum and masses—be grown out of a single sapphire crystal. Such is the sensitivity of this type of system that even the random motions of the atoms inside the crystal can have a disturbing effect. To eliminate this, the device would have to be cooled down to near absolute zero.

## TO PROBE TIME AND SPACE

The motivation for detecting these almost inconceivably weak phenomena might seem baffling. They are a far cry from the anti-gravity devices of science fiction, and there seems to be no hope of using controlled gravity in a wide range of engineering situations, as with electricity and magnetism. Nevertheless there exist in the universe fantastic objects that are so compact that huge amounts of matter are crushed into a tiny volume. These objects can rotate at staggering speed. We have every reason to suppose that the barely-detectable, subtle effects predicted by Einstein's theory will be of great importance under these much more extreme conditions. A proper understanding of them will enable astrophysicists to build models of these objects with greater confidence, and to probe the structure of space and time in conditions which will never be attained on earth□

 SELECTED READINGS

*Gravitation and Space Time* by Hans C. Ohanian. Norton, 1976.

"Is Gravity Getting Weaker?" by T. C. Van Flandern. *Scientific American,* February 1976.

*The Riddle of Gravitation* by Peter G. Bergmann. Scribners, 1968.

Dr. James Zimmerman, inventor of the National Bureau of Standard's Squid, uses a jeweler's eyepiece while he makes adjustments in the Squid in his left hand.

# MEASURING MINUTE MAGNETICS

## by Dietrick E. Thomsen

SQUID—you think of a soft-shelled mollusk that may or may not be one of your favorite seafood dishes. But the word has another—and completely different—meaning. It is also an acronym, or short form, for a new and highly sophisticated device used in solid-state physics.

A SQUID is a Superconducting QUantum Interference Device.

### WHAT?

Squids are very sensitive devices for measuring weak magnetic fields. They are finding applications wherever such fields are of interest, especially in medicine, psychology, and geophysics. Someday they may be used in predicting both heart attacks and earthquakes.

Squids are an application of the Josephson effect, the discovery of which brought the British physicist Brian Josephson part of the 1973 Nobel Prize for physics. The effect is manifest in what is usually called a Josephson junction and involves superconducting materials, those materials that lose all resistance to electric flow at extremely cold temperatures. These very low temperatures are measured according to the Kelvin scale. 1° K equals −273.16° Celsius, or approximately −459° Fahrenheit.

A Josephson junction is a "weak" connection between two superconducting electric circuit elements. Its weakness may consist of a thin layer of insulating oxide or simply poor contact because of minute roughness of the surfaces of the superconductors. In the ultra-cold world of superconductivity (liquid-helium temperature of 4° Kelvin), the electrons that make the supercurrent can pass through the weak connection by a special process that is called tunneling.

If there is a magnetic field through a portion of the circuit in which the junction is located, the current that flows across the junction will oscillate in response to changes in the magnetic field. The effect is a stepwise, or quantal, one. There is a minimum permissible value, or quantum, of magnetic flux. Magnetic flux is the magnetic field strength multiplied by the cross section over which the field is spread. The junction current oscillates once whenever the flux changes by one quantum.

### MAKING A SQUID

If two Josephson-junction circuits are arranged in parallel so that both surround a certain area, the current will oscillate once for every time the flux changes by an amount

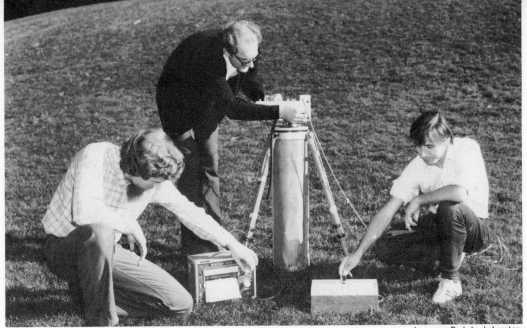

Professor John Clarke and some students are using a Squid to search for geothermal energy sources and oil deposits.

equal to the quantum divided by the enclosed area. This is the way a squid is made: the two parallel circuits are laid down around a cylinder through which the field to be measured is passed. Field strength equals flux divided by area, so with a large enough area in the cylinder's cross section, extremely small changes of field strength can be measured. A figure recently quoted by John Clarke of the University of California at Berkeley is $10^{-10}$ gauss. The gauss is a unit used in the measurement of magnetic field strength. The earth's magnetic field, which is extremely weak compared to industrial magnets, is about half a guass.

Squids are proving useful in a number of studies where sensitivity to minute magnetic fields can yield information. Medicine, psychology, geophysics, and metrology are especially active right now.

## USE IN GEOPHYSICS

Geophysics is one of the branches of science most concerned with magnetic fields. Many of its particular phenomena are noted for imposing minute fluctuations on the earth's surrounding magnetism. Clarke says he and his associates at Berkeley have been in the field testing the usefulness of squids in prospecting for such things as geothermal energy sources or oil deposits. Squids may also be used to help search for other minerals.

And then there are earthquakes. Mechanical strain on a geologic fault, or crack—the San Andreas Fault in California, for example—produces changes in the local magnetic field. The degree of strain, or stress, in rocks is believed useful in predicting earthquakes, and squids may become an effective way of monitoring the strain.

## USE IN PHYSIOLOGICAL STUDIES

Biology, medicine, and psychology account for particularly intense experimentation on the possible application of squids. Many of the body's organs—the heart, the brain, muscles, for example—generate minute electrical currents. Measurement of these currents has been used in medical diagnosis for a long time. Where there are electric currents, there are also magnetic fields, and squids are being used to determine what the magnetic fields can reveal about the health and functions of the various organs.

As Samuel J. Williamson of New York University points out, there is a severe technical difficulty involved in measuring physiological magnetic fields: they are characteristically about 1/1,000,000,000 of the earth's field, and we learned previously how weak the earth's field is. So how are scientists to measure them in the presence of fields from power lines and electrical appliances that are characteristically much stronger?

One approach is to construct a magnetically shielded chamber in which to do the work. David Cohen of the Massachusetts Institute of Technology is said to have the chamber with the lowest magnetic noise, or outside interference, yet.

But such an approach takes space and expense. The NYU scientists have tried another approach. They have succeeded in altering the circuitry of squids so that they respond only to spatially varying magnetic fields and not to uniform ones. This effectively subtracts out the noise due to power lines and such, and Williamson says his group can work quite well even above the magnetic fields produced by the electrical supply of a busy New York City subway line.

Much of the current work is concentrated on seeing what magnetograms, or the patterns produced by changes in magnetic field strength, can tell physicians and psychologists that other means of observation cannot. It is already clear that magnetocardiograms can show up conditions that electrocardiograms miss. One of the advantages of magnetocardiograms is that they can sense effects of direct currents, which electrocar-

diograms cannot. Also, the magnetogram can be taken without skin contacts. This means it is faster to take and that it senses the heart's condition more directly. In electrograms, the skin adds a contribution of its own. The exercise right now is to make magnetic surveys of a large number of hearts and then have the data studied by experienced cardiologists so as to establish norms and criteria for distinguishing healthy from diseased conditions.

Much of the NYU work, Williamson says, is psychological. In one experiment, subjects are shown a pattern of stripes and asked to press a button to signal that they have understood it. The more complicated the pattern, the longer the response time. But, Williamson says, the magnetograms or measurements of the brain's magnetic field strength, indicate that the difference lies in the visual response, or the time taken to see and understand. The response time of the visual cortex, or, in other words, the seeing and understanding of the pattern, seems to vary with details of the pattern. People with diabetes or kidney disease seem to take longer to respond. Preparations are under way to com-

National Bureau of Standards

Squids are expected to become quite common in the near future, with their use spreading to many different fields.

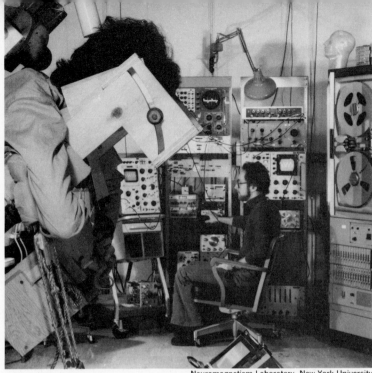

Squids are now being used in physiological studies. Photo at left shows laboratory version of a squid used to study the function of the heart.

Neuromagnetism Laboratory, New York University

pare the responses of people with severe mental disturbances with those of normal subjects.

These are just a few of quite a number of magnetophysiological studies going on in laboratories around the world. There is even a possibility of using squids to distinguish suspect tissue from healthy tissue.

## USE IN MEASUREMENT STANDARDS

Less likely to turn up in a future television series, but very important economically and scientifically, is the use of squids in establishing standard units of measurement.

Originally, the standard meter was the distance between two scratches on a platinum-iridium bar kept at the International Bureau of Weights and Measures in Sèvres, a suburb of Paris. National standards were compared with the one at Sèvres. Standards used in industry and science were established by comparison with national ones and so on till one reached the meterstick hanging by the blackboard in the schoolroom.

The succession of comparisons introduces many opportunities for error to creep in. Now the meter is defined as a number of wavelengths of a particular color emitted by the inert gas krypton, and any laboratory with the proper lamp and a good device to count wavelengths can set up its own accurate standard meter independent of the bar at Sevres.

Donald B. Sullivan of the National Bureau of Standards in Boulder, Colorado, suggests that the squid's ability to measure magnetic change step by step could lead to a redefinition of electric and magnetic units. Then any laboratory with a squid could set up its own independent electromagnetic standards. Squids could be especially useful, Sullivan thinks, in establishing more precise standards for oscillatory quantities in the high range of radio frequencies. It is possible to extend such accuracies to the range above 10,000,000,000 hertz, or cycles per second.

## SQUIDS TO BECOME COMMON

This very appealing instrument with the somewhat marine-biological name also seems susceptible to mass production. The technique of making the squid itself, of laying down the superconducting circuits, and the Josephson junctions on a cylinder is not difficult to do industrially, and technology can supply the refrigeration necessary to maintain the liquid-helium temperature. It will still be a somewhat bulky apparatus, and prospectors are unlikely to carry squids in the pockets of their jeans, but, according to some cost estimates, an organization that can afford a new automobile can afford a squid. The estimates range from $5,000 to $13,000 depending on how much of the ancillary technology is counted in the cost of the squid□

# TRAVELING FASTER THAN LIGHT

## by James S. Trefil

HOW familiar the scene is. The handsome spaceship captain leans forward and snaps out a command:

"Ahead Warp 8, Mr. Chekov."

"Aye, aye, Kepten."

And the gallant starship *Enterprise* moves out at 512 times the speed of light.

Or how about that other favorite device of the writer—the hero who travels backward or forward in time to visit another age? Pure fiction, isn't it?

Or is it?

For the last several years, theoretical physicists have been speculating about the existence of objects which, should they ever be found, could conceivably make something like the *Enterprise* a reality someday, and might even have something to do with time travel. These hypothetical objects are called "tachyons"—"swiftly moving ones" (from the Greek root *tachys,* meaning swift). If they exist, they would have the property of moving faster than light. By contrast, all the more mundane matter that we know about that moves at less than the speed of light would be lumped under the general heading of "tardyons," or "slowly moving ones."

Most of us have heard that it's impossible to move faster than the speed of light, and that this cosmic speed limit is somehow imposed by Einstein's theory of relativity. Does this mean that scientists now believe Einstein was wrong? Not at all. What the emergence of the tachyon idea means is that scientists have taken a closer look at the theory of relativity and have concluded that, under certain conditions, faster-than-light travel is not forbidden. But to understand how this conclusion has been reached, we'll have to understand exactly what it was that Einstein said in the first place.

### THEORY OF RELATIVITY

We've all had the experience of riding in a car or a train and dropping something, either intentionally or by accident. Strange as it may seem, just thinking about an everyday occurrence like this can lead us to the principle of relativity. No matter how fast you are moving, 50 kilometers (about 30 miles) per hour in a car or more than 950 kilometers (600 miles) per hour in a jet, if you drop something it will fall right at your feet. The laws that govern the fall of the object don't seem to depend on how fast you're moving.

Let's look at this in a slightly different way. Suppose you are sitting on a moving motorcycle and a friend of yours is standing on the ground. While you are watching the object falling straight down, what does he see? Well, during the time it takes for the object to fall to the ground, he will see the motorcycle move along the ground a certain distance. Consequently, he will see the object fall in an arc. You say it fell straight down, and he says it fell in an arc. This apparent contradiction is resolved by saying that each of you is watching the same event from a different point of view (the technical term is "frame of reference"), and therefore each saw something different.

What isn't so obvious, but is true nonetheless, is that if you and your friend were to make some measurements—you on the motorcycle and your friend on the ground—you would come to the conclusion that even though you see different things when you watch something fall, you agree on the basic laws which govern falling bodies. You would, for example, both find that the object takes the same amount of time to reach the ground.

And that is the Principle of Relativity. It states that no matter what frame of reference you are in, the laws of nature that hold for you are exactly the same laws of nature that hold in any other frame of reference. In other words, every point of view is correct, even though each point of view corresponds to a different description of what happened. But what does this idea have to do with the speed of light?

Up to now we've talked about only one law of nature, the law that governs falling bodies. There are many other laws, of course, and one set governs the behavior of electricity and magnetism. The speed of light is built into these laws. It follows from this fact that if the laws that govern electricity are to be the same for every frame of reference, then the speed of light has to be the same for any two observers, even if they are moving with respect to each other. In other words, if you were on your motorcycle going 50 kilometers (about 30 miles) per hour and you flashed a beam of light at your friend on the ground, he would see the light moving at 300,000 kilometers (186,000 miles) per second and not at 300,000 kilometers (186,000 miles) per second plus 50 kilometers (30 miles) per hour.

## CLOCK PARADOX

Let's take the famous "clock paradox" as an example of the surprises that follow from relativity. Einstein is supposed to have come to the theory of relativity by imagining what would happen if you traveled away from a clock at the speed of light. If you

The man on the motorcycle sees the ball fall straight down. An observer on the side of the road, though, sees the ball fall in an arc. This illustrates the relativity of motion: Different people see the same event in different ways.

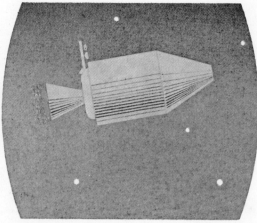

According to relativity, an object shortens as its speed approaches that of light.

think about it for a minute, you'll realize that if you did this, you'd always "see" the same position on the hands of the clock, so that as far as you were concerned, the clock would be stopped, even though someone standing next to the clock would see it moving as usual. This would happen because the light wave that carries the signal that says "it's 2 P.M." moves away from the clock as fast as you do, so when you looked, you'd always see 2 P.M.

Think about it a little more, and you'll realize that if you traveled a bit slower than light, it would appear that the clock had slowed down, and if you traveled a bit faster than light, it would appear that the clock was running backwards. In other words, what you see a clock doing depends on how fast you or it is moving, and two observers moving with different speeds will see the same clock running at different rates.

Is this result really so paradoxical? Actually, it's no more so than the fact that you saw something fall straight down while your friend saw it fall in an arc in our earlier example. What every observer has to agree upon is the fact that the laws of nature are the same, but individual events, like the ticking of a clock, needn't be perceived in the same way.

This result—that moving clocks appear to be running slower than stationary ones—is hard to believe, but this difference has actually been measured by flying very sensitive clocks on airplanes.

## CAN'T ACCELERATE TO SPEED OF LIGHT

There are other surprises in special relativity. It turns out that arguments based on the same principles as the ones we used in the clock paradox result in statements that virtually every property of an object changes when it moves. Its time slows down, its length contracts, its energy appears different, and it gets heavier. This last property explains the conventional statement that faster-than-light travel is impossible, because if we try to accelerate an ordinary object to a high speed, we'll find it getting heavier as it goes faster. This means that we'll have to exert more force to get an equivalent increase in speed on a quickly moving object.

As we approach the speed of light, we need more and more force, until we are just a hairsbreadth from it. To raise the speed that last fraction would require an infinite force. Since this isn't available in the universe, we have to say that if the theory of relativity is correct, no object now moving at less than the speed of light will ever be accelerated by conventional means to a speed greater than the speed of light. This argument is the basis for the usual statement that faster-than-light travel is impossible.

## BUT IF TACHYONS ALREADY EXIST

But it doesn't prove that at all, because the same argument could be used to "prove" that travel *at* the speed of light is impossible

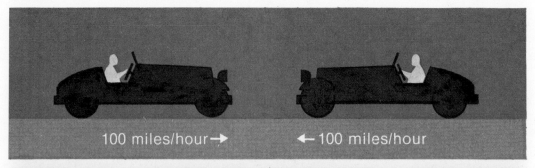

100 miles/hour →     ← 100 miles/hour

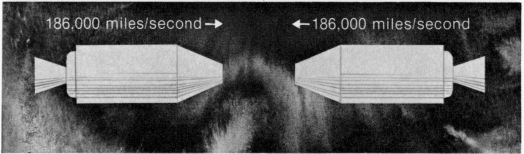

186,000 miles/second →     ←186,000 miles/second

The law of addition of velocities: Each car travels at 100 miles per hour; they approach each other at 200 miles per hour—100 + 100 = 200. Two space ships travelling near the speed of light, however, approach each other at the same speed—186,000 + 186,000 = 186,000.

as well, and we know of at least one thing that travels at the speed of light—light itself. What the argument actually says is that things going at less than the speed of light (the things we've called tardyons) will always be tardyons, and that things now traveling at the speed of light will always do so. There is nothing in the argument that says we can't go one step further, either. Suppose that somewhere in the universe there is something that actually travels faster than light—a real tachyon. From the theory of relativity we could say that such an object must always be a tachyon and must always have been a tachyon, but we can't say that such a thing is impossible. The fact that we can't turn a tardyon into a tachyon doesn't prove that tachyons don't exist, any more than our inability to accelerate a tardyon to the speed of light proves that light doesn't exist.

Modern physicists often quote something called the Gell-Mann dictum, named after the Nobel laureate in physics Murray Gell-Mann. It goes like this: "Whatever isn't forbidden is required." In other words, if there's no reason why something shouldn't exist, then it must exist. If we accept this idea, then we would have to conclude that there must be faster-than-light objects unless some reason can be found for denying them.

## STILL SOME PROBLEMS

Actually, we've already hinted at what this reason might be when we talked about the clock paradox. You will recall that when we moved away from a clock face at more than the speed of light, the clock appeared to run backwards. This is a hint about one very important and puzzling property of tachyons and, indeed, the main reason that they were not accepted as a possibility until very recently: they seem to involve us in time travel.

Let's think about an experiment we might do if we could control tachyons. We could set up a tachyon transmitter at one point and a tachyon receiver somewhere else. We could then send signals via tachyons, just as we now can send out signals with radio or light waves. The tachyon would leave the transmitter (which would use up some energy and give it to the tachyon) and, sometime later, would arrive at the receiver, which would then gain the energy that the transmitter has lost.

The only way we'd know that we were dealing with a tachyon would be by noticing that the time it took to go from the transmitter to the receiver would be less than the time it would have taken light to travel the same distance. But aside from this, there is nothing at all strange or paradoxical about the emission and reception experiment we've described.

The funny business begins when we ask how this experiment would look to other observers—say observers flying by in a spaceship and watching through the window. Remember, all points of view are supposed to be equally valid. Suppose there are two men in the rocket, each with a stopwatch. If the man in the front stops his watch when he sees the receiver activated, and the man in the rear stops his when he sees the transmitter activated, they can compare the times on their watches after the experiment. If the rocket ship is moving fast enough (but still less than the speed of light), they will find that the front stopwatch will have recorded an earlier time than the rear one.

In other words, the tachyon will be "received" before it is "transmitted." Furthermore, if they could measure the energy changes involved, they will see the receiver lose energy, instead of gain it, and they will see the transmitter gain energy instead of lose it. Surely there is no way of reconciling this sort of thing with any rational interpretation of relativity.

Until recently people thought that this seeming inconsistency was a strong argument against the existence of tachyons. After all, one of the basic laws of nature says that an effect must come after its cause. In this example, one observer sees events which follow this principle, and the other sees events which do not. Therefore, it was argued, the existence of tachyons is inconsistent with the laws of nature.

Well, not quite. Let's describe what the men in the rocket ship see in a little more neutral language. They see the apparatus which we called a "receiver" lose energy, and

The clock paradox. One twin goes on space trip, at relativistic speeds. The other twin stays home.

The travelling twin returns 40 years later, to find his brother has aged—although he has not.

then, sometime later, they see the apparatus we called the "transmitter" gain energy. They wouldn't say that cause-and-effect was violated at all, but that a man on the ground had got his labels mixed up. The thing which loses energy is what should be called a transmitter. Then their description of what they see is perfectly sensible: the transmitter sends something out, and that something is received later. In short, they see the tachyon going the other way.

So then both the observer on the ground and those flying overhead agree that "effect" follows "cause." What they disagree on is which event is to be labeled "cause" and which "effect." Likewise, they disagree on what piece of apparatus is the transmitter and what is the receiver. This situation is analogous to the case of the object dropped from a moving motorcycle: the observers disagree on the description of events, but agree on the laws that governed those events.

## COMMUNICATION IN TIME

Once we accept that, however strange the tachyon's behavior might appear, it does not violate any law of nature or of logic, the apparent backwards-in-time motion of a tachyon seen by some observers leads to another topic that science-fiction writers have elaborated on over the years: communication in time. Let's go back to our observers in the rocket to see how.

Suppose the man in the front of the rocket had a tachyon transmitter and the man in the rear a receiver just like the ones on the ground. Now suppose the man in front sends a tachyon to the man in back as soon as he sees the ground receiver interact with the first tachyon. To the man on the ground, it will appear that the tachyon in the rocket ship is sent by the man in back. If we choose the speed of the rocket properly, we can even have the tachyon in the rocket transmitted before the one on the ground.

The possibilities in a situation like this are mindboggling. What if, after seeing the second tachyon "sent," the man on the ground refuses to send the first one and perhaps even destroys his transmitter? Then the second tachyon wouldn't have been sent. But it's already been received. . . .

A tachyon is sent from a transmitter (left) to a receiver (right). An observer on the ground would notice only that the tachyon signal took less time to cover the distance than a light signal would. For a rocket, passing overhead, the situation is totally different. The rocket automatically records the time the tachyon is sent and, also, the time it is received by the receiver. The printout shows that the tachyon was "received" before it was "sent."

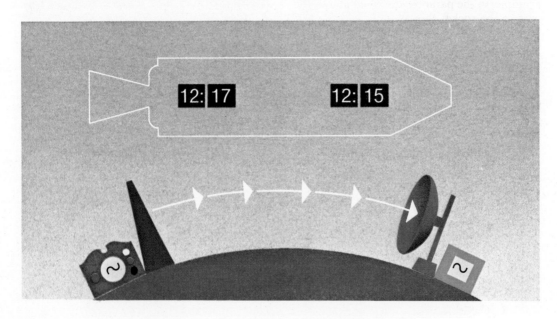

In tachyon world, cause and effect seem reversed. At left, tachyon car has an accident. Right: Same car is seen *later* in incident that caused the accident.

## PARADOX CAN BE SOLVED

Actually, physicists have thought quite a bit about this type of paradox involved with tachyons. I think it is fair to say that at the present time, all of the paradoxes can be resolved at the particle level, although the resolutions become stranger and stranger. For example, in the paradox described above, the man in the rocket ship actually sees the first tachyon "sent" from the ground receiver. If the ground transmitter is destroyed, the man in the rocket will see that tachyon go right through the spot where the transmitter was and eventually be absorbed in a remote corner of the universe. He still sends the second tachyon, though, since the receiver was activated.

From the point of view of the man on the ground, the first tachyon will appear to move in the opposite direction—from a remote corner of the universe to the ground receiver. So just after he has destroyed his transmitter, he sees the tachyon he would have sent come zipping in from outer space, so that his receiver goes off no matter what. In terms of particles, there is no paradox: both tachyons always get sent.

So where do we stand now on the question of faster-than-light travel? We know that the existence of tachyons wouldn't violate any general principles of physics, and that an entire world of faster-than-light objects could exist side by side with our own. We have no experimental evidence that they do exist, although this isn't so surprising. Except for the fact that they travel faster than light, we have to guess what other properties they might have, which makes it difficult to think of experiments to find them. A good analogy to this sort of situation would be the existence of radioactive elements before the discovery of ways of detecting radioactivity.

If at some time in the future someone does come up with a way to detect tachyons, and maybe even control them to the point of being able to emit signals, there would be some interesting consequences. For one thing, the question of whether or not advanced civilizations exist in the galaxy could be settled, because we could have practically instantaneous communication over interstellar distances.

At the same time, the existence of tachyons would pose some pretty sticky philosophical problems about the nature of causality. Physicists have argued that there would be other problems as well: they might not obey the same kinds of laws that govern other subatomic particles.□

View of Stanford University's high-energy storage ring SPEAR, one of the first facilities to be used to extract and use synchrotron radiation.

# SYNCHROTRON RADIATION

IT'S a fact of life: in order to see something, the "light" you shine on it has to have a shorter wavelength than the object you expect to see. For that reason scientists have, over the years, developed some ingenious ways to see smaller and smaller things by illuminating them with "light" of shorter and shorter wavelength.

The advantage of the electron microscope over the conventional visible light microscope is an example. Physicists studying nuclear particles have carried the techniques even further. They use extremely high-energy electrons—the equivalent of very short wavelength illumination—to determine the structure of subnuclear particles. To conduct studies of that kind, they use massive particle accelerators to boost the energy, or speed, of the electron "bullets," which then bombard specific targets or collide against their antimatter, positrons.

Until the physicists are ready to maneuver them into a collision, these high-energy electrons are kept on tap by being circulated in a closed loop or storage ring. The particles normally would move in a straight line; however, their paths can be curved by a series of high-powered magnets placed around the ring. But there's another fact of life: when charged particles move through a magnetic field, they lose energy in the form of radiation that spins off to the side of the storage ring. This energy is known as synchrotron radiation. This loss slows down the speeding particles, much to the annoyance of the high-energy physicists. To keep the particles moving at the high speed they need to stay in orbit, the physicists replace that lost energy with a radio-frequency acceleration "boost."

One physicist's nuisance is another's golden opportunity, however. The energy that is "lost" is thrown off against the walls of the synchrotron or storage ring like mud thrown from a spinning car wheel.

## TRASH TO TREASURE

This energy consists mainly of X-ray and ultraviolet radiation—an ideal illuminating source for looking at structural details of molecules and atoms. So physicists, biologists, and other scientists came up with an ingenious idea to turn so-called trash—lost energy—into a sought-for treasure—a source of "light" that would enable them to "see" smaller things than ever before possible. They slit a hole in the outer wall of the ring to catch the "lost" radiation as it flies off the circulating electrons.

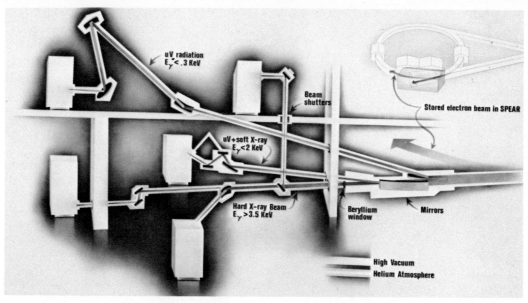

Stanford University

As electrons move through SPEAR's storage ring, they lose energy that spins off to the side of the ring. This energy is split and directed by mirrors into five ports, shown as rectangular boxes in the art above, each of which can be used for a different synchrotron radiation experiment.

One major technical consideration is protecting the ultrahigh vacuum within the storage ring. If particles or air should enter the ring through the slit, the electrons would crash into the foreign molecules and lose energy.

In the 1950s, pioneering work at Cornell University and the U.S. National Bureau of Standards paid off. The idea proved successful: "waste" radiation from orbiting electrons could be captured and used. In the late 1960s, Tantalus I, the storage ring at the University of Wisconsin, was set up to provide a steady source of ultraviolet and soft X-ray radiation. At Stanford University, physicists saw their chance to take advantage of one of the high-energy storage rings: SPEAR. Storage rings such as DORIS in West Germany and synchrotrons such as DESY in West Germany, ARUS in Russia, and NINA in England could also be used.

Stanford physicists began planning in the 1960s to slit the SPEAR ring, and in 1970 a proposal for extracting radiation was ready, prepared under the direction of Sebastian Doniach, now director of the Stanford Synchrotron Radiation Project (SSRP). On July 6, 1973, at 10:42 A.M., synchrotron radiation was first beamed from a window cut in the SPEAR ring. Less than a year later, five research stations were in operation in the steel prefabricated laboratory.

## MANY USES

The range of synchrotron radiation extends from the infrared region through the visible light region to the X-ray region of the electromagnetic spectrum. In recent years, synchrotron radiation has been most useful as a source in the ultraviolet and X-ray regions.

Only a few years ago work in the ultraviolet and X-ray range was for the most part limited to the scattered beams emitted from ultraviolet discharge lamps and X-ray tubes. Synchrotron radiation has proved remarkably useful in many ways that are impossible with similar radiation from conventional ultraviolet lamps and X-ray tubes.

For one thing, the photon beams emitted from the storage-ring source have extremely high intensities—50 to 1,000 times more intense than those from conventional sources. Researchers can accumulate data with amazing speed. For instance, X-ray pictures can be taken 50 to 100 times faster than with the classical X-ray tubes; and X-ray absorption graphs can be made more than 1,000 times faster.

Synchrotron radiation also provides a continuous spectrum of energies, so that extremely narrow bands of any desired wavelength can be obtained, often considerably narrower than conventional line sources.

Scientists at work on Tantalus I, a University of Wisconsin facility being used for synchrotron radiation.

These narrow energy bands can be used for a large number of experiments. Moreover, the photons emitted are nearly perfectly polarized, in the same plane as the electronic orbit. This feature, Doniach points out, will become increasingly important in fields of crystal physics, solid-state studies, and molecular spectroscopy.

And because the electrons are circulated in the storage ring in bunches, the radiation comes in pulses that are a fraction of a nanosecond in duration. One nanosecond is equal to 1/1,000,000,000 of a second. Such pulsation is useful in the study of atomic and molecular motions, chemical and enzymatic reactions, and other time-dependent phenomena.

### CAPTURING THE ENERGY

The window cut in the Stanford SPEAR ring provides a flat beam of radiation about 10 centimeters (4 inches) wide and less than 3 millimeters (1/10 inch) high. This beam is split and directed by mirrors and crystals into five ports within the synchrotron-radiation laboratory. Each port can serve many different experiments. After one group has completed its experiment, another group can attach its equipment to the port, sometimes in a matter of minutes. Altogether, some 19 projects are in operation at one time or another.

Hard X rays with energies above 3.5 kilo-electron volts (3,500 electron volts) pass readily through a vacuum-tight beryllium window and then continue in an atmosphere of helium to three of the five experimental stations. Soft X rays, less than 2 kilo-electron volts (2,000 electron volts) are reflected sideways through a 4-degree angle to a fourth station, and ultraviolet, less than 300 electron volts (eV), is reflected upward through an 8-degree angle to the fifth station. Each outlet has a device to block out all radiations except those of the desired wavelength.

### PARASITES ON THE STORAGE RING

One of the main hitches to being part of the high-energy storage ring is that synchrotron-radiation researchers can operate only when the ring is on.

"In other words, we're parasitic," says Doniach. "When those high energy guys cut the power, we have to turn off our experiments. And if they run at such low energies that not enough of our radiation is produced, we have to wait with our X-ray experiments until they turn up the juice." Counting shutdowns for maintenance and for special experiments, the actual experimentation at SSRP runs about six months of the year.

But no one's complaining. At the moment this is the only way for experiments to be done with synchrotron radiation in the X-ray region. When SPEAR is on, researchers work seven days a week, around the clock.

### A "DEDICATED" SYNCHROTRON

Another type of facility for synchrotron radiation is a low-energy machine with a cut-off wavelength in the ultraviolet region. Tantalus I, a 240,000,000 electron-volt storage ring at the University of Wisconsin, has been successfully producing an extremely reliable and versatile source of radiation in the infrared, far ultraviolet, and soft X-ray regions, with photons up to about 300 electron volts, and wavelengths of about 40 angstroms. (An angstrom is 0.00000001 centimeter.)

"Tantalus' sole purpose," points out Ednor Rowe, director of the University's Synchrotron Radiation Center, "is to provide a constant and reliable source of radiation in the infrared, ultraviolet, and soft X-ray regions for all qualified investigators. It's a national facility." Unlike the Stanford project and other synchrotron-radiation research facilities, Tantalus does not depend on high-energy physics experiments for its existence. The Wisconsin facility, supported by the U.S. National Science Foundation since September 1974, was designed and is operated only to produce synchrotron radiation, and thus the photon beams can be tailored to the needs of the researchers. Also, programs can be carried out without any unexpected shutdowns. Finally, because of the design of the Tantalus, the researchers can work with their equipment close to the ring of circulating electrons.

## WHAT THE PHOTONS PROBE

Physicists classify the general type of experiment that can be done with a synchrotron source of radiation into two groups: spectroscopy and diffraction. Spectroscopy deals with the interaction of electromagnetic radiation and matter, and in it the photon energy is changed. Diffraction scatters the photons with no loss or change of energy.

The process of spectroscopy is considered inelastic; the energy of the ingoing photon changes as it is absorbed, split up, or scattered. Diffraction is considered an elastic process. Here the outgoing photons have the same energy as the incoming particles, but travel in a new direction.

## "SEE" THE STRUCTURE OF MATTER

Several experiments at SSRP and Tantalus are turning out results unobtainable with any other radiation source. One continuing experiment at Stanford, for instance, is letting scientists "see" special structural features of matter, such as the distances between atoms. X rays of well-defined energy are directed onto a target—an element, a simple compound, amorphous material, dilute alloy, or a biological material. The target can be a solid, liquid, or gas, and can be at temperatures from room temperature to that of liquid

nitrogen (about −210° Celsius, or −346° Fahrenheit). Then scientists watch what happens when the X rays knock loose electrons that are close to the nucleus of an atom.

When the energy of an incoming X ray is absorbed by an electron, that electron may spin completely out of the atom. This recoil affects the absorption coefficient, which can be measured by means of special devices placed just in front of and just behind the target material. The X rays are counted before they hit the target and after they have been transmitted through the target. A computer calculates the ratio of these measurements to show the amount of absorption. New measurements starting from the new energy settings are then made. Several thousand measurements are made in rapid succession.

As the X-ray energy is increased, it reaches a point where it is sufficient to knock an electron out of an atomic shell. This onset of the process causes a sharp increase in X-ray absorption, called an edge. For X rays at energies above the edge, the absorption slowly decreases. The phenomena that have particularly interested scientists are the "wiggles" in the absorption curve above the edge. These small bumps indicate the influence of neighboring atoms on the absorption of the X-ray photon. The pattern, then, presents information on the atoms in the environment of an atom whose electron has absorbed an X ray.

Another series of experiments going on both at Tantalus and at SSRP is designed to study a problem that scientists have long been curious about: determining the structure of matter by the measurement of photoelectron emission—the energy and angular distributions of electrons as they are knocked out of materials by ultraviolet and X-ray photons. These experimental results, together with other data also obtained with the aid of Tantalus, are now providing reliable information on the electronic structures of elements, alloys, and compounds, and on how the electrons are distributed in the one or two layers of atoms at and also beneath the surface. Results of this research will contribute to better understanding of semiconductors and insulators.

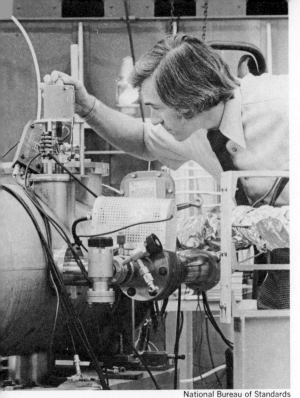

National Bureau of Standards

Scientist at work at the National Bureau of Standards's low-energy ultraviolet storage ring.

## TO OBSERVE MOLECULES MOVING IN LIVING TISSUE

Biologists are using the main X-ray "biology" line at the Stanford facility to observe biological changes on a molecular level—for instance, the movements of protein molecules in retinal rods of frog eyes as they respond to light or the molecular activity of frog-leg muscle as it contracts or relaxes. These movements of protein and other molecules in living tissue are captured on X-ray photographic film, giving scientists a clue to the behavior of molecules as the tissue reacts to different stimuli.

## RADIATION IN THE FUTURE

The potential use of synchrotron radiation for research is enormous. For instance, scientists believe that experiments in understanding the detailed structure of a silicon film could lead into activities such as producing a substance with the same electrical properties, at less cost, as single crystals of silicon that convert sunlight directly into electricity. Through experiments for understanding the optical response of metals, semiconductors, and insulators to ultraviolet and X rays, scientists hope to improve the optical

capabilities of high-energy lasers and of lenses for space astronomy. Other experiments are helping to explain the spectral-radiation distribution from space.

Research is increasing faster than space and time on the radiation beam outlets allow. There are two other facilities in the United States at present, in addition to Stanford and Wisconsin. One is the low-energy ultraviolet storage ring at the National Bureau of Standards at Gaithersburg, Maryland, and the other is the high-energy synchrotron at Cornell University in Ithaca, New York. Another facility, a National Synchrotron Light Source, devoted solely to synchrotron radiation, is to be built at the Brookhaven National Laboratories on Long Island, New York; it is expected to be operational in the early 1980s.

Following the early experiments in the United States in the mid-1950s, larger machines in other countries were soon used to produce synchrotron-radiation, first in Japan and then in Germany. Today there are more than 20 synchrotron radiation facilities throughout the world, most of them parasitic upon the already established high-energy physics rings. Germany, England, Japan, Italy, and the Soviet Union have made substantial commitments for developing synchrotron-radiation research.

"The technique that was just a laboratory curiosity little more than a decade ago," points out Doniach, "has now become a sophisticated facility increasingly in demand by scientists in all fields. With this radiation source illuminating the molecular world of matter with a flexibility never before available," he says, "the more scientists look, the more they want to see. The hard part now is keeping up with their demands" □

SELECTED READINGS

"Casting light on materials structure: synchrotron radiation" by D. E. Thomsen. *Science News*, December 24, 1977.

"Synchrotron radiation: large demand spurs new facilities" by A. L. Robinson. *Science*, July 8, 1977.

"Uses of synchrotron radiation" by E. M. Rowe and J. H. Weaver. *Scientific American*, June 1977.

**320**   PHYSICAL SCIENCES

The Nobel Foundation

Princeton University

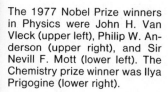

The 1977 Nobel Prize winners in Physics were John H. Van Vleck (upper left), Philip W. Anderson (upper right), and Sir Nevill F. Mott (lower left). The Chemistry prize winner was Ilya Prigogine (lower right).

The Nobel Foundation

The Nobel Foundation

# THE 1977 NOBEL PRIZES IN PHYSICS AND CHEMISTRY

THE 1977 Nobel Prize in Physics was awarded to two Americans and one Briton for their work in solid-state physics, which has provided the basis for many modern technological developments, including computer memories, copying machines, and other electronic devices. The recipients of the prize were Dr. Philip W. Anderson of the Bell Telephone Laboratories in Murray Hill, New Jersey; Dr. John H. Van Vleck of Harvard University; and Sir Nevill F. Mott of Cambridge University in England.

The 1977 Nobel Prize in Chemistry was awarded to Ilya Prigogine, a Russian-born scientist from the Free University in Brussels, Belgium, for his "contributions to nonequilibrium thermodynamics, particularly the theory of dissipative structures." This work explained how life could have arisen on earth.

## THE PRIZE IN PHYSICS

The Swedish Royal Academy awarded the 1977 Nobel Prize in Physics not for spe-

cific discoveries but rather for the lifetime work of three scientists whose discoveries have provided the foundation for practically all that is now known about the physics of solids. Working independently, the three men unravelled many of the mysteries concerning the magnetic and electrical properties of solids and opened the door to a whole new branch of solid-state physics—the study of amorphous semiconductors.

Amorphous semiconductors are electronic switching and memory devices. They are made of glassy materials that have an irregular, unorganized atomic structure, unlike that of crystals in which the constituent atoms are aligned in an orderly way. Since amorphous solids are somewhat easier to prepare than complex crystal devices, some scientists feel that they will play an increasingly important role in the development of new devices such as lower-cost solar energy converters as well as provide newer materials for the electronics of computer memories, calculators, and copying machines.

Dr. Van Vleck's work was perhaps the most theoretical. Called the "father of modern magnetism" by many other scientists, he began studying the magnetic properties of solids in the 1930s. He explained the action of subatomic particles in solids, often reducing the descriptions to fundamental mathematical formulas that could be widely applied. His work was basic to many subsequent developments, including electron interactions in computer memory systems.

Dr. Anderson worked primarily with amorphous solids. In the late 1950s he began studying electron transport within such materials. He discovered that an electron can be located or pinpointed in a material like glass, rendering it an electrical insulator, but be free to move in other amorphous materials, making them electrical conductors. These discoveries, now known as the Anderson localization theory, were brought a step closer to practical application by Dr. Mott.

Dr. Mott explained how Anderson's theories accounted for the electrical conductivity of amorphous solids and went on to describe how such materials could be used in electronic devices.

*John Hasbrouck Van Vleck* was born in Middletown, Connecticut, in 1899. He earned a bachelor's degree in physics from the University of Wisconsin in 1920 and a doctorate from Harvard University in 1922. He remained at Harvard for his entire career, much of the time as Hollis professor of mathematics and natural history, the oldest endowed chair at an American university. He is now an emeritus professor.

*Philip W. Anderson* was born in Indianapolis, Indiana, in 1925. He earned his bachelor's, master's, and doctorate degrees from Harvard University. Since 1949 he has been associated with Bell Laboratories in Murray Hill, New Jersey, where he is now director of the physical research division. Since 1975 has been professor of physics at Princeton University.

*Sir Nevill Francis Mott* was born in 1905. He was a student of Lord Rutherford, the pioneer in studies of the atom, at Cavendish Laboratory at Cambridge University. After

receiving his doctorate, he was professor of physics at Bristol University for a while, but returned to Cavendish where he became head of the laboratory. He retired in 1971.

## THE PRIZE IN CHEMISTRY

According to the classical laws of physics, energy tends to dissipate and organized systems tend to drift into chaos. This law always presented a problem to scientists trying to explain the origin of life on earth as the spontaneous result of the interaction of chemicals, because for life to have arisen higher degrees of organization, not less, were necessary. Dr. Prigogine was able to explain this apparent contradiction and in the words of a Nobel committee member "make us believe that life's origin was not coincidental and that it may be possible to trace it."

Dr. Prigogine worked with mathematical models that, like living systems, dissipated energy at the same time that they were able to sustain themselves and grow in size and organization. He predicted that such systems, which he termed "dissipative structures," were at work when life began on earth. His work was only theoretical however, until the late 1960s when chemical reactions that confirmed the theories were discovered. In one such reaction, a solution of chemicals was able in a certain environment to spontaneously sort itself out.

Dr. Prigogine explained that the classical laws of physics and chemistry apply in closed systems but not in open systems, like that which existed in the prebiotic world. In such open systems growth and increasing complexity and organization can occur as a limited number of members—molecules in the case of the prebiotic earth—interact with one another and with their environment.

*Ilya Prigogine* was born in Moscow in 1917. His family left Russia when he was very young, travelled through Lithuania and Germany, and finally settled in Brussels, where he completed his education. He now divides his time between the Free University in Brussels, where he is professor of physical chemistry and theoretical physics, and the University of Texas at Austin where he is director of the Center of Statistical Mechanics and Thermodynamics □

IBM

Scientists have developed a new information-display technology that uses a small solid-state laser to write information in a liquid-crystal medium. Characters are formed in the liquid crystal and projected on a translucent screen as typewriter characters. In the photo above, IBM scientist Anthony G. Dewey, one of the developers of the new information display terminal, holds the laser in a pair of tweezers.

# TECHNOLOGY

## contents

# TECHNOLOGY
## review of the year

Bell Labs

Cable for lightwave communications system is put into plastic tube before being placed underground.

Bell Labs

Bell Lab scientists demonstrate the new computer-controlled digital sound synthesizer they developed.

**Optical phone lines.** Ever since electric and radio waves were first used to carry messages it has been clear in principle that light waves could be similarly modulated to carry messages. The production of such message-carrying optical lines awaited two technical developments: a source of light that was coherent (beams that spread little or not at all as they travel), and the development of materials out of which guides to carry the light without absorbing unacceptable amounts of it could be made. The development of lasers and of light-carrying fibers has now progressed to the point where optical message-carrying lines are now possible. In mid-1977 Bell System began testing an optical telephone line in Chicago, Illinois. The line runs from the Brunswick building, an office building in downtown Chicago, to the Illinois Bell Franklin central station, and from there to its Wabash central office. The new system is carrying voice and other signals on pulses of light over almost 2.5 kilometers (1.5 miles) of underground cable using hair-thin glass fibers. Each of the 24 fiber lightguides in the 0.7 centimeter-diameter cable is able to carry 672 simultaneous conversations or their equivalent in other signals. In late 1977 General Telephone & Electronics announced plans to install a similar system along a 10-kilometer (6.5 mile) route between Brussels and the nearby city of Vilvoorde in Belgium and to test it for a period of two years beginning in late 1978. Because light beams can carry more messages at lower energy cost than electric phone lines can, the new developments are expected to be widely applied in the future.

**Laser developments.** The first lasers worked in the infrared region of the spectrum. Making lasers that produce shorter and shorter waves—through the visible range of the spectrum into the ultraviolet—has been a long and difficult task. Now the U.S. Naval Research Laboratory reports that it has produced a laser that emits at the ultraviolet wavelength. This development will undoubtedly further increase the range of uses for lasers. ■ Meanwhile, more conventional lasers are finding more and more uses in industry. The Microtrac particle size analyzer, a Leeds and Northrup instrument that uses a laser beam to measure the size of particles, is being used increasingly to measure ore size, determine grinding sizes, analyze foodstuff particles, and blend materials. Able to detect superfine particles, it is also being investigated as a new and extremely sensitive detector of particulate matter in the air.

**New breeder reactor.** Advocates of nuclear power are facing a serious problem. As supplies of uranium that are fit to refine for reactor fuel dwindle, the advocates recognize the need for some sort of breeder reactor that produces more fuel than it burns. The usual type of breeder reactor burns uranium 235 and produces the byproduct plutonium, which can be used to fuel other reactors. But plutonium presents many problems, important among which is the danger that a plutonium-reactor economy could lead to widespread proliferation of nuclear weapons. It does not take much plutonium to build a bomb. Any nation with a breeder reactor or a plutonium-fired reactor has a legitimite reason to import and transport plutonium, and would be in a position to manufacture nuclear weapons. Furthermore, terrorist and criminal groups might be able to hijack plutonium shipments and engage in nuclear blackmail. A partial solution to this problem has been found. It is a light-water breeder reactor that is fueled with uranium 233 and uses the thorium cycle to breed. Each atom of the uranium 233 that fissions releases two or three neutrons. Only one of these neutrons is necessary to keep the chain reaction going. The extra neutrons are absorbed in a blanket of thorium that surrounds the reactor core. Each neutron that is absorbed turns a thorium atom into an atom of uranium 233, so the reactor produces more fuel than it destroys by fission. The possible insurance against proliferation results from the danger and difficulty of transporting uranium 233, which emits gamma rays that are very dangerous to living cells. The careful handling needed to transport uranium 233 would deter criminals and would make any government activity expensive and highly visible to the world. The first commercial-scale test of the thorium breeder is going on at Shippingport, Pennsylvania. It will test the feasibility of commercial installations of this type by supplying electricity to the Duquesne Lighting Company.

**Particle beams.** Scientists at Los Alamos Scientific Laboratory in New Mexico are experimenting with methods of making large pulses of electric power by explosions and then accelerating subatomic particles with the resultant pulses. These ultra-strong pulsed-power devices have many applications in research and development, including the study of the behavior of materials in strong magnetic fields. Some of these devices also have potential as weapons: the pulses of electric power can be used to accelerate large numbers of protons, or positively charged subatomic particles, to make a powerful particle beam. The technique for these devices is to set up a magnetic field in a box of a certain size and then to compress the box suddenly by detonating explosive charges packed around it. The sudden compression squeezes the magnetic energy into a small space, making a much stronger magnetic field in the small space than could be done with electromagnets. The magnetic pulse can then be converted to a high-power electric pulse and used in many ways.

**Other developments.** Automatic focusing became the latest new technique in the burgeoning camera market. A Konica 35-millimeter rangefinder camera equipped with a Honeywell-developed automatic-focusing device led in the development that is expected to spread quickly throughout the camera industry. ■ A new computer-controlled sound synthesizer that is able to play up to 30 musical instruments simultaneously and make musical sounds never before heard was also unveiled.

Technology also continued to try to meet some of the world's energy problems. Liquid-junction solar cells combining liquid and solid parts were one of the latest developments in attempts to make solar cells more efficient in converting the sun's energy into electricity. ■ The major automobile manufacturers also continued efforts to develop more efficient, less polluting automobiles. Among the approaches being studied and tested were stratified-engine cars that can run on gasoline, diesel fuel, methane, kerosene, or a mixture of these fuels; turbocharged engines; and the increased use of light-weight materials such as graphite and aluminum to make cars lighter and more fuel-efficient.

Dietrick Thomsen

ERDA

Tests of the Shippingport reactor included analyses of its various parts such as this bottom plate.

Konica

The Konica 35-millimeter rangefinder was the first of the new automatic focusing cameras.

# PLANETRAN

## by Robert M. Salter

Rensselaer Polytechnic Institute

An artist's conception of tubeflight vehicles that could be used to relieve air and road congestion and speed travel time between major population centers.

NEW YORK to Los Angeles in 21 minutes . . . Fantastic? Only in the world of science fiction? Maybe . . . Maybe not.

I would like to describe a new subway concept called Planetran. Planetran is not an ordinary subway system. Rather it is one moving at many thousands of kilometers per hour. Its cars travel in underground evacuated tubes and are electromagnetically supported and propelled. Cars float on these electromagnetic fields just as a surfboard rides ocean waves.

Planetran can cross the United States in an hour or so and perhaps even in 21 minutes. It can be extended to a worldwide network using under-ocean tunnels to connect the continents. It is designed to connect with existing subway and local transit systems in the same stations. It provides safe, convenient, low-cost, efficient, and non-polluting service. Its tunnel complex can also be used to house transmission and auxiliary freight-carrying systems.

The Planetran concept was put forward some years ago in a search for a transport method operating at speeds comparable with aircraft. A high-speed train by conventional standards is one like the Japanese "Kodama" which operates at speeds in excess of 160 kilometers (100 miles) per hour. Experimental surface transit vehicles using magnetic levitation have attained 480 kilometers (300 miles) per hour. However, even at these speeds terrestrial systems cannot compete with aircraft over long distances. Planetran can.

## SPEED

Planetran can readily exceed conventional aircraft speeds and even those of future hypersonic planes. Further, Planetran does not need to climb to high altitudes to find favorable atmospheric conditions for high speed.

The fastest Planetran case examined—across the United States in 21 minutes—assumes a propulsion of one *g*—that is, a force equal to the force that gravity exerts on an object, equal to its weight. A maximum of 22,400 kilometers (14,000 miles) per hour is reached. The cars would be continuously accelerated until they reached the midpoint of their trip and from then on would be continuously decelerated. With properly positioned seats, passengers would feel these propulsive forces as additional weight.

Experimental facilities are not yet available to determine passenger response to such accelerations and limits for comfort acceptability. Thus we don't know how realistic the 21-minute case is. It should be remembered, however, that airborne systems might need 21 minutes just to get to and from high alti-

tude. Further, aircraft do not have Planetran's prospect for terminating in a downtown subway station with one minute headway.

It may be more desirable for passenger comfort to have higher accelerations at the start and finish of each trip with no forces in between rather than the steady force of the example given above. At a thrust of 0.6 *g* for only four or five minutes at each end of the Planetran link, a trip between the U.S. coasts with one stop at Dallas, Texas, would take 54.5 minutes. The cars would reach a speed of almost 5,800 kilometers (3,600 miles) per hour. For two thirds of the trip no thrusts would be felt and for the other third the passengers would feel only one sixth heavier. Obviously a critical consideration is the tradeoff of transit time for passenger comfort and the type of acceleration schedule.

## ROUTE SYSTEM

The determination of a route system for Planetran depends on a careful study of transportation needs and population densities as well as of land configurations. As now

Map showing possible Planetran and rail routes coordinated across the United States in the early stages of a Planetran or Planetranlike program.

adapted from "Trans-Planetary Subway Systems" by Robert M. Salter, The Rand Corporation

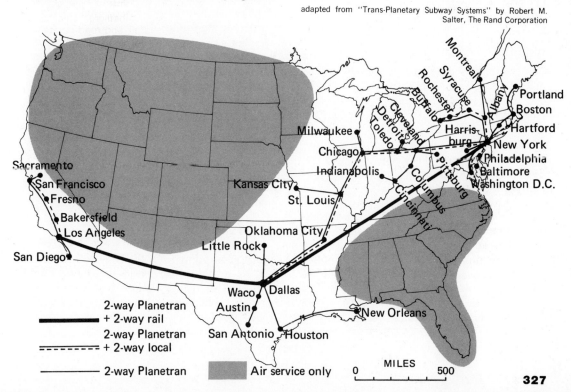

2-way Planetran + 2-way rail

2-way Planetran + 2-way local

2-way Planetran

Air service only

MILES

0    500

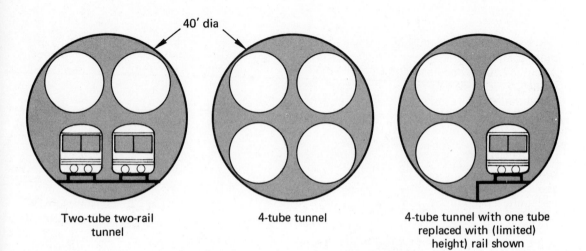

40′ dia

Two-tube two-rail
tunnel

4-tube tunnel

4-tube tunnel with one tube
replaced with (limited)
height) rail shown

adapted from "Trans-Planetary Subway Systems" by Robert M.
Salter, The Rand Corporation.

Four possible tunnel arrangements for a Planetran
or Planetranlike system.

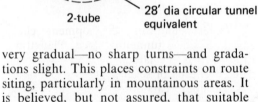

2-tube

28′ dia circular tunnel
equivalent

visualized, Planetran would connect with already existing airports and local mass transit facilities so that a passenger could, for example, step off a subway and get on a Planetran in the same terminal.

## UNDERGROUND REQUIREMENTS

Planetran's evacuated channels can be placed above ground and there may be special instances where this is appropriate. However, to provide a truly high-speed system we must go underground. Aesthetic considerations, favorable location of utilities, and protection against sabotage all argue for the desirability of underground placement of the system.

We must place tunnels 100 meters (300 feet) or more down to find solid rock formations. In some places depths of more than one kilometer will be necessary, particularly when tunneling under ocean straits or mountains. Extensive lengths far underground are not desirable, however.

To assure safety, efficient operation, and passenger comfort, Planetran tunnels should be as straight as possible. Curves should be

very gradual—no sharp turns—and gradations slight. This places constraints on route siting, particularly in mountainous areas. It is believed, but not assured, that suitable routes can be found.

Tunnels will present the major problem—and the major cost—of Planetran. The best system compromise is one that minimizes tunnel cost at the expense of other system components. Planetran vehicles should, for example, be long and narrow to minimize tube size and allow placement of several tubes in one tunnel.

Small tubes have other advantages: they allow easier vacuum pumping and tunnel packing and permit the use of smaller acceleration equipment.

## MASSIVE UNDERTAKING

A system such as we have been talking about—one going from the U.S. or Canadian east coast to the west coast with one (or two) stops and involving tunnels with provisions for two tubes and perhaps also for fast rail lines—would involve somewhere near 12,000 kilometers (7,500 miles) of tunnels.

How does an undertaking of this magnitude compare with other world projects? About 12,800 kilometers (8,000 miles) of tunnels were drilled in the 1960s in the free world alone. This figure is expected to double in the 1970s. Italy alone has over 1,600 kilometers (1,000 miles) of freeway with numerous tunnels. As for under-ocean projects, a tunnel under the English Channel is now being actively planned. The Japanese are about half way under the Hokkaido Strait with quite a deep tunnel. Offshore wells have been dug 10 kilometers (6 miles) deep.

Such tunnel projects, together with mines, storage caverns, pipe lines, and power conduits are all supporting the development of both undergrounding technologies and geologic methods. Present day tunneling methods will be enhanced as more and more sophisticated devices such as tunnel boring machines, water jet drills, and hypersonic laser and particle beams become available.

## CHALLENGES—BUT NO NEW TECHNOLOGY

Other significant development challenges besides tunneling face Planetran. Prominent is the lateral acceleration problem. At speeds of several thousand kilometers an hour, cars must maintain a very precise course to avoid sideways forces on passengers. At the maximum speed, curves must also be very gradual. Since Planetran

"tracks" are magnetic fields, exacting control of the fields themselves is necessary.

Recent progress in compact, reliable, and low-cost microcomputers paves the way for such systems control. Hundreds of these computers distributed along Planetrans' electrical guideway structure would be able to detect and correct any tiny departures from the vehicles specified cruise and acceleration schedule.

These microcomputers would also be able to detect any disturbances caused by outside events—by, for example, an earth tremor affecting the tunnel region—and keep the magnetic field guide in a fixed position.

Provisions must also be made for emergency stopping; fail-safe overall designs in operational and car life-support systems; quick opening, computer-controlled gates, or valves, at tube ends; terminal car-handling facilities; tube vacuum-pumping and sealing; and overall system maintenance. None of these challenges requires scientific breakthroughs or even new technology.

## ENERGY SAVER

Planetran is a highly energy-conservative system. Cars contain ultra-cooled supermagnets for levitation. Travelling electromagnetic waves in Planetran guideways oppose the magnetic fields of the cars in a way that provides support and thrust. For every car that is being accelerated in one direction,

adapted from "Trans-Planetary Subway Systems" by Robert M. Salter, The Rand Corporation.

Tunnel shell

Vacuum tube

Earth tremor shakes tunnel

Vehicle path remains fixed in space although tunnel shakes

Inertial detector mounted on tube

Inertial detector signal

Inertial detector picks up signal

Control electronics

Rollers

Vernier control magnet windings to "shim" planetron thrust/support magnet field

Stabilizing control signal

A computer-controlled inertial detector system would keep Planetran on a steady course even if earth tremors should shake the tunnel.

Massachusetts Institute of Technology graduate students William R. Snow (left) and Kevin S. Fine stand beside an electromagnetic mass driver that uses magnetic repulsion to send a small "bucket" (held by Fine) down the tube at 110 kilometers (70 miles) per hour. The system is being developed for use in launching spacecraft but the basic principles used in the system can also be applied to land transportation.

there is one in an adjoining tube that is being decelerated. Cars being decelerated return electrical energy to the overall system.

Microcomputer control will make it possible to tailor electrical systems to specific needs all along the route and lead to a high level of energy efficiency. The vacuum tubes can also be designed and maintained in energy efficient ways.

Overall Planetran cars are more efficient than aircraft. It is estimated that Planetran will use only a few per cent as much energy per passenger kilometer as an airplane.

## ENVIRONMENTAL BENEFITS

Transportation systems pose well-known problems to the environment. The controversy over the noise of supersonic planes has perhaps obscured some other environmental effects of aircraft. None of the energy required to levitate and propel an aircraft is recoverable. It all goes into the atmosphere along with combustion products. Long-term buildup of these products is a matter of concern and a process that we are just beginning to understand.

Many nations are interested in developing new, more efficient mass transportation facilities. Here a model of a magnetic railway system under consideration in Germany.

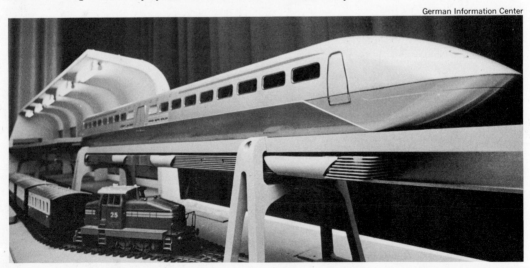

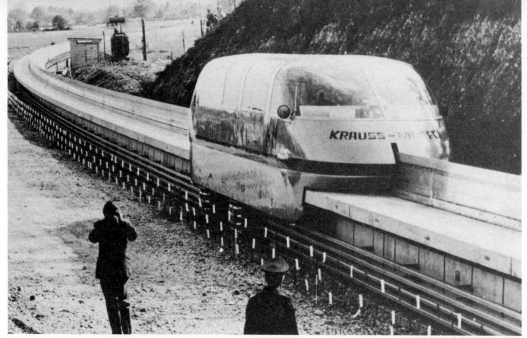

Prototype "Transrapid" system being tested in Germany as a possible answer to mass transportation and traffic problems.

Planetran would alleviate these hazards to the environment. Since the system is underground, right-of-way costs, surface congestion, grade separation problems, air pollution, and noise pollution would also be eliminated.

### TUNNEL SHARING

The high cost of Planetran could be reduced if other facilities shared the use—and cost—of the tunnel. A controlled access tunnel such as that necessary for Planetran is a virtual necessity for superconducting power cables, for example. Laser communication channels also require the protection of enclosed channels. The underground Planetran system could also be used for pipelines for oil, water, gas, and waste disposal and for freight hauling systems.

The development of a route for Planetran also offers the potential for a fast rail system to be developed with it. Such a rail system, designed to connect with existing railroads, would carry semi-trailers, container cargo, campers, and other items too bulky for the Planetran tubes. It would share with Planetran power and service installations.

A Japanese-developed High Speed Surface Transport (HSST) vehicle that uses magnetic levitation to lift it above the track. It travels at speeds of about 300 kilometers per hour.

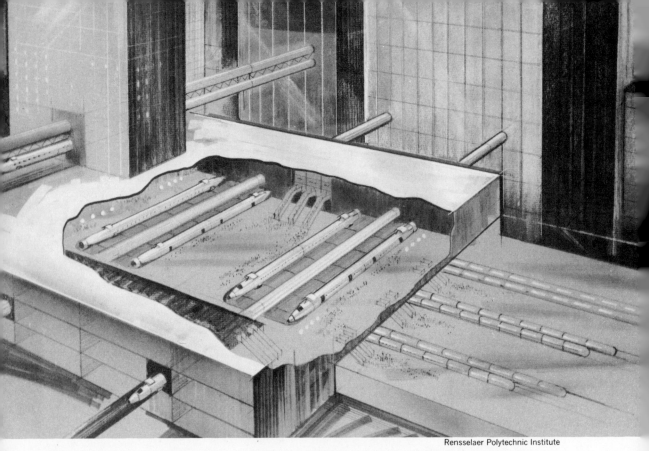

Rensselaer Polytechnic Institute

Artist's conception of a Planetranlike intermediate station in which several vehicles are loading and unloading. The system could be designed to be noiseless and be able to run through buildings.

## SYSTEM DEVELOPMENT

Development of a system like Planetran is a prodigious undertaking. By its very nature, it will be difficult to reap Planetran's benefits in piecemeal stages. Until main corridor links are operating, its high-speed nature cannot be exploited, and even then feeder lines and connections with existing transit services must be established to realize Planetran's full social and economic potentials.

The development of multiple-use tunnels now will help establish Planetran, shortening the gap between systems development and initial revenues. By building the tunnels first for other purposes—say fast rail service or military use—we improve the odds for achieving Planetran and help defray its costs.

## FUTURE PROSPECTS

Are there compelling reasons for Planetran? Yes, emphatically. We no longer can afford to pollute our skies with heat, chemicals, and noise, nor to carve up our wilderness areas and arable land with new surface transportation routes. Nor can we continue our extravagant waste of limited fossil fuel resources.

Is the idea really far-fetched? To answer that, just look back over the last 100 years in transportation. What seemed far-fetched in 1878?

Present travel and freight systems have proliferated without much attention given their relationship and without integrated plans. Without some inspiration, we may just have more of the same in the year 2078. A concerted effort is needed to at least look at where we are headed.

Planetran offers safe and highly convenient transportation service with low energy cost and minimum environmental impact. Is it not worth at least careful consideration? □

 SELECTED READINGS

*Passenger Transportation* by Martin T. Farris. Prentice-Hall, 1976.
*The Selling of Rail Rapid Transit* by Andrew Hamer. Lexington Books, 1976.

# SUPER BULB

ONE night not too far into the future your house may be better lighted, more economically, as a result of a currently promising technical development that sicentists at the Massachusetts Institute of Technology (MIT) are at work on.

It involves a new inner coating for the light bulb, and one forecast is that ultimately it can revolutionize the whole light-bulb industry. It holds out the promise of reducing electrical energy consumption by 60 per cent without any loss in light output, in the view of Dr. James D. Felske, who is the principal investigator for the project, which is being supported by a grant from the Duro-Test Corp., a manufacturer of light bulbs. In turn, Duro-Test holds a license from MIT giving it exclusive rights to the process. The process was originally researched and developed by Drs. John C. C. Fan and Frank J. Bachner of MIT as part of their work on the applications of solar energy.

The key to the development lay in a transparent film or coating that allows solar radiation to be absorbed by glass and, through a process of heat conversion, "traps" it inside.

In an ordinary 100-watt light bulb about 90 per cent of the wattage, or power, is lost as heat. The new coating will lessen the heat loss.

"This coating," says Duro-Test's engineering vice-president Luke Thorington, "conserves the heat produced inside the bulb by reflecting infrared radiation off the inner surface and back to the centrally located filament. This substantially reduces the amount of electricity needed to keep the filament hot and operating at its most efficient temperature." For example, a 100-watt light bulb with the new coating would consume approximately 40 watts of electricity.

The bulb itself is still in the experimental phase of development but should be on

In a conventional bulb (left) light and heat pass through the wall of the bulb. To produce more light, the filament must be heated more, and this requires more wattage, or power. In a newly developed bulb with a special coating on the wall (right), the heat is reflected back to the filament, increasing its heat so that it can then give off more light with less wattage consumption.

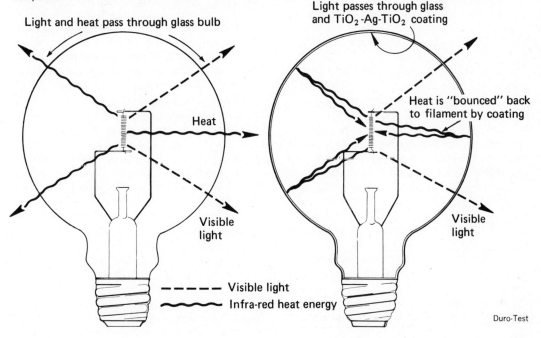

Light and heat pass through glass bulb

Light passes through glass and $TiO_2$-Ag-$TiO_2$ coating

Heat

Heat is "bounced" back to filament by coating

Visible light

Visible light

- - - - - Visible light
~~~~~~~ Infra-red heat energy

Duro-Test

the market by early 1979. "While the remarkable coating is a reality," says Mr. Thorington, "we're continuing to experiment with filaments, bulb shapes, and designs."

## WHAT'S IN THE COATING

The new coating combines certain chemical elements in a "sandwich" effect: two strips of titanium oxide with a strip of silver in between. "The expertise of MIT in adapting the coating to the inner surface of a spherical light bulb will be combined with Duro-Test expertise in the development of a filament and glass with characteristics conducive to effective lamp operation," says G. Raymond McGruther, president of Duro-Test.

MIT holds the coating's patent, which Duro-Test will manufacture. The firm will patent and market the bulb. It will probably cost more than conventional bulbs, but according to expectations, "the savings in electricity would more than pay for the bulb . . . and contribute substantially to savings in the nation's energy consumption through lighting." Such bulbs would have a life of at least 2,500 hours compared with the 750 to 1,000 user-hours of conventional bulbs.

## AND A "SUPER" BULB

In another development, scientists are exploring uses of synchrotron radiation, whose light source has been described as a "super light bulb."

A valuable research tool, synchrotron radiation's high-energy light can be used to probe the molecular structure of solids, gases, and various biological materials.

Like the new coating, the properties of synchrotron radiation were discovered almost by accident. It was found, for example, that when electrons travel at high speeds in a circular path, they "shed" an enormous amount of energy called synchrotron radiation. This radiation is in the form of light, the most intense kind, spanning a continuous range of wavelengths.

Channeled correctly, such light permits experiments that are impossible to perform with ordinary light sources. It can disclose much information about various materials and their properties, particularly the behav-

ior of electrons within them. According to Dr. Sally Johnson, a physicist at the Stanford Linear Accelerator Laboratory, where work with synchrotron radiation is conducted, "A very intense source with a continuous spectrum of light will enable us to probe matter and interactions of various kinds. Specific projects include everything from biology, physics, chemistry—including catalysts and the biological properties of material." A key application of synchrotron radiation, for example, would be in examining how the sun's infrared rays can be converted directly into electrical energy.

## NOT FOR CONSUMER USE

The properties of synchrotron radiation will not, like the new light bulb, have any real direct application for the consumer. Such light intensity only can be achieved through the technology of particle acceleration, which requires a huge facility similar to the Stanford Linear Accelerator. But Stanford's accelerator was not designed for propelling electrons in a circular motion. For this reason and to keep the United States in the forefront of this fast-developing field, a National Synchrotron Light Source is to be built at the Brookhaven National Laboratory on Long Island, New York. After completion in the early 1980s, it will be the first facility devoted exclusively to synchrotron radiation. The Brookhaven lab will be outfitted with a ring 50 meters (150 feet) in diameter where electrons will be accelerated to 2,500 million electron volts—energy that translates into a source of intense X rays. Apertures, or openings, around the ring will allow the radiation to escape into experimental devices.

Among the facility's objectives will be probing molecules of biological importance with X rays and determining the role of metal atoms scattered through their structure. The role of molybdenum in the action of enzymes that make possible photosynthesis in plants will, for example, be studied using the "super bulb" □

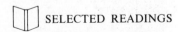 SELECTED READINGS

"Uses of synchrotron radiation" by E. M. Rowe and J. H. Weaver. *Scientific American,* June 1977.

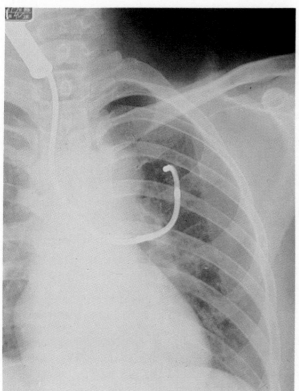

Olympus Optical Company

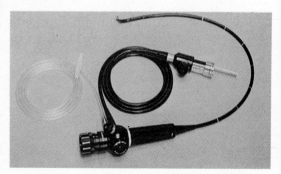

Olympus Optical Company

The bronchoscope, shown above, is an endo-scope used to see into the bronchial tubes. At left, an X-ray photograph shows almost the whole length of the bronchoscope as it probes the lungs.

# ENDOSCOPY

## by David N. Leff

THE 1960s *Fantastic Voyage* science-fiction film is coming true in the 1970s. In the movie, a team of doctors, shrunk to germ size, travels by microcapsule through a patient's bloodstream to dislodge a blood clot in the brain. Today, a new generation of miniaturized fiberoptic tubes permits direct visualization of brain, bronchial, and bile-duct abnormalities never seen before in living patients. What's more the ultrathin tubes carry tools for therapy as well as diagnosis. The tubes are called endoscopes. They are usually named according to the part of the body they are designed to examine—duo-denoscopes, for example, are used to study the duodenum, or first part of the small intestine; and bronchoscopes are used to study the bronchial tubes.

Though still experimental, the removal of gallstones by inserting a specially designed endoscope through the mouth and into the bile duct is probably the best known use of endoscopy for treatment. Going beyond this controversial procedure, a team of Japanese gastroenterologists in Kyoto can now gaze straight up the common bile duct and pancreatic duct via a fiberoptic "babyscope" pushed through a sphincter from a "mother," or master scope, in the duodenum.

Shifting the focus from the digestive tract, a Japanese neurosurgeon now looks squarely into a part of the brain through his specially designed ventriculofiberscope and does surgery there. And newly miniaturized devices promise early cancer screening in the bronchial tubes.

Modern fiberoptic endoscopy began in the United States in the late 1960s, but since then much of the advanced research and development has taken place in Japan.

Endoscopy pioneers Masatsugu Nakajima, Shigeto Ikeda, and Keiichi Kawai. Drs. Nakajima and Kawai developed the babyscope. Dr. Ikeda developed instruments to explore the lungs.

## LOOKING AT THE UNSEEN

In the X-ray room of a branch hospital of the Kyoto Prefectural University of Medicine, gastroenterologist Masatsugu Nakajima gently pushes a duodenoscope down his patient's throat. So far, standard. Then, under intermittent fluoroscopic guidance, a 2.3-millimeter (0.09-inch) diameter babyscope emerges from the larger tube's flexible, remote-controlled tip. This slender fiberoptic bundle penetrates farther into the body to shed light on a possible abnormality in the common bile duct or duct system of the pancreas.

Dr. Nakajima, designer of the direct-vision babyscope, fingers a special manual plunger, or thruster, to advance the extruding subscope without damaging its strand of some 2,000 image-conducting fibers. Dr. Nakajima twists the flexible subscope right, left, up, and down by rotating the tube while advancing and withdrawing it under fluoroscopic and duodenoscopic control—and sometimes by turning the patient. Moments earlier a special dye had been injected through the duodenoscope into the bile and pancreatic ducts. Now a colleague peers through an eyepiece to view the color and texture of the ducts and search for any abnormalities.

This procedure was introduced from Japan to the United States in 1970, but only a very few U.S. and European endoscopists have the prototype babyscope sets.

Dr. Nakajima developed his babyscope jointly with Professor Keiichi Kawai, also of Kyoto. Both say that their device is still experimental. If and when fitted with a controllable tip and an extra channel for removing bits of tissue, the babyscope should prove to be "one of the most reliable diagnostic tools" and "a new concept" in viewing the digestive tract.

Some leading U.S. specialists voice some skepticism, however, questioning the scope's cost and wondering how the fine frail fibers will hold up in actual practice.

## SNARING STONES WITHOUT SURGERY

Slitting a tight sphincter to release or retrieve impacted stones in the bile duct is a recent extension of duodenoscopy and the partial fulfillment of almost any doctor's dream: removing gallstones without surgery. Professor Kawai recalls that he conceived the method and the endoscopic scalpel for this approach in 1970 while a visiting professor in Germany. German practitioners enthusiastically espoused the technique and today many more sphincterotomies are performed in Europe than in Japan.

Of some 2,000 procedures performed by the Kyoto group since 1971, about 600 revealed the shadowy round defect marking residual stone after conventional surgery for gall stone removal. These, says Dr. Nakajima, were almost all referred for conventional surgery. Only those patients rejected as poor operative risks underwent endoscopic sphincterotomy—52 since 1973. Morbidity in this conservatively selected series has run around five per cent, mostly from transient bleeding.

At a small informal symposium in Hungary this year, which Dr. Kawai attended, European clinicians debated the relative merits of surgical versus endoscopic removal of residual stones. "I think the discussion was nonsense," the Kyoto gastroenterologist comments. "A surgical procedure always involves laparotomy, but the endoscopic approach is bloodless, noninvasive—*if the indications are correct.*" The emphasis is Dr. Kawai's. He preaches and practices rigid patient-selection criteria in electing sphincterotomy. He, for example, advises the removal of a residual stone left after cholecystectomy, or conventional stone removal surgery, and only for an impacted stone, with the patient a poor operative risk. He also insists on a long enough interval after the sphincter is slit to allow the stone to dislodge and pass before attempting further intervention.

So far Dr. Kawai has not seen a single recurrence of stone in any of the Kyoto group's series of patients since 1973, and has found no marked irregularity of biliary or duodenal function after the procedure.

Gallstone removal via endoscopic sphincterotomy has been hailed as "remarkably simple and safe in man" by gastroenterologist Peter B. Cotton of London's Middlesex Hospital. In the United States the American Society for Gastrointestinal Endoscopy ran a two-day course devoted to sphincterotomy for stone.

Does this mean that the technique is the coming answer to the ancient injunction, "Thou shalt not cut for the stone"? Dr. Jack A. Vennes of the University of Minnesota, the first U.S. clinician to acquire the babyscope, says, "Taking a look at the future, I think endoscopic sphincterotomy will probably become a standard approach to relieve common bile duct obstruction in patients at operative risk, and in the longer run for the majority of patients with small-to-medium-size stones. The patient with a single large calculus will not be a candidate. I expect the technique will become more precisely learnable and teachable—and safer.

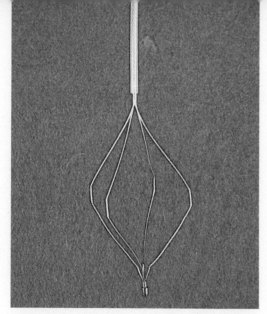

Olympus Optical Company

The basket snare, shown above, is a device to grasp, or snare, a gallstone and remove it from the body.

"It's a technique with very little room for error," warns Dr. Vennes. "One is working in a small anatomic area . . . It's fraught with danger." He and his associates in Minneapolis have used the techniques on only 20 people, while working to improve the instrumentation "with an eye toward safety."

The other eye is fixed on the U.S. Food and Drug Administration, which has not accorded investigational-device status to any of the devices used for stone removal. The result: most of the growing band of U.S. endoscopists taking up the procedure must hand-carry their minihardware from Germany or make their own.

## USE FOR OTHER GI DIAGNOSES

Gastroenterologist Tadayoshi Takemoto of the Tokyo Women's Medical College is more directly involved in early detection of malignancy in the esophagus and other parts of the gastrointestinal lining. He and his associates are using standard endoscopes, not new miniaturized ones, in new ways to differentiate cancerous from precancerous tissues.

By spraying a special dye, methylene blue, from the endoscope irrigation channel onto the stomach wall, Dr. Takemoto is able to distinguish true gastric cancer from transitional structures between normal and tumor.

A still earlier precursor of cancer involving unusual growth of the mucous lining of the stomach can also be distinguished by the telltale vital staining procedure.

Such malabsorption disorders as sprue and celiac disease are also now being studied through the use of endoscopes and special dyes.

### CLIMBING THE BRONCHIAL TREE

The gastrointestinal tract is not the only part of the body being explored with endoscopes. Dr. Shigeto Ikeda of the National Cancer Center Hospital in Tokyo is working to perfect fiberoptic instrumentation for reconnoitering the bronchial tree. Among his latest innovations: a 6-millimeter (0.25-inch) flexible catheter that has a maneuverable tip for selective or diffuse perfusion of the bronchial passages with opaque dye.

Outlining the bronchial passages enables Dr. Ikeda to locate the one closest to a lesion he intends to biopsy. Next, using a newly designed two-channel flexible bronchofiberscope, he inspects, irrigates, and photographs the target tumor. Then he nips off a biopsy specimen with a novel "window" forceps, 2.4 millimeter (0.1 inch) in diameter.

Dr. Ikeda hopes to be able to develop devices that will pass through the scope and allow him to burn off small tumors that his techniques enable him to spot early.

### EYEING THE BRAIN

In their trips through the human body with fiberscope and camera, Japanese endoscopists have explored many minute, remote recesses, including the knee joint and heart chambers. So far, these remain areas of research out of bounds for routine clinical use.

One neurosurgeon, however, has entered the brain's ventricles via endoscope, as well as the spinal canal. He is Dr. Takanori Fukushima of the University of Tokyo.

An operative cerebral ventriculofiberscope, 4 millimeters (0.15 inch) in diameter, with a tip that can turn up and down to peer inside the third ventricle of the brain, was made to his specifications. He has used this on 61 patients. With the patient under general anesthesia, Dr. Fukushima inserts his seeing-eye tube through a small frontal burr hole. Of his brain tumor patients, he was able to obtain biopsies from 21.

Left: Bronchofiberscope, together with staining technique, reveals condition of lungs. Right: Duodenoscopic view of bile duct.

Olympus Optical Company

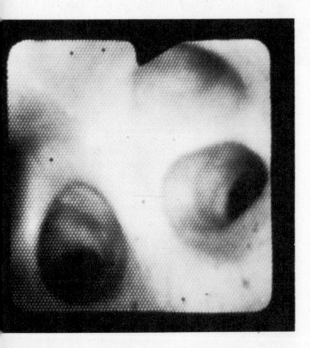
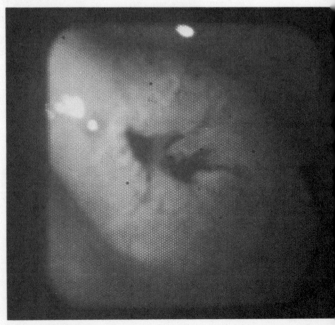

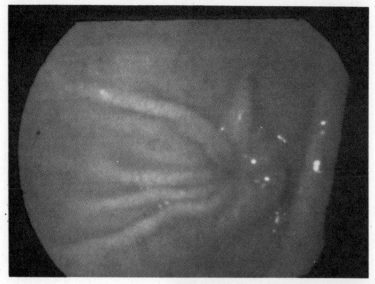

Olympus Optical Company

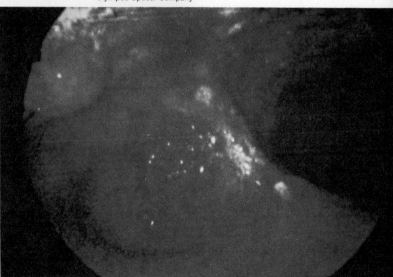

Two endoscopic views of stomachs. A normal stomach is shown above. At right, endoscope shows an ulcer and a polyp in wall of stomach.

Besides direct visual diagnosis and biopsy, his ventriculofiberscope has also permitted some endosurgical operations.

Dr. Fukushima's latest instrument gives him a better-than-ever look into the spinal canal. Instead of a bundle of fine glass fibers, he uses a rod made of a new kind of optical glass, developed in Japan, that acts as a light-wave carrier. After trials on ten fresh cadavers, Dr. Fukushima used his new device on six patients and reports obtaining clear, clinically useful photographs. This newest and slimmest fiberoptic tube is almost one millimeter thinner than the duodenal babyscope.

## STILL LARGELY RESEARCH TOOL

Although Japan has led the world in developing highly advanced tools and techniques of fiberoptic endoscopy, in Japan itself the devices are largely limited to teaching hospitals and research centers. Dr. Takemoto knows why: "Endoscopic examination may give fruitful results but it doesn't pay. The doctor's only reward is a high level of diagnosis and therapy" □

### SELECTED READINGS

"Techniques tomorrow" by B. Sherman. *Modern Photography*, March 1972.

Electronic Switching Systems have revolutionized telephone service. Using solid-state memory and control sections, the systems are reliable, rapid, compact, and cost efficient.

Bell Labs

# A NEW TELEPHONE SYSTEM

## by Joseph Zmuda

"CALL me from that phone over there," said Gerald Kruse, equipment supervisor at a large San Francisco, California, telephone exchange. I did, and his phone began to ring even as I pulsed out the last digit on the pushbutton phone I was using.

"That's electronic switching at work," Kruse started to explain; but before he could finish, I heard a short beep tone on the line. "This is a call coming in for you," he said.

I pushed down my switch hook, then released it. Kruse was on hold, and I heard another voice: "We're ready for the next demonstration," it told me.

I pressed the switch hook again to put that call on hold and bring back Kruse. Then we all hung up to try a new trick: three-way calling. I phoned Kruse and put him on hold by pressing the switch hook. I heard a pulse interruption, then a new dial tone. Pulsing a second number brought back my other caller, a maintenance man elsewhere in the Pacific Telephone building. After I touched the switch hook again, Kruse was on the line with us.

"You can go on doing this almost indefinitely," he explained, "as long as each new line you bring into the circuit is equipped with the three-way calling feature."

Our conference call over, I hung up and punched out a special code. Then Kruse and I went to another part of the building, knowing that any calls we got would follow us there.

### NOT FUTURISTIC—THEY'RE HERE

There was nothing futuristic about the telephone services I had just been using. They—and other features like Speed Calling and International Direct Distance Dialing—are already available to millions of U.S. telephone subscribers as part of improved switching systems. After 1978, even mobile telephone users should have some of these custom calling services.

All these improvements are taking place behind the scenes as part of a new revolution in telephone central-office design called the Electronic Switching System, or ESS for short.

Few of us realize that the telephone sitting on our desk or hanging on the wall is merely the first link to a vast, invisible, switching network that provides communication to all parts of the world. While the telephone instruments in our homes change little over the years, modern technology is making big changes in the rest of the network. For example, the invention of the transistor at Bell Laboratories in 1948 has led down a long road of research and development to ESS.

## ESS

ESS takes the place of conventional switching systems that rely primarily on electromechanical call processing. In ESS call switching is still performed by mechanical (though ultramodern) relays, but its control and memory sections use solid-state components—122,700 transistors in the metropolitan-type No. 1 ESS that I was visiting. All these transistors are mounted, together with other circuit components, on plug-in modules that are easily replaced in event of failure.

Along with the reliability and the rapid action of near-total automation, ESS also saves money through more efficient maintenance procedures. It's more compact, too: this particular ESS machine, which is capable of handling up to 110,000 calls per hour, occupies just half of one floor of the building. The neat and aesthetically pleasing banks of modern equipment give the office room the feel of a data processing center.

## TOUCH-TONE AND BEYOND

There is one revealing sign in our homes and businesses of the change in telephone technology, the pushbutton Touch-Tone phone. While all switching systems can be adapted to Touch-Tone calling, ESS features it as part of its program design. But even in the way it handles Touch-Tone calls, ESS is different, because it responds instantly to Touch-Tones and dial pulses. That's how my call to Kruse got through so quickly—

Bell Labs

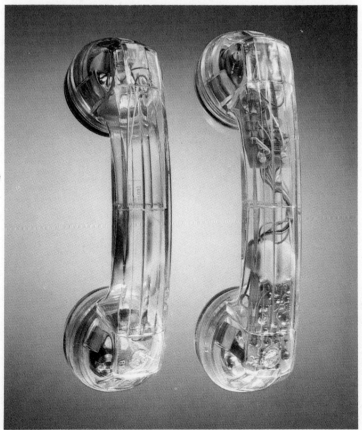

Even handsets are being improved. Extra circuitry in the right-hand set allows for extra amplification of calls for customers living far from switching offices and reduces the expense of providing rural service.

operating more than 2,000,000 separate operations in the time it takes to complete a call.

## A SWITCHBOARD YOU TALK WITH

ESS has still another virtue: easy programmability. Conventional exchanges must be rewired in order to change your phone number or the type of service you require. With ESS the phone company can alter the programming of any line through teletypewriters located in the central office and plant service center. This means quicker service changes, since phone company clerks can now program ESS directly, rather than having to wait for maintenance personnel to make needed wiring changes.

It also gives the customer some instant programming capability, using the pushbutton (or dial) phone instead of a teletype. If you phone in an activation code and a phone number, your calls are automatically transferred to that number till you dial the deactivation code.

With this Call Forwarding feature, you don't have to risk missing important calls, whether you are going next door or even out of town. When calls are forwarded, the calling party is billed the normal rate to your phone while you pick up the additional message units—or toll charges—to the forwarded location.

## SPEED CALLING, TOO

Speed Calling, another ESS service, allows an individual to reduce the number of digits needed to dial frequently called numbers. Depending on which service you order, you can store up to eight or up to 30 commonly called numbers in the ESS memory system, and then dial them (even long distance numbers) by entering only three or four digits instead of the usual seven or ten. Aside from its speed, this service cuts down on misdialing.

## INSIDE ESS

But the advantage of ESS may be less in the extra services it can provide than in the efficient way that it performs them. Mechanical switching machines delegate pieces of common equipment to customers for the duration of each call. But ESS cuts down equipment needed by constantly scanning every line it handles and switching only when it senses it can perform a useful function. The semiconductor logic circuitry of ESS's Central Control interrogates each line five times a second, sensing when a customer has picked up his phone, needs a dial tone, or has begun to dial. Then it moves on to see what everyone else's phone is doing before coming back to the first customer—200 milliseconds later.

Information about calls in progress and about the condition of equipment is continuously updated in a temporary memory called the Call Store. Central Control even checks itself; and data about troubles there or elsewhere in the ESS system is immediately printed out on the same teletype that

Bell Labs

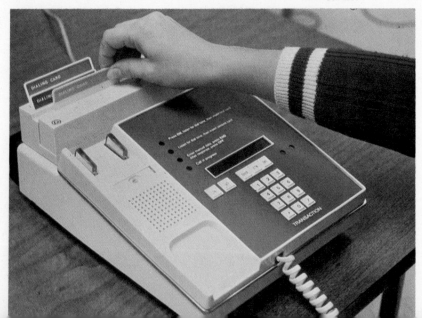

Efficient credit authorizations, check verifications, and other fund transfer operations are possible with the new Transaction II telephone, controlled by a microprocessor.

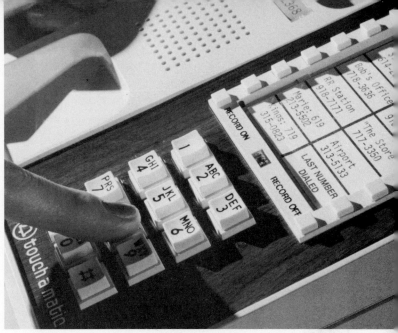

With a speedy automatic dialing telephone, people may dial frequently called numbers that are stored in a special memory section by entering only a few digits.

the ESS personnel use in communicating their instructions to the machine. In addition, should a major trouble occur in Central Control, a duplicate is ready to take over until repairs are completed.

How Central Control will operate in any given situation is determined by information stored in a semipermanent memory, the Program Store. Thousands of thin, aluminum memory cards, each containing thousands of magnetic data bits, form a data bank to which Central Control refers 180,000 times per second for instruction on what to do with the calls it senses.

Smart? Actually Central Control is, like all computers, an idiot that can do only one thing at a time. But since it does them at electronic speeds, it processes calls hundreds of times as fast as older switching systems.

## ESS ISN'T EVERYTHING

ESS is not the only new development to improve your phone service. For example, some phone offices are now using microfilm and minicomputers for high-speed directory assistance.

Instead of having operators leaf through stacks of telephone books, directory pages are recorded on microfilm, 1440 pages to a strip, with up to 60 strips—15,000,000 listings—controlled by one minicomputer. To locate a particular listing, the information operator presses a key corresponding to a particular directory and then the first four letters of the last name. The computer locates the page and flashes it onto a TV-type screen. And systems already exist to have computers "print" directories on microfilm to enable quick updating of new subscribers and number changes.

Bell Laboratories is constantly dreaming up new ideas—like Picturephones—that someday may be available to everyone. Solid-state amplifiers are now being built into handsets used by rural customers to boost the volume of telephone conversations that have gone through long, rural lines. The Bell System is already using a new round storage battery, good for 30 years' service, and one whose principles may someday be applied to automotive use.

Finally, a touch of the awesome future is provided in the design of pocket-size cordless telephones: women might wear them around the neck, and men could have one in a billfold format. Also just beginning are interconnections between phones and telephone exchanges involving fiber optics—hair-thin glass fibers carrying light instead of electricity. Impossible to believe? Some still say that about ESS □

## SELECTED READINGS

*Modern Communications Switching Systems* by Marvin Hobbs. TAB Books, 1974.

*The Telephone Book* by H. M. Boettinger. Riverwood Publications, 1976.

*The Video Telephone: Impact of New Era in Telecommunications* by Edward M. Dickson and R. Bowers. Praeger, 1974.

Electric cars, such as the Studebaker runabout (left) built in 1902, were considered outmoded by the 1920's. Renewed interest, due to the energy crisis and pollution problem, has led to the recent development of experimental electric vehicles. Below: the Electrovette, a modified Chevrolet Chevette powered by a 240-volt battery pack in the rear-seat area.

The Bettmann Archive

General Motors Corp.

# ELECTRIC VEHICLES

by Neil Gluckin

SOUPED-UP golf carts? Doodle bugs? Or the cars of the future? Call them what you will, there may be 20,000,000 electric vehicles—EVs for short—on U.S. highways by the year 2000. The more realistic executives of the automotive industry already are anticipating commercial production in large quantities.

EVs will create no pollution, guzzle no gasoline, cost no more than a few pennies per kilometer to operate. Under the hood, ingenious technologies will be at work. Sophisticated batteries, high in energy, low in weight, will provide juice enough to cruise for several hundred kilometers at 85 to 90 kilometers (about 55 miles) per hour before recharging. Recharging will be simple—just plug the EV into a standard outlet. Advanced regenerative braking systems will retrieve electric current as the EV slows down and recycle it into the propulsion system, extending battery life. Flywheels made of lightweight materials and spinning at high speed in a vacuum will store energy in the form of momentum until the EV needs a boost—climbing a hill, for instance, or passing another car.

IN PLANNING

So-called hybrid vehicles will carry both electric motors and internal-combustion engines. The electric motors will be used for stop-and-go driving in cities, where hydrocarbon emissions associated with internal-combustion engines are a serious problem, while the internal-combustion engine will be used for open-road travel. EVs will be safe, their proponents say, and will compete with gas-powered automobiles for the consumer's dollar. The expensive peak-and-valley pattern of demand for electricity will be evened out by all those EVs charging their batteries during the night.

Who could resist such a Utopian vision? Certainly not the U.S. Congress, which overrode a President Ford veto to enact the "Electric and Hybrid Vehicle Research, Development and Demonstration Act of 1976." The Act made available a hefty $160,000,000 to spark EV technology and demonstrate its commercial feasibility—quickly. The clock is already running: the U.S. Energy Resources Development Administration (ERDA) has been assessing the current state-of-the-art with respect to hybrids and electrics and

plans to put 2,500 EVs on the road by December 1978, to be followed by another 5,000 by October, 1984.

ERDA already has issued contracts for developing battery systems and for the building of "proof-of-concept" vehicles using such innovations as flywheels, regenerative braking systems, transistorized power-control systems, and matchbook-size microcomputers, which manage energy flow from batteries to motor. ERDA has also issued contracts for the building of EVs "from the ground up," and is looking for small businesses to bolster the effort.

NOT NEW

In 1899, a Belgian electric racing car (carrying so many batteries it weighed two tons) set a world land speed record of 105 kilometers (65.79 miles) per hour. In turn-of-the-century Chicago, electric cars outnum-

The Bettmann Archive

Thomas Edison and E.R. Erskine sit in a 1910 electric car designed and developed by Erskine.

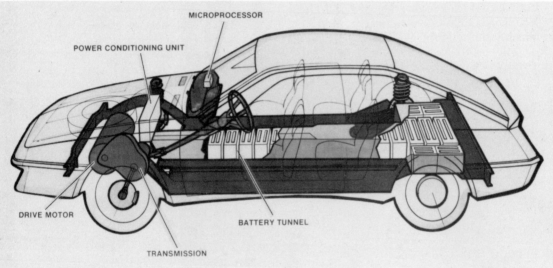

MICROPROCESSOR

POWER CONDITIONING UNIT

DRIVE MOTOR

TRANSMISSION

BATTERY TUNNEL

G.E./Chrysler Corp.

Top: Design for a four-passenger electric car being developed by G.E. and Chrysler Corporation for the U.S. Dept. of Energy. Chrysler is designing the car; G.E., the motor and controls. Below: Key chassis features include 18 lead-acid batteries.

bered gas buggies by more than two to one. Thanks to the lightweight internal-combustion engine and the abundance of gasoline, most EVs were in mothballs by the 1920s.

The pollution problem of the 1960s and the energy crisis of the 1970s made the EV look good again. Today more than 500,000 special purpose electric vehicles are in use in the United States, ranging from golf carts and forklifts to postal delivery vans and airport buses. At least four companies manufacture first-generation EVs for on-the-road use, and more than 100 others are involved in research or development, or both.

The typical EV of 1977 is operated almost like a conventional automobile, except in place of a gasoline gauge, a meter shows battery-charge levels. The EV is turned off at red lights to avoid wasting energy by idling, and it must be recharged at regular intervals. Comparing operating expenses can be tricky, but according to electrical engineer Ernest H. Wakefield, an EV owner for the past eight years, electricity costs about $0.01 per kilometer versus $0.025 per kilometer for gasoline. When batteries are counted as fuel costs, however, expenses for both begin to look similar.

## PERFORMANCE

The big—and crucial—difference between EVs and conventional cars is performance. Inadequate acceleration and range, difficulty climbing hills, and poor handling are among the most frequent complaints about EVs. To be competitive with gasoline cars, cites a study by the National Academy of Science, a family model EV would need a 320-kilometer (200-mile) range and a cruising speed of nearly 90 kilometers (55 miles) an hour. Today's average EV has a maximum speed of 80 kilometers (50 miles) per hour and a range of only about 50 to 65 kilometers (30 to 40 miles) between rechargings.

So, scientists have their work cut out for them. In its first group of EVs, ERDA wants a car that will remove psychological barriers. It should have a 120-kilometer (75-mile) range, top speed of 90 kilometers (55 miles) per hour, accelerate from 15 to 45 kilometers (approximately 10 to 30 miles) in ten seconds, recharge within six hours, satisfy appropriate safety requirements, and cost no more than $5,000 in 1975 dollars. In a second prototype, to be delivered by 1984, ERDA wants a range of 160 kilometers (100 miles) and, more important, technological breakthroughs.

## SUPER BATTERY NEEDED

That means, above all, better batteries. A 5.5-kilogram (12-pound) vehicle battery stores about the same energy as a half ounce of gasoline. So without a low-cost, high-en-

The "Copper Electric Town Car" is America's most advanced electric vehicle. It has a range of slightly more than 100 miles at a cruising speed of 40 mph and a top speed in excess of 50 mph.

Right: Interior of the "Copper Electric Town Car." The instrument panel includes a voltmeter showing the strength of the battery, a speedometer, and two ammeters. Below: Underhood view shows the drive motor in the center, an accessory battery pack on the right, and a one-gallon gasoline tank for conserving electric power on the left.

Copper Development Association

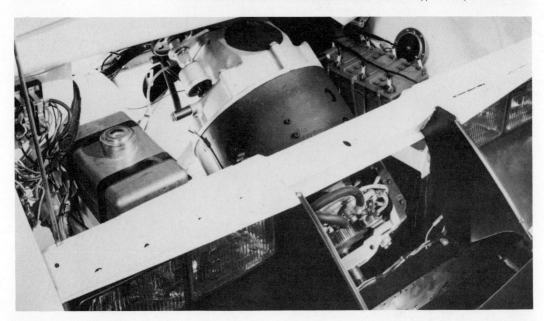

ergy battery, experts say, EVs will never be appealing enough to justify production in significant quantities. Yet for all the millions of dollars spent on research over the years, the "breakthrough" battery remains where it has been for the past decade, "just around the corner."

Somewhere over the rainbow may be more like it for the real pot of gold, a true "superbattery" with high-energy density for long range, and high-power density for quick pick-up and speed. The pinch in these powerhouses comes from exotic elements like sodium, sulfur, and lithium, which possess high-energy electrochemical properties. Energy cells using some of these elements have been built and demonstrated, but few have been scaled up to battery size.

Beyond that, superbatteries remain impractical for on-the-road use because of the high temperatures at which they must operate, generally over 300° Celsius (575° Fahrenheit). This heat exposes sealing and container materials to severe corrosion problems, which explains why much current research is aimed at finding materials that can stand up under superdemanding operation conditions.

## TEMPORARY SOLUTION

Widely seen as an intermediate-term solution to the battery problem is the Nickel-Zinc system, which ERDA hopes to use in at least some of its first 2,500 EVs. Far from a breakthrough, and well below the 100-180 watt hours per kilogram capacity of the superbatteries, Nickel-Zinc nevertheless seems able to satisfy ERDA's short-range requirement of 36 watt-hours per kilogram and 800-1,000 charging cycles. These batteries are expected to be available within one to five years.

The only system ready for commercial use in EVs today is lead-acid, the basic golf-cart battery. The problem with lead-acid is its low energy density, which means very limited range. For reasonable performance in stop-and-go urban driving, according to one study, lead-acid batteries must be equal to half the total weight of the vehicle, and that translates into less space for passengers and cargo. Improved lead-acid batteries should arrive any day now, however, and they might require only 30 per cent of vehicle weight to provide a cruising speed of 83 kilometers (52 miles) per hour and a top speed of 93 kilometers (58 miles) per hour for 800 cycles.

## A GOOD BET

Facts and figures make the $160,000,000 electric vehicle race look like a good bet. U.S. Representative Mike McCormack, a former atomic energy scientist and one of the authors of the Electric Vehicle Act of 1976, points out that 90 per cent of all distance provided by private vehicles in the United States is generated in short commuting trips, with each of those vehicles using about 8 liters (2 gallons) of gasoline a day. Many of those short-haul trips are made by second and third family cars, a market that will grow to 32,000,000 cars by 1980.

"Judging by the statistics available on use patterns," says Fred J. Port, chairman of the Electric Vehicle Council, "it seems a rea-

The prototype of a gasoline-electric car. It is powered by a 12 cu. in. gasoline engine coupled with a series DC electric motor. The car runs in either the electric or the hybrid mode.

General Motors Corp.

Dr. Craig Marks (left) and Dr. Charles E. Winters examine the heart of a hydrogen-oxygen fuel-cell power system for a van. In front of them are liquid hydrogen and oxygen tanks. Beneath the bench seat is a reservoir of potassium hydroxide. The system has a range of 100-150 miles.

sonable guess that electric cars could do the job done by one-half the vehicles in this market." Rep. McCormack estimates that 10,000,000 EVs on the road in 1990 would represent a savings of 80,000,000 liters (20,-000,000 gallons) of gasoline (500,000 barrels of oil) per day, or $2,700,000,000 a year, figuring imported oil at $15 per barrel.

The superbattery needed for electric vehicles is still the central problem, though. The problem centers around a simple engineering fact: Batteries are storage devices; engines are power devices.

## A SLEEPER

After an International Electric Vehicle Exposition and Conference in Chicago in early 1977, one EV enthusiast declared, "We're in the big leagues now," and another foresaw the end of an "image as an eccen-

tric's gadget." The affair—dubbed EXPO I—included some 75 exhibitors and a parade in and around Chicago's Loop.

Not everyone believes that technology can be made to follow a timetable, of course, but few doubt that the benefit would be enormous. Rep. McCormack's appraisal has an appealing hint of the crossed fingers with which a lot of scientific work is done:

"Of all the proposed technologies dealing with alternate energy sources or methods of conserving energy," he said in a recent speech, "the electric car program is the biggest 'sleeper' " □

 SELECTED READINGS

"Cars of the future." *Forbes,* October 15, 1976.
"Electrics get federal recharge" by T. Orme. *Motor Trend,* June 1977.

Jen and Des Bartlett, Photo Researchers

Snow geese and Canada geese in Sacramento North Wildlife Refuge in California. Wildlife refuges are playing an increasingly important role in safeguarding the populations of many species of birds and other animals.

# WILDLIFE

## contents

# WILDLIFE
## review of the year

Inevitably as people continue to develop the land to adapt it for their use, there is less suitable space for wildlife. How well wildlife actually fares in any given year is discernable only in later years as part of a general trend. Even seemingly monumental issues like large oil tanker spills that kill seabirds pale beside the effects that steady loss of habitat has on wildlife's future well-being. In 1977 more than 2,000 hectares (5,000 acres) of rural land in the United States were lost each day to development, but there were also some bright spots in wildlife preservation efforts.

**Habitat.** The old saying "Habitat is wildlife," is more true now than ever before. Without adequate food, water, and shelter, not a single species of wildlife can survive in the wild. Because it is impossible to preserve all land now undeveloped, a new concept of "critical habitat" is receiving increased attention. According to this concept, a realistic setting aside of habitat that is absolutely necessary for a creature's survival in the wild is preferable to broader, less intensive efforts to safeguard the species' entire range. For example, it will probably do the grizzly bear more good to have its den areas well isolated from human activities than for its entire range to receive mediocre protection.

Joseph Van Warner, Audubon/PR

Some birds, including the ospreys shown above, need dead trees for nesting and feeding.

New attention has focused on the need for preserving a specific kind of wildlife habitat: dead trees, which are needed for nesting or feeding by 85 species of U.S. birds. As demand for timber grows, fewer dead and dying trees are left standing on public or private land. The U.S. Forest Service has begun a program to leave sufficient trees on land it administers to provide for the scores of birds that eat harmful insects and need dead trees for continued survival.

Some wildlife—even endangered wildlife—have, however, been able to adapt to people-caused habitat changes with some surprising success. The once-rare white-tailed kite whose favored habitat of California grasslands and marshes has been degraded has learned to harvest the bountiful mice and insects in median strips and road edges along the California freeways. These medians and road edges also provide relatively secure nesting areas for the kite.

Richard Ellis, Photo Researchers

Painting of a bowhead whale and two belugas. Bowhead populations are seriously reduced.

**Wetlands.** Wetlands are critical life support systems to hundreds of wildlife species. Many are tidal-marsh ecosystems, rich in plant nutrients and among the most productive lands on earth, producing four times as much plant life per hectare as cropland. In 1977 President Carter took two steps to help safeguard them: (1) he directed all executive agencies to refrain from supporting construction in wetlands when there is a practical alternative, and (2) he added more than $10,000,000 to the Department of Interior's budget for the acquisition of breeding and wintering habitat for migratory waterfowl and promised much more in coming years.

**More money helps.** Budget requests for the U.S. Fish and Wildlife Service have been increased. The higher budgets will pay for six new refuges and for increased research and will allow the service to put its personnel and technological resources to work effectively to repair, maintain, and safeguard the nearly 13,000,000 hectares (33,000,000 acres) in the 384 refuges of the system.

**Weather.** Although weather grabs the headlines when a harsh winter storm kills many deer and songbirds, even severe winters back-to-back like those of 1976-77 and 1977-78 do little more than temporarily reduce wildlife numbers. It is the carrying capacity of the land—food, water, and vegetative cover—that determines how many individuals of which species can survive over a long period of time. Several harsh winters seldom affect the land's carrying capacity, and wildlife's intricate biological response to adversity usually produces enough young to send populations back to normal after what seem like massive die-offs.

**Endangered Species.** There is little doubt that more creatures will be added to the Endangered Species list—both the international and the U.S. lists. The length of the list has become less important than what significance is attached to the listing of a species. The U.S. Endangered Species Act, for example, forbids the use of federal money for projects that would destroy species listed as endangered or destroy the habitat necessary for them to survive. This has led to controversy between some federal agencies and conservationists. Conservationists, however, claim that in the vast majority of cases it is not an "either-or"—federal project or wildlife—choice, but that with proper planning most projects can proceed without grave risk to endangered species. For example, a proposal to build a dam in Tennessee in waters that are home to endangered snail darter fish can, conservationists argue, simply be delayed until efforts to transplant the fish to nearby streams prove successful.

**Whales.** In 1977 the United States completely banned commercial whaling within 320 kilometers (200 miles) of its coast and firmly supported a 10-year moratorium on commercial whaling. However, despite some controversy, the United States supported the International Whaling Commission when it decided only to limit native Eskimos from taking more than 12 bowhead whales for subsistence needs but did not completely forbid the taking of bowheads, the whale species with perhaps the lowest population.

**Non-game wildlife.** Traditionally game wildlife—those that can be hunted or on whom there are regulations and seasons for taking—have received the bulk of attention from wildlife agencies. Only now are non-game animals beginning to receive the attention they deserve with regard to habitat acquisition and maintenance, research into their life cycles, and reintroduction of species to areas where suitable habitats are again available.

**Two Success Stories.** The whooping crane, symbol of U.S. endangered wildlife, is on the road to a more secure existence. Latest figures show that 29 young birds hatched to make a total of 126 in the wild and in captivity. Even more significant, 16 whooper eggs were placed with their greater sandhill crane cousins, and 12 survived. This foster parent approach seeks to establish two separate breeding populations of whoopers so that a disaster could not wipe out the entire wild population.
■ The peregrine falcon also had a good year. Of 71 young peregrines hatched in captivity and released to the wild, 54 appear to have survived.

Robert Strohm

Allan D. Cruickshank, Audubon/PR

The whooping crane (above) and the peregrine falcon (below) are two success stories for conservationists. Both birds, protected in the wild and bred in captivity, are on the road to a more secure existence.

Eric Hosking, Audubon/PR

Tom McHugh, Photo Researchers

Red wolves, though protected by U.S. law, are seriously endangered. Photo above shows a red wolf pair; the female is on the left.

# THE WOLF THAT LOST ITS GENES

by James H. Shaw and
Peter A. Jordan

REMNANT populations of one of North America's most critically endangered mammals live within an hour's drive of Houston, Texas. Most travelers passing through the prairies and marshes along the upper Texas Gulf coast would probably not suspect that a large carnivore, averaging some 25 kilograms (55 pounds), still inhabits this farm and ranch country that has been settled for more than a century. Although the howl of the red wolf can still be heard from Galveston Bay to the southwest corner of Louisiana, perhaps fewer than one hundred animals, the last of their kind, still survive in the wild.

The red wolf (*Canis rufus*) once occurred throughout the southeastern United States from southern Florida to central Texas and possibly as far north as the Carolinas and Kentucky. Along with other large carnivores, red wolves were persecuted by

generations of farmers and ranchers who feared for their livestock. Government agencies also trapped and poisoned the animals. These efforts, together with habitat alterations as the land was logged, grazed, and farmed, resulted in the animal's disappearance from most of its geographic range.

Just short of annihilation, the red wolf was officially recognized as an endangered species in 1965, and lethal control measures by federal agents were halted. Today, when a rancher claims that wolves are killing his stock, a federal trapper is dispatched to capture the suspect. Should the animal turn out to be a red wolf, it is relegated to a captive breeding program.

## PROTECTED—BUT STILL IN DANGER

Most endangered species can survive given adequate legal protection and sufficiently large reserves of critical habitat. The red wolf is now protected by federal and state laws and there seems to be enough suitable habitat to sustain several populations. But a more subtle form of extinction threatens the species—genetic dilution through hybridization with another, far more numerous and adaptable species, the coyote (*Canis latrans*).

Although the natural occurrence of interspecies hybridization is rare among free-living mammals, human disturbance of animal populations and their habitats increases the chances of this happening. The result can be an alteration of the genetic characteristics of one or both species.

As red wolf numbers declined, the coyote, a species more resistant to trapping and poisoning and better suited to disturbed habitats, began extending its range eastward, bringing the two into increasingly greater contact. Most members of the genus *Canis* are interfertile, there being no physiological barriers against hybridization. Furthermore, the hybrid offspring may also be fertile, either breeding among themselves or backcrossing with either parent species.

Under normal conditions, different species of wild canids do not interbreed and thus maintain genetic distinctiveness because they are separated by geography, by territorial instincts, or by differences in courtship patterns. Evolutionists predict that hybridization is most likely to occur when a rapidly expanding species comes into contact with a less numerous close relative. Fluctuating populations and altered habitats also enhance the prospects for hybridization. Since all these conditions were present as coyotes invaded areas where red wolves were being drastically reduced, the normal behavioral safeguards against interbreeding failed and hybridization began.

## ITS GENE POOL IS DISAPPEARING

The coyote-hybridization threat, together with very low red wolf numbers, requires that management be approached in terms of saving the red wolf's "gene pool." This term refers to the sum of genetic information carried by all members of a "deme," or interbreeding group. On a larger scale, it is all the genetic information possessed by a se-

Highly adaptable coyotes have spread into the red wolf's traditional territory and through interbreeding with their less numerous and less adaptable relatives are threatening to destroy the red wolf's gene pool.

The gray wolf is closely related to the red wolf. Its geographic range and behavior patterns make it less vulnerable to interbreeding with coyotes and thus less threatened.

ries of related demes that may make up the entire species.

Traditionally, wildlife management has largely been a numbers game, the objective being to either increase, decrease, or maintain population sizes with little or no regard for genetic changes. Management of a gene pool is broader because it considers not only numbers of individuals but also the amount of genetic variability preserved.

When working with remnant populations, wildlife managers must try to save all remaining genetic variability in order to assure the species' adaptability to future environments. The smaller the remnant population's gene pool, the more vulnerable it is to dilution through interspecies hybridization. To preserve a gene pool, the species' genetic limits must be identified.

Defining the red wolf's gene pool is difficult for several reasons. First, individual specimens range in size from that of large coyotes to that of small gray wolves (*Canis lupus*). Second, because so little is known of the red wolf's behavior, it is extremely difficult to distinguish typical red-wolf behavior from the behavior of coyotes or other closely related species. And finally, the extent of the geographic overlap that once existed between the red wolf and the gray wolf in the eastern United States will never be known because both long ago disappeared from that region.

So we will never know whether the red wolves of the south maintained themselves as a clearly distinct entity from the larger gray wolves to the north or whether the two merged into a continuum characteristic of single, widely distributed species. Most taxonomists, those who specialize in classifying organisms, describe the red wolf as a distinct species. Some claim it is merely a small subspecies of gray wolf. Still others suggest that it represents a stable hybrid complex between the coyote and the gray wolf.

Most likely the issue will never be completely resolved because of so much missing evidence, but we believe that the bulk of the evidence supports the separate-species view. Furthermore, for conservation-management purposes the animal should be given the benefit of any lingering doubts and recognized as a distinct species.

## STUDY OF RED WOLF IN THE WILD

When we first became involved with the red wolf in 1970 its endangered status had been clearly established. We began a detailed field study of the animal, concentrating on collecting ecological and behavioral data to aid management efforts and facilitate understanding of gene pool management.

We needed a study area that had a relatively high red-wolf population density and that did not contain coyotes or hybrids. A 1970 red-wolf survey indicated that Chambers County, Texas, along the eastern shore of Galveston Bay, offered the best potential. Ranchers there proved cooperative, freely allowing us to trap, release, and track wolves on their land and sometimes recording useful observations. At the center of this area lies the Anahuac National Wildlife Refuge, which had already become a sort of center for red wolf research. Anahuac had kennels for holding wolves, and refuge manager Russel Clapper and his staff generously provided vital logistic support.

Elusive species can best be studied in the free-living state by the use of radio-location telemetry. The U.S. Fish and Wildlife Service loaned us radio-telemetry equipment and supplied the services of Glynn Riley, a skilled trapper and self-taught biologist experienced in safe and effective live trapping of red wolves.

In the summer of 1971, Riley found unusually small canid tracks in the vicinity of the Anahuac refuge, indicating that at least one coyote or possible hybrid was living among the last red wolves. It was probably the same animal we captured the following November—a 16-kilogram (36-pound) adult female with a narrow, coyotelike head. We held her for five days while we searched the surrounding area for additional small tracks made in her absence. Fortunately, none appeared, so we concluded that she was probably the only abnormally small *Canis* in the study area. She was then fitted with a radio transmitter collar and released at her capture point. We hoped to learn whether or not such an atypical animal would be accepted socially by local red wolves.

The additional nine canids captured in the study area were markedly larger than coyotes and typical of red wolves before the coyote hybridization began. Four adults weighed from 24 to 35 kilograms (52 to 76 pounds); five immatures, from 20 to 23 kilograms (45 to 50 pounds). One young male became the only fatality when hunters found and shot the trapped animal.

## THREAT EXPRESSION

Red wolf facial-threat expressions proved to be unusually interesting. While all North American canids can threaten with a snarl, only the coyote is known to threaten with a wide gape of the mouth. Those animals that, on the basis of size, appearance, and capture location, were judged to be pure red wolves threatened only with a snarl and could not be induced to gape. Wild canids

As red wolf–coyote hybrids, such as this, begin to breed, backcrossing with a member of either parent species or breeding among themselves, the factors separating the red wolf and coyote species will become more and more blurred.

captured outside the study area and judged to be hybrids threatened with a gape. We and other researchers in the field believe the ability to gape is inherited rather than learned, and may well be one of the more valuable criteria for distinguishing trapped red wolves from coyotes and hybrids.

## ENZYME STUDIES

To make genetic comparisons between species, subspecies, or local populations, population geneticists are relying increasingly upon comparisons of the molecular structure of enzymes. These structural differences are simple, are direct reflections of genetic variations, and usually tend to be less altered by environmental changes than are many external characteristics, such as body size or color. Any observed differences in enzyme structure indicate that animals carrying them are members of demes that have been separated for quite some time.

We collected blood samples from our trapped animals and sent them to Robert Storez of Yale University who was studying enzyme relationships within canids. Storez isolated some thirty enzymes from the blood and examined differences in the molecular structure of each enzyme. He then compared our samples with others collected from known coyotes and gray wolves. His results showed that the animals in our study area ranked about midway between gray wolf and coyote populations. Outside the study area, populations suspected by other criteria of being hybrids proved virtually identical to coyote populations. This enzyme comparison could prove useful for monitoring populations that are suspected of undergoing hybridization.

## RED WOLVES THINK SMALL

Our main research effort was devoted to the ecology and behavior of free-living red wolves. Food habits, determined from the contents of scats, showed that these red wolves invariably killed animals smaller than themselves. Leading prey were nutria, a large aquatic rodent introduced from South America, swamp and cottontail rabbits, and cotton rats. Despite the numerous cattle and occasional deer in the study area, we found no remains of these larger animals in red wolf scats throughout the study's fifteen-month duration.

Home ranges averaged about 4,500 hectares (17 square miles) for our radio-equipped red wolves, far smaller than gray wolf home ranges but similar to those of most coyotes. Red wolves proved to be primarily nocturnal, even in winter, an activity pattern more typical of coyotes than of gray wolves.

Within its remaining range, the red wolf forms small, unstable social groups, an arrangement well suited for hunting small prey. Gray wolves, in contrast, usually form packs that permit them to prey upon larger animals. Sightings of up to six or seven red wolves have been reported, but the vast majority of year-round observations are of one or two.

## ADDED DANGER OF PARASITES

Parasites of serious consequence flourish in the warm, damp climate of the Texas Gulf coast. Serious infestations of heartworms, hookworms, tapeworms, and sarcoptic mange have been found in captured red wolves.

Since heartworms are mosquito-borne and hookworms are transmitted through contact with wet soil, we suspected that a positive correlation exists between rainfall and red wolf mortality. Residents of the study area recalled a sharp increase in red wolf numbers from 1961 to 1964, exceptionally dry years, particularly during the spring whelping periods. Although this is only circumstantial evidence, it suggests a causal relationship between rainfall, parasitism, and red wolf mortality. It also supports the view that the Gulf coast region, while providing abundant natural foods for red wolves, is only marginally suitable for them because of the heavy parasite burden.

## BEHAVIOR SIMILAR TO THAT OF COYOTES

Overall we found that the ecology and social behavior of the red wolf within its remaining range were similar to those of the coyote and generally different from those of the gray wolf. These similarities between the

The coyote, like the red wolf, does not form large packs but rather stays alone or hunts in small groups. Similarities in ecology and behavior such as this may help explain why the normal barrier against hybridization failed.

Wildlife Unlimited, Photo Researchers

red wolf and the coyote may explain why the behavioral barriers against hybridization between these species were breached. On the other hand, the gray wolf's tendency to form strong group bonds that maintain distinct territories and repel intruders minimizes opportunities for breeding with outsiders.

## RECOVERY PROGRAM

The U.S. Fish and Wildlife Service has developed a recovery plan for the red wolf. Curtis Carley was assigned as biologist in charge of field operations and Russel Clapper was appointed leader of the Red Wolf Recovery Team. The recovery plan consists of three strategies: maintenance of a captive breeding colony, reintroduction of red wolves into areas where they once occurred, and curbing hybridization within the animal's remaining range.

## CAPTIVE BREEDING

A captive breeding colony has been established at the Point Defiance Zoo in Tacoma, Washington. In 1977 captive red wolves produced four litters totaling fourteen pups. This breeding colony could provide long-term survival insurance if all else fails.

The captive breeding strategy, while a necessary last resort, has several drawbacks. High costs and limited space make it difficult to preserve a large enough gene pool. A long-term captive population may undergo unnatural selection, losing critical genetic information unrelated to survival in captivity, but essential for survival in the wild. Saving a species only in a zoo is something of a tie game with extinction. Only by insuring that the red wolf can persist in the natural, free-living state can the species genuinely be preserved.

## REINTRODUCTION INTO FAVORABLE AREAS

Reestablishing red wolves somewhere within their original geographic range presents a difficult and critical challenge. One problem involves the source of red wolves to be transplanted. Captive-reared individuals may not have the hunting skills and wariness of humans necessary to survive in a new environment. Removing wild red wolves from the Gulf coast might hasten the demise of the last known wild population. Sites for release are also a problem. The hybridization threat will persist if coyotes are in the area, and coyotes have invaded much of the southeastern United States in recent years. Southern Florida and some islands along the Atlantic and Gulf coasts are essentially coyote-free, and there may be other areas yet undiscovered. The first transplant attempt did not

This radio-equipped female red wolf will be tracked by wildlife researchers. They hope to learn more about the animal's habits, relations with coyotes and other animals, and chances for survival in new territories.

U.S. Fish & Wildlife

provide a very encouraging start, however.

Bull Island lies about five kilometers (three miles) off the South Carolina coast, and seemed a reasonably good site for an experimental red wolf release. A pair of radio-collared wild-caught red wolves were released in December 1976. For about a week the pair explored the island; then the female suddenly swam to the mainland and had to be recaptured. Later the male was also recaptured.

## EXISTING WILD POPULATIONS LOSING OUT

The third aspect of the red-wolf recovery plan is the effort to maintain existing wild populations along the Texas and Louisiana coasts. During our 1970/1972 investigations, the wild red wolves seemed to be relatively homogeneous and robust, but even then we accounted for one apparent hybrid within the study area. Our radio tracking, incidentally, showed that this suspected hybrid regularly associated with a large male red wolf. After her death we examined her reproductive tract and found that she had been bred, presumably by her frequent companion. The Fish and Wildlife Service has since sampled wild canid populations more extensively, eastward into southwestern Louisiana. While some large, wolflike animals are being found, the ratio of apparent hybrids to red wolves seems to be increasing rapidly.

Curtis Carley now believes that there is little hope for preserving pure red wolves within the animal's remaining range. Accordingly, the Fish and Wildlife Service is now attempting to capture the last apparently pure red wolves for inclusion in the captive breeding colony. If the tide of the coyote invasion is overwhelming and the remaining red wolves are unable to maintain their genetic integrity, then this is the only course left open. It will, however, invariably hasten the rate at which the remaining wild red wolf population is genetically swamped by the coyote.

Whenever an animal population is drastically reduced, there is danger of irretrievable loss of genetic information. The possibility that some genes will be completely lost from the population by chance alone increases as the population shrinks. As more genes are lost, the population's chances of adapting to future environments diminish and the threat of extinction increases □

 SELECTED READINGS

"Carolina haven for red wolf" by P. Laurie. *Audubon*, January 1977.

*The Ecology and Behaviour of an Endangered Species* by L. David Mech. Doubleday, 1970.

"Courage and art of wolf maintenance" by J. March. *Audubon*, November 1977.

Jane Burton, Bruce Coleman

Octopuses have been given a bad name, but they are really quite tame, intelligent, and even lovable creatures. Here we see a beautifully colored octopus moving gracefully near the ocean bottom.

# EVERYBODY LOVES AN OCTOPUS

## by Betty Pratt-Johnson

EVERYBODY loves an ocotopus . . . except another octopus, maybe—for octopuses like to be alone. "In captivity you can't keep two together in a tank," said Gil Hewlett, Vancouver Public Aquarium Curator. "Octopuses have their own territory. They're always solitary except at mating time."

And that is how four Vancouver divers found two octopuses on the day of the most exciting hunt of their lives, a day when they caught three enormous specimens of *Octopus dofleini*, 27, 31, and 34 kilograms (60, 70, and 75 pounds) of writhing eight-armed powerful but delicate giants which they brought back to the aquarium alive. This north Pacific species is generally considered to be the largest in the world. A mature animal may touch the sides of a circle with a diameter of 10 meters (32 feet). However, the octopus is not a fearsome monster, and has probably the most misunderstood nature in the animal kingdom.

### FOUND ALMOST EVERYWHERE

Octopuses are found in nearly all coastal seas of the world from the tropics to the Arctic and Antarctic. There are at least 150 known species ranging from the giants of the Pacific northwest to the midgets in the South China Sea.

In the Indonesian area, the largest octopuses are only a few centimeters long, and even they are very scarce. There are small species elsewhere too, such as the smooth-skinned *Octopus leioderma*, which shares Pacific northwest waters with the giants. But most octopuses are middle-sized and grow to about a meter (about three or four feet) across.

Octopuses may live at the extremes. Some—even the large *O. dofleini*—are found in intertidal regions. Over the years, yachtsmen have seen many of them sunning themselves on the shallows of Octopus Point

An octopus typically has a large, horny, parrotlike beak with which it bites and cuts up its prey. Poisonous saliva usually first stuns the prey.

in Sansum Narrows off the shores of Vancouver Island.

Other octopuses may live as deep as one and one-half kilometers (one mile), or on the ocean floor. In 1964 Dr. Sharon Proctor and Dr. Vicki Buchsbaum Pearse pulled up a large deep-ocean octopus west of the Seychelles in the Indian Ocean.

"It was thirty centimeters [12 inches] long," said Vicki, "a large specimen for this species (*Amphitretus pelagicus*). We didn't have a closing net, but we estimated the depth of the trawl to be mostly from 400 to 525 meters [1,300 to 1,700 feet]. The octopus' eyes were particularly large. Its body was covered with a gelatinous sheath. It was faintly blue, and quite translucent. The web was extremely large, coming almost to the tips of the arms, thus giving it expanded swimming ability. This animal is probably truly pelagic, never touching bottom."

Bottom-dwelling octopuses such as *Opisthoteuthis depressa*, also living in the Indian Ocean at great depths, have bodies flattened to fit the bottom topography.

## EFFICIENT FOOD GATHERERS

The natural food of these animals is usually shellfish such as crabs, clams, lobsters, or abalones. Occasionally they will catch a fish swimming by. Some species such as Hawaii's "day octopus," *Octopus cyanea*, hunt by daylight, but most octopuses are shy and lie in wait for random prey or hunt nocturnally.

An octopus grabs its food with the circular suckers on one or more of its eight strong arms. In most species there are 240 suckers running the length of each arm in double rows, varying from the size of a pinpoint up to 6 centimeters (about 2½ inches)

in diameter. A 2-centimeter sucker requires a pull of 170 grams to break its hold, which, multiplied by the 2,000 suckers found on most common octopuses—even a small one—equals considerable pulling force. With these powerful suckers the octopus carries the prey to its mouth where its beak bites it, injecting poison from its salivary gland. This saliva stuns or kills the prey. Some octopuses drill holes through clam shells with their radulas, or rasping tongues, in order to reach the flesh, and then use their tongue to scrape out any small remaining particles. An octopus can consume its favorite shellfish, the crab, in thirty minutes.

In some deep-water octopuses (*Cirromorpha*) the radula is almost entirely absent, presumably because they eat mostly soft foods. Some species also feed on bottom debris.

Common octopuses have some exotic eating habits too. They are territorial—to the point of being cannibalistic—and will devour an intruder that dares to crowd their space. They have even been known to start eating themselves just prior to death.

## WANT TO BE LEFT ALONE

Despite the strange facts of life concerning the way octopuses relate to each other, all their reported contacts with people—even in the wild—are either friendly or tinged with fear on the part of the octopus.

Diver Larry Hewitt who wrestles giant Puget Sound octopuses for fun and food, feels the octopus's greatest desire in life is, not surprisingly, to be left alone. "When faced with a fight-or-run situation, they run!" He believes that tall tales of attacks have come about because when an octopus is molested it will latch onto the closest hard object. If you are trying to catch him, that object will be you. The experienced diver will place the octopus against his chest and in most cases it will ride contentedly to the surface in this friendly hug. Then, if you want to be rid of it—just tickle it.

Another diver, who has caught more than 450 kilograms (1,000 pounds) of octopus in a day to sell as bait, asserts that it is impossible to make this Pacific giant bite. In his experience octopuses always refuse to retaliate and restrict the use of their beaks to devouring prey.

## EXPERTS AT HIDING

If a frightened octopus will not attack a diver, it will do various other things—mostly to save itself. Octopuses are protected by the speediest color-changing system in the animal kingdom, exceeding even the well-known quick-change chameleon. A frightened octopus will probably first turn white with fright, then red with rage to alarm its enemy. It may also turn greeny-white or brown or reddish-brown or speckled for camouflage.

The skin of the disturbed octopus may become pebbly and push up over the eyes into points resembling horns, which may account for the nickname of "devilfish." Next, it will probably squirt sepia, or ink, to distract its predator, usually an eel, and numb its sense of smell. Afterward, the octopus will swiftly escape and hide in some den in the rocks.

An octopus always looks for a cave or crevice or some enclosure to contain it, almost as if it were trying to find a protective shell like most other mollusks have.

## CLEVER AND TAME IN CAPTIVITY

Though octopuses prefer solitude in the wilds, in captivity they become tame and affectionate according to the Vancouver Public Aquarium curator, Gil Hewlett. "They like to be stroked. They are quite intelligent and may play jokes too. Once we had an octopus that had a habit of squirting passersby.

"However, their curiosity and intelligence sometimes work against them. Another time we had an octopus that pulled the plug in the night and died after the water drained from its tank.

"Then one morning while making rounds we discovered a more mysterious casualty. We found that half of a 30-centimeter- (1-foot-) long skillfish had been eaten and there was nothing else in the tank with it. The next day we caught the octopus red-handed, climbing into the skillfish tank to eat the rest of its meal. You must keep the tanks tightly sealed with fine screening at the top because a 27-kilogram (60 pound) octopus can creep through a hole about 5 centimeters (2 inches) in diameter. You must weight down the cover of the tank too, or an octopus will cleverly find how to push it up and escape."

Farther down the Pacific coast at Point Defiance Aquarium in Tacoma, Washington, I met Cecil Brosseau, a man who has lived at Point Defiance since he was a boy, and met his first octopus on the beach there when he was ten. Since then octopuses have always been his favorite animal. Before his retirement as its director, he brought this curious

Each of an octopus' eight arms is equipped with a large number of round suckers. The animal uses these suckers to carry prey to its mouth. The photo shows a closeup of some suckers.

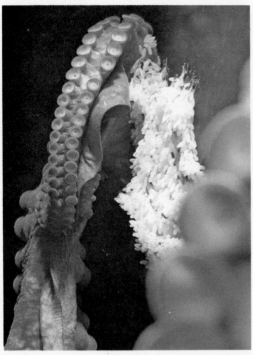

Tom McHugh, Photo Researchers

Octopuses are dedicated mothers. After she mates, the female lays her eggs and weaves them into strands that she protects, cleans, and aerates until hatching time.

creature to the fore in the aquarium. There are octopuses everywhere: in the huge central tank mingling with other animals; in the more conventional eye-level tanks displaying its natural habitat; and in three waist-high open-topped tanks—each occupied by a single animal.

"Octopuses usually live five or six years," he told me. "After mating both male and female die. This has always been the case in the aquarium. Now we're quite sure this also occurs on the outside because if these animals did continue to live for years and years, they would become monstrous. They would all weigh about 1,000 pounds [450 kilograms] or more."

The octopus' growth rate depends partially upon its temperament. If it is a very shy animal and seldom ventures out of its den to eat, it will grow slowly. If food is plentiful and it is aggressive, it could double its weight in a year. This happens often with aquarium animals. Brosseau once had a 32-kilogram (69-pound) octopus that increased to 50 kilograms (109 pounds) within nine months.

Cecil Brosseau's specialty is helping man and octopus overcome their fear of one another. "It takes a good week to get an octopus to lose its fear of you," he said. "But people can overcome their fears immediately. They can be deathly afraid of octopuses and within five minutes you can teach them not to be. It happens every day. You talk them into touching the animal. Then they play with it. Then they don't want to leave. That's why we display octopuses this way [in the open-topped tanks]."

Embryologist and cytologist Dr. John Arnold, who has been working with octopuses for over twelve years, claims that octopuses always seem to have individual personalities and are quite intelligent, and tells about a little one from the waters off Bimini in the Bahamas that he started feeding small snails. Given a half dozen shells each day, it would gather them under its web and carry them around, eating them one at a time when it became hungry. Then the octopus learned to pry open Dr. Arnold's fingers in search of the snails. To avoid overfeeding, it would sometimes be given an empty shell. But then the octopus soon learned to insert an arm tip into each shell to see if it held anything before it bothered to take it.

"Some octopuses tend to react differently to different individuals," Dr. Arnold continued. "The most striking case I know of happened here in Hawaii. I had fourteen adult day-active octopuses, each of which was kept in an individual fiberglass laundry tub. Every morning when I came to work the octopuses would apparently sense my footsteps, and they would stick an arm or two up through the wire on their tank lids. On the other hand, there was a woman who felt squeamish about octopuses when she first worked in the lab. Sometimes she would stop to look at them, declare them to be the ugliest, slimiest things she'd ever seen, and rap on the sides of their tank. Soon they got to know her. Even after she stopped intentionally annoying them, they would squirt water through the tank lids whenever she walked by. No one else in the laboratory evoked such a response."

Dr. Katarina T. Borer describes an incident which further illustrates the intelligence of octopuses. She tried to capture *O. bimaculoides* in a sand-filled depression in a rock at low tide. After initial contact the octopus, apparently to avoid her, disappeared in the sand and held its breath. But Dr. Borer waited until the octopus finally betrayed its presence by releasing a jet of water from its siphon.

## DEDICATED MOTHERS

Focusing on another intriguing facet of the octopus' nature, F. G. Wood, formerly curator at Marineland in Saint Augustine, Florida, described the maternal role of the octopus. The female octopus, he feels, is one of the most diligent and faithful mothers in the sea.

According to Wood, after the female octopus (*Octopus vulgaris*) mates, she returns to her solitary life and lays her eggs, which are about one-half the size of a grain of rice. As each egg emerges she weaves and cements their stems together to form 10-to-12-centimeter (5-to-6-inch) strands, that are subsequently hung under a ledge or in a cave. There may be 1,000 eggs in a strand, and as many as 325,000 eggs may be produced over a period of about two weeks. During the four to six weeks it takes the eggs to hatch, the mother octopus cares for them without pause. By blowing water on the strands and running her arms through them, she keeps the eggs clean and well aerated. She refuses all food from the moment she starts nesting, and repels any intruders, including octopuses much larger than herself. Then, when the eggs hatch, her job is done, and she dies. It is a story of total dedication.

## UNFAIRLY GIVEN A BAD NAME

Moving to another area of behavior, Mr. Wood said, "Squids will bite readily when handled—unlike most octopuses." When I heard this I realized octopuses might have acquired a bad name by being mistaken for this close relative. For though

A. B. Joyce, Photo Researchers

Only the blue-ringed octopus of the Australian waters is seriously poisonous to humans. Even it, though, probably attacks only when provoked.

all octopuses have powerful beaks, reports of octopuses biting people are rare. The octopus' beak and venom are meant for its natural prey—not people. Only the blue-ringed octopus of Australia (common name for both *Hapalachlaena maculosa* and *Hapalachlaena lunlata*) is seriously poisonous to humans. Considering that it is quite common around the Australian coast, reported deaths from this small but extremely venomous creature are few and probably result from maltreatment of the octopus.

Everyone who has become familiar with the octopus has found it to be not a gruesome monster of the deep, but an intelligent creature with a distinct, even lovable character □

 SELECTED READINGS

*Octopus: Physiology and Behaviour of an Advanced Invertebrate* by M. J. Wells. Halsted Press, 1977.

*Octopus and Squid: The Soft Intelligence* by Jacques-Yves Cousteau and Philippe Diole. Doubleday, 1973.

"Tentacle tales" by Roger Caras. *Wildlife*, August 1977.

Image Bank

The thickly coated bear passes most of the winter in a state of dormancy, waking up on some mild days to venture forth from his winter's den.

# MAKING IT THROUGH THE WINTER

## by Anne LaBastille

DAY and night the winter winds of 1977 blasted my log cabin in upstate New York. Arctic air leaked through the chinking. The seemingly endless snowfalls threatened to bury the cabin or buckle the roof. My woodpile sank lower and lower. But if my own devices for survival seemed puny in the face of such a season—the coldest on record for most of the United States—what of the wildlife outside? I knew some individuals would not make it, despite their marvelous winter adaptations. What I could not have known, then, was how high the final toll would be.

• Millions of fish suffocated in the U.S. Midwest as shallow lakes became so thickly iced that oxygen was cut off.

• Wild turkeys in Pennsylvania were forced to follow deer, seeking leftover acorns that the larger animals were able to dig from the snow.

• Long-tailed birds, such as pheasants, starved when their tails became iced to the ground.

• Dozens of sea turtles were found frozen stiff but still alive along the coast of Florida.

• Thousands of waterfowl died in New Jersey when the ice covered their plant food.

• Blue crabs and shrimp in the Atlantic Ocean were killed by the winter chill of the water.

• Trout eggs and aquatic insect larvae were destroyed by the scouring action of bottom ice.

• Carolina wrens were decimated throughout most of the U.S. Northeast because the food they depend on was snowed under.

The wonder of it all was that there were any creatures left by the time spring finally came. As it turned out, of course, I thrilled once again to the sights and sounds of wildlife thriving all around me in the Adirondacks. True, it had been an unusually severe winter. But in the greater scheme of things, it was just another interruption. After millions and millions of years on earth, wildlife has learned how to cope with such interruptions.

### MOVE AWAY OR TOUGH IT OUT

In the most simplistic sense, animals survive bitterly cold weather in one of two ways. If they're lucky, they can migrate away from it—go where it's warmer. If they are not so fortunate, then they must stay and tough it out, each species in its own fashion.

Fully two thirds of the birds in the northern U.S. and Canada escape the cold by flying to the Deep South, Mexico, Central America, or farther. But migration is not reserved solely for birds. Monarch butterflies and many other insects journey over well-established flyways. Several kinds of bats also head for the tropics or subtropics each fall. Many of the baleen whales, including the humpbacks, depart frigid arctic or antarctic seas for warmer, ice-free waters.

But what about all of the creatures that stayed behind in the harsh winter of 1977? These are the animals that undergo another set of changes.

## HIBERNATION

For some animals, there is the "little death" of hibernation, a trancelike state that is the ultimate in energy conservation. Many frogs, turtles, and toads overwinter by burrowing into the mud bottoms of lakes and swamps. Snakes hole up in rocky dens, sometimes in great numbers, piled around like so much spaghetti.

In the fall, woodchucks, ground squirrels, and other hibernators begin slowing down. They stop their frenetic gorging and laying-on of fat to laze in the sun. One day their body heat begins to drop, hour by hour, until their body temperature nears freezing. The heartbeat slows, blood pressure plummets, and magnesium and a chemical called noradrenaline increase throughout the animal's system. These chemical changes effectively anesthetize the creature and cut the clotting time of its blood so that a wound sustained by a hibernator would scarcely even bleed.

For those birds that try to tough it out, life becomes difficult as ice covers much of their favorite food source.

George Bakacs, APF

New York Zoological Society

Snakes typically spend the winter curled up in a rocky den.

The ground squirrel offers a striking example of the changes that occur. This hyperactive little mammal becomes virtually inanimate. Its respiration slows from 100 breaths per minute to 4. Its heartbeat goes from about 250 beats per minute to 10 and its body temperature crashes from 36° Celsius (97° Fahrenheit) to 4° Celsius (39° Fahrenheit).

Another very active creature, the jumping mouse, has some further refinements and apparently is able to control the length of its hibernating period. Recent research done in Utah by Jack Cranford of the University of Utah indicates that jumping mice have varying periods of hibernation at different elevations and seem to be able to respond to soil temperatures rather than air temperatures—the higher up, the colder the soil, hence the longer the hibernation.

In the spring, reawakening occurs with astonishing swiftness. In marmots, for example, body temperature may rise 20 degrees Celsius (35 degrees Fahrenheit) within an hour. The ground squirrel's temperature climbs from 4° Celsius (39° Fahrenheit) back up to its normal 36° Celsius (97° Fahrenheit) in about four hours—roughly the time it takes for the animal to stir, open its eyes, make its first movements, and then crawl out the entrance of its den.

Townsend P. Dickinson, PR

Jacana

Many birds and mammals add insulation to get through the winter. Top, a tufted titmouse with its feathers fluffed out. Bottom, a squirrel with thick coat and fluffy tail.

## TORPOR

Another way of getting past winter's ordeals is in a torpor, or dormancy. This is a deep sleep rather than hibernation and the animal's body temperature usually remains close to normal. Breathing rate and circulation do, however, usually slow slightly during periods of dormancy.

Dormant animals like chipmunks, striped skunks, opossums, raccoons, and black bears can easily wake up on mild days every few weeks. They then sally forth to feed, defecate, and even mate in late winter. They return to a reduced activity level on the coldest days.

Late one January, I almost literally stumbled onto a bear's den. I was snowshoeing through a balsam thicket. The cold air was dead calm—one of those days when the smoke rises straight up from chimneys and smokestacks. Suddenly, I stopped dead, then backed slowly away. Right there in my path, the faintest wisp of steamy air was rising from a mounded snowbank. If I hadn't noticed it, I might have crashed in right on top of the bear that slept there. A bear doesn't take kindly to being abruptly awakened— particularly if it's a female that, during her torpor, has given birth to two tiny youngsters that she is carefully protecting and feeding.

## ADD INSULATION

In lieu of snug dens, other animals depend almost entirely on their own physical adaptations to get through winter. Many birds and mammals grow longer, thicker plumages and pelts. The hollow guard hairs of the caribou and deer hold dead air close to the skin, which makes for super insulation. The woolly undercoats of arctic foxes trap an extraordinary amount of air, a most energy-efficient insulator. In fact, this northern fox can sleep outdoors at temperatures as low as minus 40 degrees without undergoing cold stress.

Still other insulating methods are used by birds. For example, chickadees and blue jays fluff out their feathers until they look like colored Christmas balls perched on bare branches. Wolves and coyotes use a similar tactic, puffing their hair out, curling into tight balls, and using their fluffy tails to protect their faces. Still other animals beat the cold by shivering and by huddling together in groups.

Both photos, Karl H. Maslowski, PR

The weasel's brown summer coat turns white at the first signs of winter. With its white coat, it blends in with the snow and is better able to survive the winter.

## ENERGY CONSERVATION

"Acclimatization" to winter also means internal changes, even for nondenners. Blood chemistry, blood pressure, and circulation all change. More blood may be pumped to the paws, ears, tail, and nose, where the extra warmth is needed. Because of such changes, the red fox can stand winters that are more than 50 degrees Celsius (about 100 degrees Fahrenheit) colder than the usual summer temperatures in their home range.

A fascinating major research investigation of seasonal adaptations of white-tailed deer is being completed by Aaron N. Moen, an associate professor of wildlife ecology at Cornell University in New York. Moen has been studying the reactions of whitetails to their environment since the mid-1960s. Deer

in his laboratory herd, kept in a large pen, are at ease with humans and accustomed to wearing tiny radios. These radios transmit electrocardiograms, and over 3,000 hours of measurements have been made on these penned deer. While the deer are transmitting heart-rate information, they are observed with binoculars and their behavior related to heart rates. Because of the gentle treatment the deer receive, they have natural reactions to changes in weather and seasons rather than to stress because of being penned.

Moen's work has revealed that the deer employ a most interesting and useful strategy during the winter: they exhibit true energy conservation. He compares it to cutbacks in spending by people who are short of money: deer balance their inner resources with those available from the outer world. In wintertime, deer often move into coniferous cover on level bottomlands. They concentrate on smaller and smaller areas. They move slower and forage less. They appear to be more lethargic. There is a similarity between this response and hibernation, although deer do not go to the extremes that woodchucks and other hibernators do. But the deer do conserve energy, and many of their body functions, including thyroid activity—which regulates metabolism—drop to seasonal lows. There is a definite "metabolic depression."

Any disturbance of deer in winter, such as by snowmobiles or packs of dogs, goes against the deer's energy conservation plan. Deer observed in winter may even appear to be unperturbed by disturbances, but their hearts are likely to be beating at a fast pace and limited energy reserves are used up unnecessarily. This could prove fatal in hard winters.

Moen's research should result in a stronger biological argument for the management of deer in winter: allowing animals in winter-concentration or "yarding" areas to remain as undisturbed as possible. This may also mean better control of snowmobile traffic and free-ranging dogs, coupled with maintaining as much natural food and cover as possible for deer, year-round.

## YET MANY DIE

Despite all the strategies for winter survival, animals do die and sometimes perish in great numbers. Freezing to death is common, and happens in animals much as it does in humans. First the limbs chill and may become frostbitten. Then cold stress, or hypothermia, sets in. The body's core cools, the brain becomes sluggish. Drowsiness and confusion follow. Next, the pituitary-adrenal system breaks down. Then comes death.

The big brown bat is a case in point. Unlike several of its relatives, who hibernate in parts of caves that stay steadily above freezing, the big brown sometimes waits out the winter upside down in old buildings or hollow trees. The bat can hang next to icicles and survive, but if a cold wave moves in swiftly, this flying mammal can be killed before it is able to wake and warm itself by body chemistry and moving around.

Freezing is not the only way wildlife dies in winter. Fish in shallow ponds can suffocate when ice is covered by heavy snow

White-tailed deer react to winter and limited food reserves by conserving energy and becoming lethargic. Their body functions drop to a seasonal low in a "metabolic depression."

A. N. Moen

Elk that didn't make it. They drowned as ice stopped their river crossing during migration to a warmer region.

that blocks sunlight, kills aquatic plants, and thereby cuts off the production of oxygen by photosynthesis. In Wisconsin during the severe 1976–77 winter, the natural resources department managed to save about 500 choice hybrid muskies in one lake by bringing in pumps and aerating the water, a rescue technique that is often used.

The cruelest death of all is starvation. This happens fairly often among deer, particularly whitetails. On snow-shrouded Tug Hill in New York during the 1976–77 winter 2.5 meters (9 feet) of snow lay on the level for months, and a total of 10.5 meters (35 feet) of snow fell. Deer were imprisoned and unable to browse. To top it off, roving groups of feral dogs moved in and attacked the weakened animals. Those creatures' fat deposits had been used up and their bone marrow had turned red and gelatinous. As many as 85 per cent of the deer in some parts of the region are believed to have died.

## LIKE A DOSE OF SALTS

But hard winters are not all bad. Biologically speaking, they act like a dose of salts, cleaning out the sick, crippled, injured, and aged individuals. Overpopulations can be cut down to size for a proper balance with the existing food and habitat. In this way, an occasional severe winter ·can rejuvenate a wildlife population.

No winter is all "good" or "bad" in human terms. U.S. Fish and Wildlife Service biologists agree that an unusually severe winter definitely has an adverse impact on much of our hunting and fishing, birdwatching, and wildlife photographing for the succeeding one to five years. Yet, in the long run, wildlife will go on living□

 SELECTED READINGS

*Animals in Migration* by Robert T. Orr. Macmillan, 1970.

"Getting warm" by Julie Ann Miller. *Science News*, January 15, 1977.

"Can humans be taught to hibernate: work of H. Swan" by A. Rosenfeld. *Saturday Review*, June 11, 1977.

"Hibernation and body weight in dormice" by N. Mrosovsky. *Science*, May 20, 1977.

*Where They Go in Winter* by Margaret Brick. Abingdon, 1977.

Male orangutan gazes out at his jungle habitat, an increasingly threatened home for him as people and the trappings of civilizations creep ever closer.

New York Zoological Society

# ORANG—ENDANGERED "MAN OF THE FOREST"

## by Maxine A. Rock

*"My friend, the jungle is dark and dangerous. Man cannot live there, and even animals are in peril. But the Mawas—well, he is half man, half beast. He fears no other jungle animal and can tear a crocodile to bits. Mawas is very strong. Be careful of him."*

A young researcher in North Borneo got that folk-tale description of Mawas—the orangutan—from his porter. The researcher spent a winter studying the elusive red ape and said later that he almost believed the description was true. The orangutan, or orang (*Pongo pygmaeus*), is the least known and perhaps most endangered of the great apes. Only in the past few years have hearty scientists ventured into the jungle to dispel the old tales and find the facts that might save Mawas, which in Malay means "man of the forest."

### ONCE WIDESPREAD

Orangs once probably roamed all of southern China. Fossil orang teeth have been found there dating back to the Pleistocene era some 1,000,000 years ago. Anthropologists think that during the Ice Age the animals were forced into the tropical regions of what is now Indonesia. There, they lived in Borneo, Java, and Sumatra. When climactic changes made these areas into islands, the orangs evolved into two subspecies—the dark red Borneo orangs and the orange-red Sumatran orangs.

When Stone Age Man—the Java Early Man—appeared, orangs on Java were hunted for food. They quickly disappeared. Now they remain only in remote parts of Borneo and Sumatra and in the mountainous southeast Asia rain forests. Only about 4,500 orangs are still left in the wild. And, because of modern machinery that makes it easier for humans to invade the jungle, orang survival is in doubt. Dr. John MacKinnon, a Scottish anthropologist who has studied these shy, sensitive creatures in the wild, recently lamented that although enough orangs are still left for the species to survive, "Wherever man has penetrated, the orang has vanished—hunted for the pot, caught for pets, or simply because his habitat is destroyed."

## FORBIDDING HABITAT

The orang's forbidding habitat has saved the animal from extinction so far. But the difficulties their habitat visits on humans is also the major reason that we know so little about orangs today. The jungles of Borneo and Sumatra are thick and hot. Human travelers who want to travel quietly, without disturbing animals, must shun machinery and chip their way through barbed palms and knifelike thorns. Slimy leeches suck at human skin, and biting flies are everywhere. Scorpions come out at night, as do giant bats. Elephants, rhinos, wild boars, tigers, panthers, and sharp-clawed honey bears all can crush or tear a person in a minute. Crocodiles and pythons live beside the coffee-colored rivers, and hunting dogs prowl the hills.

Still, the tropical forests are incredibly beautiful. Orangs thrive there, moving slowly 6 to 18 meters (20 to 60 feet) above the ground in the lower jungle canopy. Like gorillas, they build nests in the trees at night and stay in them when it is dark or raining. Their lazy days consist of slow travel, frequent naps, and endless foraging for food.

## LONE SEARCHES FOR FOOD

Between April and November the apes feast on *wadan*—tall, nutty-tasting bamboos. In June and July wild plums, lychees, figs, and other sweet fruits ripen; and the orangs grow fat and glossy. They need the extra weight to sustain them during the winter, when only leaves, bark, and wood pith are available. Because of seasonal changes and the uneven distribution of the fruit harvest, orangs are frequently on the move. They go from place to place in search of their favorite foods. Except for mothers and their clinging

infants, they almost always travel alone. Orangs would soon exhaust the food supply if they traveled in groups, so they have developed what MacKinnon described as an "easy-going, tension-free hermit life."

Unlike gorillas and chimpanzees, the other two great apes, wild orangs do not seem to need one another often for comfort or company. Now and then mating couples will travel together for a few days or weeks, and one or two stable wild families of mother, father, and infant have been observed. Generally, however, wild male orangs live a solitary life, allowing females and their young into their huge territories but vigorously chasing away other adult males. Females have only their babies for companions, although they do strike up short-lived friendships with wandering males and some other females.

Only when food becomes desperately scarce do orangs band together. Then, juveniles and females follow the booming voices of the big males, which have the greatest

Two young orangs enjoying an easy-going life. As they grow older, they will lead a solitary life, frequently on the move in search of food.

Wolfgang Bayer

Wolfgang Bayer

In the wild, orangutan females are dutiful mothers, providing food, transportation, and companionship for their cute, clinging babies.

## CUTE, CLINGING BABIES

This antisocial behavior is not present in orang babies, however. The infants are so clinging and cute, with their floppy red hair, huge brown eyes, and chubby round faces that they are often captured for sale as pets. Conservationists estimate that 625 orangs are now being held in zoos, laboratories, or private homes. It is illegal to trap or sell orangs, but poachers hunt them anyway. The poacher's method of capture is similar to that used on young chimps and gorillas: the protesting mother is cornered and shot, and the baby is torn from her corpse.

Many babies cannot stand the shock or are so weakened by subsequent abuse, cold, or malnutrition that they cannot survive. Like most other primates, orangs are also very susceptible to human diseases. The animals that do manage to survive despite these hazards are often sold to Indonesian officials, given as gifts, or kept in wealthy homes as what one Dutch researcher called "valuable playthings." The researcher lamented that although everyone knows this activity is illegal, the babies are still poached and purchased because they are rare and thus have become status symbols.

## SAVING CAPTURED ORANGS

Although it has been illegal in Indonesia since 1931 to catch, trade, or keep orangs, until very recently the law has been weakly enforced. In 1970 the World Wildlife Fund, the Directorate-General of Forestry of Indonesia, and the Netherlands Genung Leuser Committee agreed to establish a special orang reserve and a research project aimed at saving the species. The Indonesian police were instructed to cooperate with conservation officials to round up captive orangs and take them to the Genung Leuser Reserve. The reserve covers about 30 per cent of the total habitat of the species in North Sumatra. There, sick orang babies are nursed back to health and slowly reacclimated to the wild. They learn to find their own food in the forest. Then, they are released.

The idea caught on, and recently several other reserves have been established, including the Sepilok Forest Reserve in Borneo and the Lankat reserve in Sumatra. Another

knowledge of the forest and are most likely to find food because of their more extensive travels in search of new territory in their youth and in defense of territory after maturity. MacKinnon did notice, however, that some of the males are surly and selfish about their finds. He once watched a 90-kilogram (200-pound) male dubbed Redbeard dominate every orang who tried to eat a morsel from a huge fig tree Redbeard had found.

Redbeard built four nests in the tree and munched his way around the branches for a week. During that time he let a few favorite females and their young snatch a meal or two, but he bubbled a warning to any male who tried to eat. The famished males had to find food elsewhere, although there was plenty on Redbeard's tree.

is now run by Birute and Rod Brindamour, a pair of young primatologists who set up shop in the Tanjung Puting Reserve in Kumai, on the edge of Borneo.

The task of rehabilitating captured orangs provides workers with an excellent opportunity to study the animals at close range. The Brindamours found, for example, that orangs are mild and retiring. Even wild orangs will not attack humans except when provoked, and Birute described her first encounter with a huge male orang to prove the point:

"I was rounding a turn on a path.... He was just ambling along.... He stopped dead in his tracks less than twelve feet away from me.... We were on a collision course ... but, strangely, I felt no fear. I simply marveled at how magnificent he looked with his coat blazing orange in the full sunlight. Abruptly, he whirled around and was gone. There was nothing but the sound of his feet padding off along the path."

## FEARSOME-LOOKING MALES

Birute's bravery is really the remarkable part of this story, for adult male orangs do look fearsome. They can stand up to 1.5 meters (5 feet) tall and weigh 135 kilograms (300 pounds). At maturity—between twelve and fifteen years old—the males develop wicked-looking facial flanges, or jowls. They also sport leathery throat sacs that probably act as resonators for their bellowing voices. Their long, thick hair makes them look twice their actual size.

Although male orangs rarely fight, they do threaten, scream, and drop branches on other males or intruders in their territory. And they are not gentle with females. They routinely assault and "rape" female orangs. The females almost always cry and try to escape, but they are half the size of a grown male and do not have much of a chance. These assaults take place even in captivity, but researchers think that such violent cou-

Wolfgang Bayer

When they are about two or three years old, young orangs begin to toddle away from their mothers and start taking food themselves. Here we see a young orang starting out on its own but keeping its mother, in lower nest area, in view.

In efforts to help orangutans
survive, sick orangs are nursed
back to health in special reserves and then helped—as
this researcher is doing—to
become readjusted to their natural habitat.

Wolfgang Bayer

plings rarely produce offspring. Instead, zoo observers report that when male and female orangs are given spacious quarters and privacy, they become fond couples. Then the females easily become pregnant.

## DUTIFUL MOTHERS

In the wild, orang mothers provide food, transportation, and companionship for their babies. During its first year the infant clings to its mother steadily—with its mouth never far from her nipples. By the time it is two years old the baby tastes some solid food, builds a few play nests, and toddles away from its mother for a few minutes at a time. At three the youngster may still suckle and ride upon its mother, but a new baby is often born about this time. From then on the mother pays less and less attention to the toddler, and eventually the child wanders off into the forest.

Female orangs may stay with their mothers longer than male offspring do. They are less adventuresome and must learn about

baby care by handling their younger siblings. This task is critical, for female apes of other species who have had time to learn baby care from their own mothers almost always turn out to be good mothers themselves, even in captivity. In contrast, apes reared in cages with little or no social contact with their own kind are nervous, incompetent mothers, if they are able to mate and conceive at all. Their babies have to be taken away from them and raised by humans, thus perpetrating the ruinous cycle of human interference.

This cycle is important to orang survival because some observers insist that the species may not be able to survive in the wild much longer. Instead, researchers hope to breed orangs in captivity or in sheltered environments until more natural habitat is made secure by stronger Indonesian conservation laws. Indeed, no other species has so large a captive population except for Père David's deer, but orangs are poor breeders in captivity. So captive breeding must be considered a last-ditch attempt at present.

## CAPTIVE ORANGS

Perhaps the world's largest captive population of orangs is at the Yerkes Regional Primate Research Center in Atlanta, Georgia. There, scientists are trying to learn more about orang breeding from the thirty-five males, females, and juveniles in residence in the Yerkes building and in open-air enclosures at the nearby Yerkes field station. One of these scientists, Dr. Ronald Nadler, reports that although more than twenty-nine orang babies have been born at Yerkes since 1966, all the breeding animals were born wild. No orang born in captivity—at Yerkes or elsewhere, says Nadler—seems capable of bearing young. In desperation, Yerkes scientists are experimenting with artificial insemination; and the Atlanta Zoo, in cooperation with Yerkes, is keeping two "families" of the apes in spacious cages. The zoo hopes to stimulate more natural breeding this way.

## NATURAL HABITAT BEING DESTROYED

Obviously, the best place for orangs—as with other wild animals—is in their natural habitat. But giant logging machines and the land-clearing tractors of farmers are wiping out that habitat at an alarming rate. Farming practices in Indonesia are particularly wasteful. Highland rural communities practice slash-and-burn cultivation, which exhausts the soil and eventually turns it into a sterile, acid heath known as *blang*. Millions of hectares (acres) of lush rain forest have been turned into *blang* in just the past few decades. No orangs can survive in these areas.

Logging has its own perils for the easily frightened orangs. Not only do they lose their main mode of transportation, food, and shelter—the trees—but they are terrified by the noise and human intrusion. Always, they flee.

MacKinnon has visited logged jungle habitat where orangs once lived and says, "Orangs are extremely sensitive to disturbance, and while some had returned briefly to nest in logged areas, none seem to have made this their permanent home. Instead, the red apes had fallen back farther into the forest, and I could judge what effect this would have on the reproductive activity of the population. . . . Orangs are slow breed-

R. D. Nadler, Yerkes Regional Primate Center

A 10-month-old orangutan raised in captivity. So far no orangs born in captivity have been able to bear young.

ers, and it would take many years for them to recover and recolonize their traditional haunts. Indeed, I doubted if they would be given sufficient time to do so before timber-felling operations cut farther into their range. The pace of commercial expansion is simply too fast, and the orangutan seems the inevitable loser."

## FATE IN THE BALANCE

Will this timid species be able to survive at all? Habitat destruction is not decreasing, and scientists so far are unable to unlock the secret to captive breeding. But more people than ever before are interested in the red ape. And the Indonesian government, pushed along by the fervent support of international conservation organizations, seems to be taking strong steps to save orangs. So the fate of the orang now hangs in the balance.

It is up to conservationists all over the world to see that Mawas does not fade away into the ghostly silence of ruined rain forests, but that it survives to move slowly in the dappled jungle sunlight—a living testimony to our respect for creatures with which we share this fragile planet□

 SELECTED READINGS

"Hermits of the jungle" by P. S. Rodman. *International Wildlife*, May 1977.

*In Search of the Red Ape* by John MacKinnon. Ballantine, 1975.

*Orangutan: Endangered Species* by Aline Amon. Atheneum, 1976.

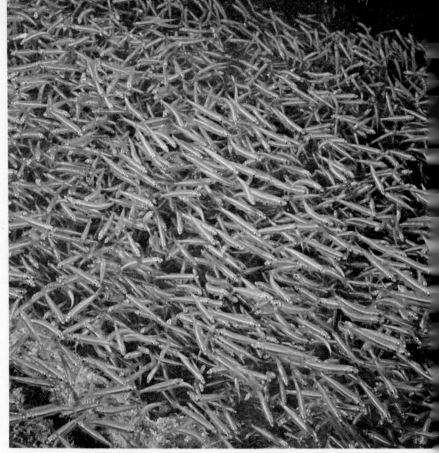

Sound production serves many functions in fish, one of which is the coordination of school movements. Here we see a school of minnows. Sounds made and detected by members of the school help to keep them together and functioning as a unit.

Michael De Camp, Image Bank

# VOICES IN THE DEEP

## by Walter B. Hendrickson, Jr.

THE silence of the deep is really a myth—it seems silent only to human ears. As Dr. Niko Tinbergen, a Dutch Nobel laureate for his work in animal behavior, pointed out, the ocean actually contains "a cacaphony of chirps, whistles, and moans."

That dolphins, porpoises, and other cetaceans, or whale relatives, can make sounds is well known and is often demonstrated at ocean aquarium shows. Dolphins have far keener hearing than humans and make a wide variety of sounds both with their mouths and their blowholes. While there is still speculation as to whether dolphins' sounds actually constitute a language, it is agreed that, at the very least, they are as elaborate as those produced by dogs and, like the latter, can convey a variety of meanings. In addition, some sounds made by dolphins and whales are used as sonar for echo-location of unseen objects underwater.

Cetaceans, however, are not the only creatures that make noises in the sea. Although not nearly as talkative as dolphins, fishes are by no means as quiet as clams (which might not be all that quiet after all). Fishes can produce sounds in a variety of ways—gnashing teeth, thumping swim bladders, or, in one case, even rattling bones and a variety of other mechanisms. These sounds often are not simply incidental to the movements of the fishes, but are deliberately created and serve a distinct purpose. For example, some catfishes coordinate the formation of their schools by rhythmic swimming movements. Most sounds, however, are social in nature, with the animal making them only during some particular behavior.

### FISH SYMPHONIES

Scientists have long been aware of the sounds produced by fishes, and other people may have heard them without knowing the source. The late Dr. John O. LaGorce, president of the National Geographic Society, speculated that large schools of fishes may have been responsible for the siren song that led ancient Greek seamen onto the rocks. A similar occurrence was reported by Lieutenant John White, United States Navy, in 1824. His ship was in the mouth of a river in Cochin-China when he heard the combined sounds of a deep-toned organ, jingle bells, a guttural frog, and an enormous harp. The natives assured him that the wierd symphony was performed by fishes.

In World War II, the U.S. Navy again began hearing voices in the deep. Using listening devices they had developed to detect submarines, navy personnel began to pick up a variety of strange beeps, grunts, and groans. At first, the navy thought that these sounds were made by other ships in the convoy, but the noises were even more numerous when ships were not around. The source

of the noises proved to be marine animals. This discovery spurred research into underwater sound sources and into the equipment necessary to study them. The latter included such devices as the hydrophone, sonar, and sophisticated sound-analysis instruments, all of which have proved of great help to naturalists investigating aquatic animal sounds.

Land vertebrates typically generate sound by using the principle of the vibrating reed. Humans, for example, force air past the vocal cords. These vibrate, generating sound, and these sounds are then modified into speech by the pharynx and mouth. The production of these vibrations is relatively easy, as air is a relatively thin, lightweight medium which offers only slight resistance to the vibration. Water, however, is much denser and such vibrations are rapidly damped out. To maintain them requires considerably more energy. To avoid this energy cost, fishes have found other ways to produce sounds.

The parrotfish emits audible sounds as it grazes on coral for algae.

Geo. Lower, Photo Researchers

Chesher, Photo Researchers

Grunts make loud, deep, grunting noises by grinding their pharyngeal teeth. They are also good at camouflage, frequently changing their color to match their surroundings.

## TEETH GRINDING

One very common method by which fish produce sounds involves the teeth. Aside from the obvious teeth of barracudas and sharks, many fishes have plates of teeth, set in rows, either inside the mouth or within the pharynx, or both. These teeth can be ground together. The effect is like that produced by moving a comb over a blade, creating a series of snapping sounds.

A good example of fishes that produce sound this way is the grunt, any one of a number of common species that are found throughout the West Indies and Caribbean and along the southeastern coast of the United States. As their common name suggests, these fishes make noticeably loud noises, all by using their teeth. Because they make this sound both in and out of water, one can observe a grunt gritting its teeth and, in fact, prove that the teeth are involved by placing a small piece of cloth between them. This prevents the fish from making noises even though it can be seen chewing the rag.

## SQUEEZING THE SWIM BLADDER

The second common technique used by fishes to produce sounds is strumming or squeezing the swim bladder. The swim bladder is a gas bag running down the interior center of the body. It is common to most fishes. While it was at one time commonly believed to function only in maintaining buoyancy, recent work has shown that the muscles attached to the bladder of some fishes vibrate or squeeze it to produce audible sounds.

Drums, gurnards, and several other types of fishes have muscles that are attached to the body wall at one end and the bladder on the other. These muscles vibrate the wall of the bladder to make a sound. Other fishes, such as the toadfish, growl by squeezing the bladder itself in rapid movements to make the sound. Finally, numerous fishes use the bladder as a resonator. Sounds made near the bladder, by teeth, bones, or other organs, are picked up by the bladder and amplified.

Fishes also use the swim bladder as a

sound receiver. Fishes have only an inner ear and lack the middle ear with which other animals transmit sound from the environment to their specific sensing cells. The interface between the gases within the swim bladder and the water around it is sensitive to the micromovements produced by sound, however, and fishes such as the herrings have sense organs that attach to the bladder to detect these movements.

SENSORY ORGANS

Low-frequency sounds, those producing not so much pressure waves as actual physical displacement of the water particles, are detected by another organ—the lateral-line system. Possessed by most fishes in one form or another, these lines usually extend the entire length along the outside of the fish's body. The lines consist of a series of minute pores, each containing a delicate sensory "hair." These hairs respond to the slightest movement of the water on the fish's surface. By noting the pattern of "hair" disturbance and the frequency, a fish can determine not only the location of a sound source (within limits), but even its probable cause, whether it be the approach of prey or the falling of a rock.

Oceanographer Theodore Walker tested the importance of the lateral lines in a school of minnows. Ordinarily, the fish would turn and swim away from his prodding finger. By placing a hood over the fish so that it covered the lateral-line pores but did not otherwise interfere with the fish, the minnows ignored his fingers. Some he could even touch.

The lateral-line system also makes up in part for the wall-eyed vision of many fishes, each eye seeing an entirely different field of view. Lacking binocular vision, many fishes, therefore, also lack visual depth perception. The lateral line provides much distance information for fishes. It is probably this process that permits fishes, such as those found on reefs, to maneuver so quickly in such a complex environment. Similarly, it allows fishes to avoid objects in turbid water and very likely is involved in the maintenance of fish schools.

SOCIAL FUNCTION OF SOUND

Such schools are coordinated not only by sensing each other's wakes via the lateral lines, but also by visual cues and, on occasion, by sounds made by each member of the group. For instance, schools of one species of catfish, when swimming at night, make sounds much like martial drum rolls. In the daytime, they typically make little if any sound except when the school is in deeper water where less light penetrates. The sounds are not made by any particular school master, but rather by fish randomly in the school.

Aside from schooling, many fishes produce sounds used in other social behavior.

James H. Carmichael, Jr., Image Bank

Many reef fishes, including the clown trigger fish shown at left, avoid corals and other objects through their lateral line senses. They pick up low-frequency sounds in the water and thus can avoid obstacles.

The small, colorful damselfish use a distinctive "chirp" sound as a mating call.

For example, Dr. William N. Tavolga of the American Museum of Natural History found that a single toadfish in an 18-liter (5-gallon) aquarium quietly rested on the bottom in a small conch shell. Adding a second toadfish, however, resulted in a series of open-mouth threatening movements and a series of contractions, each of which produced a "grunt," followed by a long, fading growl resembling a drum roll. Tavolga interpreted this entire sequence to be a territorial dispute, both the visual displays and sounds being used by the one fish to communicate with another.

### A MATING CALL

In a similar manner, some fishes produce sounds as part of their reproductive behavior. Dr. Arthur A. Myrberg, Jr., of the University of Miami, for example, recently found that many damselfishes—small, frequently territorial, and highly social inhabitants of reefs throughout the tropics—produce a complex sound during courtship. As a female approaches the nest site prepared by the male, he frequently changes color, swims rapidly up and down over the bottom, and during each downward dash produces a quick staccato sound called the "chirp." Dr. Myrberg recorded these chirps and then played back the chirps and similar sounds to groups of the fishes. He found that this sound facilitates courtship activities and that each species is capable of telling its own sounds from those of other species.

### TRAINING FISH

Fishes can also be trained to respond to sounds or to produce them. For example, the Australian Nobel Prize-winning zoologist Karl von Fisch trained a fish to come when he whistled. Going through the motions of a whistle without a sound did not prompt the fish to respond, but it would respond to the sound without the visual stimulus.

### SOUND—IMPORTANT TO FISHES

Sound has been found to be an important part of the behavior of many fishes. To some extent, this is not surprising. In contrast to the clear waters and bright lighting of the coral reefs, much of the world oceans are dark or murky. Under these conditions, the value of vision in communication and orientation is reduced or even eliminated altogether. Thus, the use of sound production and reception provides fishes living in such areas with information they might otherwise not obtain□

 SELECTED READINGS

*Lateral Line Sense Organs: Their Importance in Fish Behavior.* International School Books Service, 1971.

*Sound Perception in Fishes,* edited by W. N. Tavolga. Halsted, 1976.

*Sound Production in Fishes,* edited by W. N. Tavolga. Halsted, 1977.

# index

# Z

**Zeeman, E. Christopher** (Eng. math.) 101
**Zinjanthropus** (anthro.) 268
**Zoology**
    animal experiments with Laetrile 238
    dinosaurs 150
    dovekies 282
    electromagnetic pollution's effects 195
    fish 378
    hybridization of wolf and coyote 354
    mammoth 119
    marine environment 77
    mountain wildlife 209, 210
    ocean ecosystem 214
    ocean floor 137, 67
    octopus 361
    orangutans 372
    rain forest's fauna 200 fol.
    regeneration 89
    sudden death 57
    Tibet 67
    wildlife 352
    winter's effects on wildlife 366
    *See also* individual names of animals

---

**ACKNOWLEDGMENTS.**    Sources of articles appear below, indicating those reprinted with the kind permission of publications and organizations.

**SUNSETS,** Page 8: Reprinted with permission from *Sky and Telescope,* September 1977. © 1977 Sky Publishing Corporation.

**STARS WITH COMPANIONS,** by William K. Hartmann Page 13: *Astronomy,* September 1977. Copyright © 1977 by AstroMedia Corp. All rights reserved.

**WHITE HOLES,** Page 19: Copyright 1977 Smithsonian Institution, from *Smithsonian* Magazine November 1977.

**ROBOT PROBES,** Page 27: *Astronomy,* September 1977. Copyright © 1977 AstroMedia Corp. All rights reserved.

**VOYAGE TO THE OUTER PLANETS,** Page 33: Prepared from a NASA news release.

**HOW WELL DO YOU READ BODY LANGUAGE?,** Page 42: Reprinted from *Psychology Today* Magazine. Copyright 1977 Ziff-Davis Publishing Company.

**LEBOYER'S BABIES,** Page 50: Reprinted with permission from *Science News,* the weekly news magazine of science, copyright 1977 by Science Service Inc.

**SUDDEN DEATH,** Page 52: Reprinted from *Psychology Today* Magazine. Copyright 1977 Ziff-Davis Publishing Company.

**AGORAPHOBIA,** Page 58: excerpted from *Nothing to Fear: Coping with Phobias* by Fraser Kent. Reprinted by permission of Doubleday & Company. All rights reserved.

**METHANOGENS,** Page 68: © 1977 by The New York Times Company. Reprinted by permission.

**WHY DO LEAVES TURN COLORS IN THE FALL?,** Page 71: From *Garden* magazine of the New York Botanical Garden © 1977. Reprinted by permission.

**THROUGH A KELP FOREST,** Page 77: Reprinted from *Pacific Discovery,* Volume XXVI, number 6, pages 23–29. Copyright 1973 by California Academy of Sciences.

**POISONOUS GARDEN PLANTS,** Page 81: from *Garden* magazine of The N.Y. Botanical Garden. Copyright © 1977. Reprinted by permission.

**BIOELECTRICITY AND LIMB REGENERATION,** Page 89: Reprinted with permission from *Natural History* Magazine, October 1977. Copyright © The American Museum of Natural History, 1977.

**CATASTROPHE THEORY,** Page 100: © 1977 by The New York Times Company. Reprinted by permission.

**IF COMPUTERS COULD REASON,** Page 103: © 1977 by The New York Times Company. Reprinted by permission.

**CRYPTOGRAPHY,** Page 108: Copyright 1977 by the American Association for the Advancement of Science.

**NEW HOME COMPUTERS,** Page 113: Reprinted from *Popular Science* with permission. Copyright © 1977 Times Mirror Magazines, Inc.

**FUTURE CLIMATE,** Page 120: reprinted from *U.S. Environmental Data Service.*

**HOT SPOTS,** Page 127: Reprinted with permission from *Natural History* Magazine, April 1977. Copyright © The American Museum of Natural History, 1977.

**GALÁPAGOS RIFT,** Page 134: reprinted from Summer 1977 *Oceanus,* publication of Woods Hole Oceanographic Institution.

**EARTHQUAKE LIGHTS,** Page 147: reprinted from U.S. Geological Survey *Earthquake Information Bulletin.*

**WERE DINOSAURS WARM-BLOODED?,** Page 150: Adapted with permission of John Ostrom; paper originally presented at annual meeting of The American Association for the Advancement of Science, February 1977.

**AN ADVANCED SOLAR HOUSE,** Page 158: Reprinted from *Popular Science* with permission. Copyright © 1977 Times Mirror Magazines, Inc.

**WHEN WE'LL START RUNNING OUT OF OIL,** Page 164: reprinted from the October 1977 issue of *Fortune* magazine by special permission. Copyright © 1977 Time Inc.

**ALCOHOL—BRAZIL'S ANSWER TO THE ENERGY CRISIS,** Page 170: Reprinted from *Sci-*